# ESTIMATION THEORY

PRENTICE-HALL INTERNATIONAL, INC., *London*
PRENTICE-HALL OF AUSTRALIA, PTY., LTD., *Sydney*
PRENTICE-HALL OF CANADA, LTD., *Toronto*
PRENTICE-HALL OF INDIA (PRIVATE) LTD., *New Delhi*
PRENTICE-HALL OF JAPAN, INC., *Tokyo*

# ESTIMATION THEORY

**Ralph Deutsch**

Research and Engineering Division
Autonetics, North American Aviation, Inc.

**Prentice-Hall, Inc.**
*Englewood Cliffs, N. J.*

Current printing (last digit):
11 10 9 8 7 6 5 4 3

Library of Congress Catalog Card Number 65–23424
Printed in the United States of America
28995C

To

Charlotte
Leslie
Barbara

# PREFACE

*Estimation Theory* was established as a mathematical technique in 1806 with the first publication on least squares estimation by Legendre. For many years *Estimation Theory* was used mainly by astronomers as a means of reducing observations to obtain the orbital elements of minor planets and comets. Gradually estimation techniques were absorbed into statistics, but not immediately into the fields of *acceptable* mathematical pursuits because even statistics had not yet been admitted to these cloistered domains. During the last few decades, probability and a large portion of statistics has finally been incorporated into the rigid framework of theoretical mathematics, primarily through the elegant use of measure theoretic concepts. This same period has been one in which *Estimation Theory* has also been formalized and a period during which the large emphasis placed on estimators justifies the present status of *Estimation Theory* as an independent entity and not simply as an isolated topic in statistics.

While the rigorizing of statistics and probability was taking place, another seemingly isolated series of investigations was to have an even larger impact upon estimation. Prior to about 1940, estimation techniques were primarily concerned with the *classical problems* of determining the *best estimates* of distribution parameters on the basis of a selection of samples taken from a given population. Communication analysts were concerned with, what at first glance, seemed to be an unrelated problem. Given a continuous, or discrete, set of observations containing a signal in the presence of noise, they wished to formulate theories and synthesize equipment which could effectively detect the presence, or absence, of the signal. Later, the communications problems were extended to include the estimation of parameters that characterize the signal which is to be detected. Thus, for example, radar system designers are not content simply with solving their signal detection problems, they also wish to know the range, amplitude, and the phase of the received radar signals.

Although at first, signal detection and signal parameter estimation were attacked on a somewhat *ad hoc* basis, it was eventually discovered that when carefully interpreted, these problems fell naturally into the framework of modern statistics; provided that the proper extensions are made from the classical discrete statements to those applicable to stochastic processes.

While it is *relatively* easy to define the term *Estimation Theory*, I found it far more difficult to select topics that should be included in this book. As I have discovered from prior experience, in spite of all kinds of rationalization, the selection of topics is somewhat arbitrary and in the main reflect the interests of the author. Topics were selected so that a somewhat coherent treatment could be presented of some of the major aspects of the theory.

The objective of the book is to present an introduction to both the *classical* and *modern* techniques for estimating parameters from experimental data. It is assumed that the reader is already founded in statistics, probability, and some of the more elementary aspects of noise theory. The *customary* introductory material on these subjects is omitted. The reader is provided with definitions of many of the terms borrowed from these fields and representative references are furnished to enable him to pursue any required elaboration of background topics. While the presentation is intended as a fundamental introduction to *Estimation Theory*, it is not necessarily elementary in all aspects. Keeping in this vein, only formal and heuristic mathematics are used in most arguments. Rigorous justifications and theorems for the same points are usually left for augmented reading in the referenced technical literature. The reader will require a certain undefined degree of mathematical and practical physical system maturity which cannot be blithely collated one-to-one with a list of university courses. The more obtuse sections can readily be omitted leaving a remainder that should be suitable as an introductory text to *Estimation Theory*. Advanced topics were included to extend the usefulness of the work as a reference source.

The presentation has been purposely kept brief and on the austere side in the hope that many of the developments will appear to be as transparent, as many of them truly are. Matrix formulations are used almost from the start in keeping with the present day literature which immediately treats the $n$-dimensional cases rather than the older scheme of proceeding from *one*, *two*, and then finally to $n$-dimensions. Space has been preserved by restricting most of the discussions to random variables for which the existence of probability density functions were assumed. The more general treatment of distribution functions can be formulated in an analogous fashion by readers wishing to weaken the restrictions on various specific arguments. Another space saving device was the treatment of discrete variables in Chapters 1–10 and continuous random processes in Chapters 11–13. Again, by analogy either set of arguments can be extended from discrete to continuous, or vice versa. Finally, many of the well-known statistical problems of estimation have been either omitted or only briefly considered because of the vast literature available on such subjects. These topics are primarily those of estimating particular moments of a distribution, ratios of population parameters, etc., from samples drawn from populations known to have a given type of distribution.

Chapter 1 is a prologue offered as a simple change from the conventional title of *Introduction.*

The principle theoretical foundations of estimators are contained in Chapter 2 and extended with geometrical interpretations in Chapter 3. In essence almost all the theoretical foundations are contained here, and, in an overly generalized sense, the remainder of the book is concerned with details and window-dressing.

Chapter 4 is primarily of historical interest. It was included because of the author's feeling that all too frequently we forget our debts to the originator of a scientific discovery in the sense of omitting the reading of the original paper in favor of more up-to-date digests or review articles. The danger in this almost universal attitude is that the flavor and true insight of the originator may all too frequently be lost or obscured. It is hoped that a survey of some of Gauss's original arguments and comments may well serve as a sobering influence on those who believe that only recently discovered mathematical techniques are useful and that the *classic* or *older* methods are undoubtedly passe or sterile.

Least squares estimates are almost synonymous with estimation. Chapters 5 and 6 outline the theory of both linear and nonlinear least squares estimators.

An underlying theme of the book is the treatment of a theory in more or less elegant fashion—which is then almost immediately followed by statements pointing out the practical and somewhat prohibitive difficulties encountered in actually carrying out the required numerical evaluation of the estimator. Although the subject of numerical analysis is, at least practically, intertwined with estimation, only two of the most common troublesome numerical problems are discussed in Chapter 7. These are the problems involved with computing matrix inverses and the problems of solving a system of equations by successive approximations.

Chapter 8 is devoted to a selection of recursive estimators which are currently enjoying a large popularity because of the comparative ease in which they can be implemented as contrasted with their related nonrecursive embodiments.

No book on estimation would be complete, even in its most abbreviated form, without a discussion of the method of maximum likelihood estimation. Chapter 9 is concerned with this method as well as with the method of moments which is intimately connected with sampling theory—an adjunct to almost every reduction of experimental data.

Associated with the evaluation of an estimator are the companion questions of the magnitude of the estimate error and the confidence which can be placed in the estimation results. Chapter 10 discusses sources of estimation errors, confidence limits, and alternate error measures. The alternate measures are not based upon firm theoretical arguments but have the saving grace of being far simpler to evaluate than most confidence limits.

Chapter 11 is the breaking point between the more classic point estimation problems and the modern communication problems associated with random processes. The Wiener-Kolmogorov linear prediction and smoothing theory is introduced by illustrating several simplified versions which avoid the real troublesome theoretical arguments of the original papers.

Kalman and Bucy have recently provided an alternate approach to the Wiener-Kolmogorov theory which has certain inviting features. Instead of centering the results on the solutions of the Wiener-Hopf integral equation, Chapter 12 demonstrates how the filtering and smoothing formulations can be transformed to the solutions of differential equations.

The book is appropriately terminated with Chapter 13 on Decision Theory. The appropriateness of this termination is that, as pointed out in the text, all of *Estimation Theory* could be included as a special topic in Decision Theory. This generalized approach was not taken because it was felt that the gains obtained by such generalizations are somewhat doubtful if the reader interested in the limited theory and application of estimators had to travel the larger and more inclusive route of decisions. This is in itself undoubtedly a concession to the *classical* development of estimators as well as to the size of the book. At some arbitrary point, it is almost always necessary to draw a line between all inclusive generalities and the practical necessities of limiting a subject to digestable chunks.

It is my pleasant duty to thank Mr. M. Blum (The Rand Corporation) and Prof. J.B. Cruz, Jr. (University of California, Berkeley) for their review of the manuscript. Their suggestions have led to the correction of errors and to the clarification of several topics. Acknowledgement is due to the management of the Autonetics Division of North American Aviation, Inc., for their encouragement in the preparation of the final version of the manuscript. Finally, I wish to thank my wife for her many invaluable contributions, including the editing and typing of the preliminary drafts, as well as for her patience and encouragement which were of significant value in leading to the completion of the manuscript.

RALPH DEUTSCH

*Sherman Oaks, California*
*December 1965*

# CONTENTS

# ESTIMATION THEORY

# Chapter 1

# PROLOGUE

## 1.1
## *ESTIMATION*

The direct approach for introducing a subject such as estimation theory would be to state an unambiguous, precise definition of the term, couched in mathematical terminology. Although such directness has certain elegant attributes, it would not serve as a useable introduction unless accompanied by suitable modifiers and examples demonstrating that realizations of the definition and modifiers do indeed lead to practical problems encountered in physical situations. An alternative approach is to define loosely the meaning of estimation, motivate the definition by common examples from everyday experience, and, finally, demonstrate that these concepts can be meaningfully incorporated into a mathematical statement.

The *process of estimation* can be defined as the process of making a decision, or judgment, concerning the *approximate value* of certain undefined objects when the decision is weighted, or influenced, by *all* available information. Typical of early encounters with estimation techniques is the simple, but basic, physics laboratory experiment of estimating the length of an object by making a sequence of scale measurements. If $x_1, \ldots, x_n$ denotes the sequence of measurements, the mean (average) value, or most probable value, of the length is defined as

$$\text{avg}\, x = \frac{1}{n} \sum_{i=1}^{n} x_i. \tag{1-1}$$

One quickly discovers the property of statistical regularity. Although the individual measurements $x_i$ in the sequence exhibit irregular behavior relative to each other, their average values for large values of $n$ exhibit a striking regularity.

A similar situation arises in the experimental determination of the precision of the set of length measurements. This precision can be expressed by the standard deviation, which is defined as*

$$\begin{aligned} \text{s.d. } x = \sigma_x &= [\text{avg}(x - \text{avg } x)^2]^{1/2} \\ &= \left[\frac{1}{n-1}\sum_{i=1}^{n}(x_i - \text{avg } x)^2\right]^{1/2}. \end{aligned} \tag{1–2}$$

As the number of experiments, $n$, increases, one soon discovers that both avg $x$ and $\sigma_x$ asymptotically approach *relatively* stationary magnitudes, which tend to be independent of $n$.

The simple length-measuring experiment illustrates many of the elementary facets of estimation theory. Given a set of observations, we are asked to form judgments of the mean value and standard deviation based upon all available information. Moreover, we can carefully specify the meaning we attribute to the term *best estimate;* best is defined explicitly by estimates computed via the formulations (1–1) and (1–2).

Other pertinent questions could be raised concerning our estimates of length and measurement precision. Typical of such estimation procedures is the companion problem of determining the probability that the estimated values will lie between specified limits. Although the theory of confidence limits is related to estimation, the development of confidence limits is closer to the realm of statistics than to the treatment of estimation theory presented in this book. The development of estimation procedures will be based almost entirely upon a priori probabilities rather than upon the a posteriori probabilities of statistical sampling.

The length-measuring experiment is far less complex than the classes of estimation problems that frequently confront experimentalists. Notice, for instance, that in the formulation of the required estimates of mean value and standard deviation, the order in which the elements of the sequence of measurement are inserted into the estimators is of no consequence. Since none of the length measurements is time-dependent (neglecting personal errors), the time at which an element is measured within the sequence cannot affect the outcome.

Another illustrative problem in the estimation of parameters can be drawn from systems for determining the orbits of space vehicles. Suppose that a radar is used to track a space vehicle and one wishes to reduce the radar-tracking measurements so that they yield the orbital elements of the vehicle. The output of the radar is the vehicle's instantaneous coordinates $(R_i, h_i, A_i; t_i)$ with respect to a spherical coordinate set centered at the known geographical location of the radar; $R_i$ is the range, $h_i$ is the elevation angle, and $A_i$ is the azimuth angle at the instant $t_i$. The important point in this

*Refer to (9–17) and accompanying discussion for the reason that the s.d. is defined with the factor $1/(n-1)$ rather than the *intuitive* factor $1/n$.

illustrative example is that the desired orbital parameters of the space vehicle are not observables of the measurements. Moreover, although the orbital parameters can be assumed to be time-independent, the observables are definitely functions of time. Thus the order in which the measurements are combined to formulate the required estimated parameters must be carefully maintained in the original measured time sequence.

Suppose that the space vehicle's orbital parameters are denoted by the symbols $b_1, \ldots, b_6$. A prerequisite to the estimation of the values of $b_1, \ldots, b_6$ is the existence of an explicit transformation relating the observables $(R_i, h_i, A_i; t_i)$ to the orbital parameters. Suitable transformations have been formulated and can be obtained in the published literature on orbit determination [41,151]. The estimation problem can be stated as one in which functions $g_j$ of the observables are so formulated that the estimated values of the parameters (denoted by a circumflex accent) are

$$\begin{aligned} \hat{b}_1 &= g_1(R_1, h_1, A_1; R_2, h_2, A_2; \ldots; R_n, h_n, A_n) \\ &\vdots \\ \hat{b}_6 &= g_6(R_1, h_1, A_1; R_2, h_2, A_2; \ldots; R_n, h_n, A_n). \end{aligned} \tag{1–3}$$

It is further required that the statistical distributions of the estimated values $\hat{b}_j$ of $b_j$ be concentrated as *close as possible* to the true values $b_j$ of the orbital elements. The functions $g_j$ that satisfy (1–3) and the *closeness* criteria are called the *estimators*. If the $g_j$ are linear functions of their arguments, the estimators are called *linear*. Most frequently, the $g_j$ are nonlinear and are thus appropriately classed as *nonlinear estimators*.

The estimation of the orbital parameters is extremely sensitive to the time ordering of radar observables $(R_i, h_i, A_i)$. Because of the motion of the space vehicle along its trajectory, its velocity and position vary rapidly with respect to the radar's site. The coordinate observables can be symbolized by a sequence of position vectors $\boldsymbol{R}_i$ having the components $(R_i, h_i, A_i)$. The $\boldsymbol{R}_i$ consist of the true vector positions modified by random errors introduced by a variety of error sources and imperfections in the radar or measurement system. A time-ordered sequence of random vectors, or random variables, is called a *discrete random process*. (This is not a rigorous definition [42]). During the development of several facets of estimation techniques, we shall perceive frequently that, because the observed data is in the form of a random process or stochastic process, we can draw upon known properties of such processes as an aid in obtaining estimation solutions. This procedure will provide insight into the characteristics of the estimators.

The radar-tracking system for determining a space vehicle's orbital elements also illustrates a variety of estimation which is known as *signal filtering*. It has already been noted that the orbital elements themselves are not the physical observables, but are computed as functions of another related random process consisting of the vehicle's position vectors in a time-ordered sequence. This situation in estimation, for which the output is a function of a random process, is known as *filtering* or *smoothing*. The general case of filtering is that in which the input data or observables are a set of values of a random process over some time interval, from which one wishes to find the *best* values of a functionally related random process. The illustrative example of radar tracking does entail the general definition of smoothing if we examine the mechanism by which the radar signals are processed to provide the space vehicle's coordinates. In fact, these coordinates are themselves the consequence of an estimation, or filtering transformation.

Space-vehicle tracking can be used as an illustration of still another physically important category of estimators. Instead of processing the random sequence of position vectors to estimate the vehicle's orbital elements, we can use the same sequence of position data for another fundamental and important application. Given a sequence of measurements extending over some time interval, we frequently are concerned with the prediction of a subsequent element of this sequence at a given instant. Of course, for our illustrative example, the entire future spatial history of the space vehicle can be predicted from the knowledge of the vehicle's orbital elements. Thus the prediction problem, in the *absence of measurement errors*, can be solved by first reducing all existing data to orbital elements and then predicting the required position from the transformations between orbital elements and vehicle position. This calculation, in itself, cannot predict the physical observables, which include random and unknown errors, because the random process, by definition, is not completely determined by a set of time invariant parameters.

The estimation process, known as *prediction* or *extrapolation*, is applied to the situation in which one wishes to estimate the future values of a random process based upon the observed values of the process available during a previous time interval and certain assumed or known a priori knowledge of the appropriate probability distributions. The prediction may be of the observed random process or of some given function of the process.

Directly related to filtering and prediction of random processes is the estimation of an intermediate value in a sequence of time-ordered observables. By direct analogy to other definitions, the estimation of an intermediate value is called *interpolation*. Precise mathematical definitions of smoothing, filtering, prediction, and interpolation must be deferred until later chapters.

## 1.2
## *HISTORICAL DEVELOPMENTS*

Almost synonymous with estimation and smoothing is the process known as *least squares*. Through a period of over 160 years of widespread adoption in scientific experimental procedures, we have almost reached the stage in which, whenever confronted with a data set suspected of containing random errors, we instinctively compute the *most probable* or *best* estimate of the desired parameters by means of some variation of the method of least squares estimation.

In common with many scientific discoveries, the method of least squares was independently, and almost simultaneously, postulated by two men. The first published version was given by Legendre in 1806 [92]. Gauss is generally credited with the concept because his version in 1809 [56: Book II, Section 3] derived the method from fundamental principles. Further, Gauss claimed to have used the method of least squares as early as 1795 in connection with problems concerning orbit determination of minor planets.

Unlike several instances in which the discoverer of a scientific principle did not fully comprehend the full impact of his principle on science, Gauss exhibited particular insight into the generality of the least squares estimator for treating scientific data. The following quotations from *Theoria Motus* [56] illustrate the understanding Gauss had of the method as well as of its utility beyond the field of dynamical astronomy.

> The most probable value of the desired parameters will be that in which the sum of the squares of the differences between the actually observed and computed values multiplied by numbers that measure the degree of precision, is a minimum.
>
> The subject we have just treated [least squares] might give rise to several elegant analytical investigations, upon which, however, we will not dwell, that we may not be too much diverted from our object [determination of an orbit from any number of observations].

It is interesting to note that Gauss considered minimizing other even powers of the sum of the powers of the differences between observed data and the corresponding true values.

> But of all these principles ours is the most simple, by the others we should be led into the most complicated calculations.

This was a very prophetic statement from Gauss. All too often we shall be forced to rediscover Gauss' views. The remarkable fact is that Gauss could not have been completely aware of the entire fundamental basis of his conjecture on the simplicity as well as the significance of the second power of the differences in a least squares estimation.

After the publication of *Theoria Motus*, the method of least squares estimation was quickly adopted as a standard technique for the determination of orbits. Many of the leading astronomers since Gauss were motivated by the problems in astronomical observations to adopt and extend the method of least squares. Amongst these men are the well-known names of Bessel, Hansen, Encke, Gerling, Laplace, Poisson, Pierce, and Lagrange [24].

A curious, though not totally unexpected, coincidence appears in the list of astronomers who contributed toward the practical and theoretical development of least squares. Several of these astronomers are now almost as equally renowned for their contributions to the foundations of statistics as they are acclaimed for their contributions to dynamical theories of the solar system members. One certainly recognizes the names of Gauss, Bessel, Laplace, and Poisson in connection with statistics. In fact, until the renaissance of interest in dynamical astronomy initiated by the *space age* (1957 Sputnik I), many present-day scientists may even have forgotten that these men were primarily astronomers. It is no mere happenstance that many outstanding and lasting contributions in many facets of mathematics were motivated and generated by the practical and theoretical demands of celestial mechanics theory.

Perhaps the first major advance in estimation theory, after the least squares introduction, was the *method of moments* formulated by K. Pearson [47,115,116]. Although the method of moments is no longer widely used, one often encounters situations in which the method is applicable when other estimators exhibiting greater theoretical attributes can be employed only with a large amount of labor. The main disadvantage of the method of moments is that it has been established that estimates found with this technique are not the *best* possible from the viewpoint of *efficiency* [47].

The present firm foundations of estimation theory are attributed to R. A. Fisher. His contributions are contained in a series of fundamental papers [46,47,48]. Fisher demonstrated that the method of maximum likelihood was usually superior to the method of moments and that estimates derived by the likelihood technique could not be improved *essentially*. To students of scientific history, it comes as no great surprise that K. Gauss had, at least in particular cases, anticipated the important general method of estimation introduced by Fisher as the *method of maximum likelihood*. Although Gauss had anticipated the maximum likelihood estimator, he felt that such estimators were inferior to the least squares estimation. His opinions were disclosed in a series of correspondence with Bessel.

Fisher also introduced a set of definitions that have been adopted for describing estimators. He introduced such terms as *unbiased*, *sufficiency*, *efficiency*, and *asymptotic efficiency* into the theory of estimation. These concepts motivated a whole series of statistical theories and publications dealing with the detailed theoretical aspects of estimators. In particular, generalizations of the theory led to the relatively recent developments of nonparametric estimation in which the exact nature of the probability distribution for the random variables need not be specified. By carefully examining the foundations of estimation and introducing new concepts, Fisher freed estimation theory from the tight confines that had existed since the work of Gauss.

Almost concurrent with R. A. Fisher's statistical investigations was the rapid development of communication theory by engineers and physicists. Communication theory, as originally conceived, was applied to the transmission of intelligence by electrical means. By the very nature of the transmission media, communications were found to be perturbed by a random process, or noise, introduced by thermal motion in resistors, electron motion in vacuum tubes, galactic and ionosphere noise in propagation, etc. Communication engineers were vitally concerned with the effect of these noise sources on the intelligibility of signals within communication channels. The first attempts to reduce the effects of unwanted noise introduced filters designed to estimate the power-frequency spectrum of the desired signal. These attempts were in the proper direction but were severely limited because of the lack of an estimation theory that could be used to synthesize the required noise-separation filters.

A fresh approach to the study of information transmission in the presence of perturbing noise is generally attributed to N. Wiener (1942). However, an independent and similar theory had already been published by A. Kolmogorov in 1941 [85, 152]. Wiener made two important contributions. First, he demonstrated that estimation theory could be applied to synthesize an electrical filter that would provide a *best* separation of a desired signal in the presence of undesired noise. Second, Wiener emphasized the viewpoint of treating signals and noise as stochastic processes rather than viewing them in terms of their frequency spectra.

Wiener's work coincided with the birth of a new branch of science: *information theory*, or *statistical communication theory*. This coincidence has resulted in the almost immediate adoption of Wiener's technique. Moreover, as usual with each significant scientific advance, a number of modifications of the original technique were formulated.

During the transmission of a signal (interpreted in a very generalized sense) containing information, it is axiomatic that the transmission channel will perturb the signal by introducing a random process called *noise* (the random process is almost always assumed to be introduced as an additive process). A transformation of the received signal is frequently desired so that as much as possible of the undesired noise can be removed, thereby recapturing a better replica of the information-bearing signal. The transformation, or filter, is nothing more than a realization of an estimator applied to the experimental data, in which the estimated parameters are interpreted as the desired information message.

At first glance, Wiener's theory appears to be essentially a least squares estimation process. This indeed is the case. However, the similarities soon disappear because Wiener made elegant use of the fact that he was estimating parameters from input data in the form of a stochastic process. Thus, by leaning strongly upon the known characteristics of stochastic processes, he formulated an *optimum* estimator which makes the *best* separation between the desired signal and undesired noise. An important point is that Wiener demanded that the optimum estimator be a linear, physically realizable filter. The concept not only proves the existence of such filters, but also, in theory, permits one to synthesize the optimal filters. Of course, because the theory provides more specific properties of the optimum estimator than are attainable from a *conventional* least squares calculation, one must be prepared to pay a penalty for the increased output. The cost is in the requirement for more a priori knowledge of the probability distributions of both the desired signal and undesired noise. We shall see that these additional requirements are essentially the reason why filter theory is classed as a facet of probability rather than as a facet of statistics.

## 1.3
## *RELATED PROBLEMS AND TECHNIQUES*

One can readily surmise that estimation theory is closely related to other mathematical problems and techniques. Certainly the terminology of *least squares* and *maximum likelihood* suggest connections with familiar mathematical methods for maximizing and minimizing functions of several variables. Thus, in the study of estimation theory, it should come as no surprise when developments are encountered which rely on results from such diverse fields as calculus of variations, Lagrange multipliers, game theory, dynamic and linear programming, and inequalities in Hilbert space [93].

The evolution and ready availability of digital computers has had an almost unexpected impact upon estimation theory. While before this age of computational ease analysts would spend a great amount of effort in formulating *closed-form* solutions or simple computational algorithms, the current tendency is to program the complete problem and let the computer grind out the answers. Nonlinear estimation problems, which heretofore had been diligently avoided, are now almost considered routine for numerical evaluation.

The impact of the computer on estimators is even more dramatic in another area. Computers are now being employed as an integral part of many systems as a control and executive element. This trend has been exploited by system designs in which the detection of a signal, or the estimation of system parameters, is an integral part of the system and not an operation carried out as a separate entity. Thus estimators are frequently built into a system and are rapidly losing their identities as techniques simply for reducing the results of a sequence of experiments.

# Chapter 2

# OPTIMAL ESTIMATES

The literature on estimation theory is plagued by such adjectives as *good*, *best*, and *optimal*. These modifiers have been used so loosely that frequently they convey almost no information. It is a natural tendency for the experimenter to want to analyze observations in order to form a *best* estimate of a desired set of parameters. The difficulty is that no universally accepted criterion for *best* estimate exists.

The dictionary defines *optimal* as *the most favorable to a given end*. Notice that even in this definition the word *optimal* conveys no meaning unless the *given-end* conditions are specified. The task of choosing the criterion for determining optimal estimators is a difficult one, and the choice is by no means governed by simple intuition. The optimum technique will depend largely upon the ultimate purpose for which the estimates are made. Because the estimates are required to reach a decision, the very nature of this decision will often influence the selection of an *estimator*, or process for combining redundant data. For practical data-reduction systems, the prediction precision is only one of several factors to be considered in the choice of the estimator. The prediction speed and required computer capability (speed and capacity) are at least equally important considerations. At times it may be desirable to trade computer program simplicity for prediction precision. Thus, when computer capacity is at a premium because of other required system calculations, a simpler estimator can often be used if one is willing to accept a possible loss in estimation precision.

If about 25–50 measurements have been made, the *best* estimate of the average value may not necessarily depend upon a lengthy calculation employing some complex estimator. If a quick answer is required, the best estimator may be to merely scan the data and *guess* the average value. Obviously the modifier *best* can vary widely in its meaning.

Another rather controversial point bears emphasis at this time. The conditions for optimal estimates will be found to vary through rather wide ranges. This variation should be expected from the arguments already given for the use of such terms as *good*, *best*, or *optimal*. However, the mathematical difficulties stemming from the adoption of any universal criterion of *optimal estimate* leads to several alternatives. Thus, depending upon the mathematical manipulation problems, one may be forced to choose optimal criteria on the basis of utility rather than elegance.

The arbitrariness of optimality was assailed by L. A. Zadeh in an editorial [164] from which the following quotations serve to keynote our approach to optimal solutions.

> How reasonable is our insistence on optimal solutions. Not too long ago we were content with designing systems which merely met given specifications. It was primarily Wiener's work on optimal filtering and prediction that changed profoundly this attitude toward the design of systems and their components. Today we tend, perhaps, to make a fetish of optimality. If a system is not *best* in one sense or another, we do not feel satisfied. Indeed, we are apt to place too much confidence in a system that is, in effect, optimal by definition.
>
> To find an optimal system we first choose a criterion of performance. Then we specify a class of acceptable systems in terms of various constraints on the design, cost, etc. Finally, we determine a system within the specified class which is *best* in terms of the criterion adopted. . . .

## 2.1 *SIMPLE ESTIMATOR*

As an introduction to estimation theory, let us recall a familiar example of an optimal estimator that arises in the development of statistical foundations. Suppose that $x$ represents a one-dimensional random variable selected from a given population. Moreover, let the probability density (frequency) function of the population be denoted by the function $f(x)$. Then the *expected* (*average*, *mean*) value of $x$ is defined as

$$\operatorname{avg} x = \int x f(x)\, dx, \tag{2–1}$$

where the range of integration is over all permissible values of $x$. The notation of (2–1) is inconvenient because of the large number of times that expected values must be indicated. The adopted conventional notation is

$$\mathrm{E}_x\{g(x)\} = \int g(x) f(x)\, dx \overset{d}{=} \operatorname{avg}_x g(x). \tag{2–2}$$

Subscripts are used on the expected value operator to indicate the particular set of random variables that are operated upon. The subscripts are usually omitted if no ambiguity exists in the expression.

An estimation example can now be stated. We wish to estimate, or choose, a real number $a$ such that the following expectation is minimized:

$$I = \mathrm{E}\{(x - a)^2\}. \tag{2–3}$$

Because the expectation is defined as an integral, it is a linear operator. Therefore, (2–3) can be expanded as

$$I = \mathrm{E}\{x^2\} - 2a\mathrm{E}\{x\} + a^2. \tag{2–4}$$

One method of obtaining the desired minimization is to establish the condition for which $dI/da = 0$. This yields the well-known result

$$a = \mathrm{E}\{x\}. \tag{2–5}$$

That is, the expected value of the square of the deviations of a random variable from a constant is a stationary value when the constant is chosen as the expected value of the random variable; it has not been established that this stationary value is actually a minimum.

The solution technique of finding conditions of zero slope for minimization problems can frequently lead to ambiguous solutions, particularly when the method is applied to multivalued and nonlinear functions of random variables. This sort of ambiguity occurs when there may exist several relative minima but only one absolute minimal value. In such situations, some additional argument must be applied to select or to prove that an absolute minimum has been selected.

A rather standard technique for establishing an absolute minimum of $I$ is to arrange the function $I$ into the sum and differences of positive terms. For example, complete the square in (2–4) to obtain the equivalent form

$$I = \mathrm{E}\{x^2\} + (a - \mathrm{E}\{x\})^2 - \mathrm{E}^2\{x\}. \tag{2–6}$$

Since each term is now a square of a real number and as such is positive or zero, it follows that $I$ will have its minimum value when the second term on the right is a minimum, or if $a = \mathrm{E}\{x\}$.

Although this example appears to be almost trivial, it will be seen that many of the theoretical arguments involving more complex estimators are founded upon the simple techniques used here.

## 2.2
## *LOSS AND RISK*

The problem of optimal estimates can only be attacked after the establishment of a general acceptable criterion of optimality. Specific practical problems are sometimes best treated with different criteria of optimality.

However, our initial approach will be to establish the properties that include a large class of estimation problems.

Let $l(b,\hat{b})$ be a function which, for each true value of a parameter $b$ and its estimated value $\hat{b}$, assigns a *loss* or *cost*. The loss function cannot always be chosen as one which most naturally fits the physical problem. Compromises in the nature of the function are usually necessary, and the selection of a loss function in a specific case is often governed more by mathematical manipulative convenience than by physical arguments.

The most widely employed loss function is the squared error

$$l(b, \hat{b}) = (\hat{b} - b)^2. \tag{2–7}$$

In this case the *loss* in assigning to $b$ its estimated value $\hat{b}$ is $(\hat{b} - b)^2$. It has been recognized for many years that the squared-error loss function is not entirely satisfactory and a variety of other loss functions have been considered as alternatives. All too often, these other functions have been rejected because of apparent manipulative difficulties. Our immediate objective is to introduce a general class of loss functions (including the squared-error) which has both mathematically and physically desirable characteristics.

The estimate error $q$ is defined as the difference between the estimated value of a parameter $\hat{b}$ and the true value $b$, i.e.,

$$q = \hat{b} - b. \tag{2–8}$$

We shall call a loss function $l$ a member of class $L$, $l \in L$, if it has the following properties:

$$\begin{aligned} \text{class } L\text{:}\quad & l(q) = 0 && \text{if } q = 0 \\ & l(q_2) \geq l(q_1) && \text{if } q_2 \geq q_1 \geq 0\text{; monotonic} \\ & l(q) = l(-q) && \text{symmetric.} \end{aligned} \tag{2–9}$$

It is generally convenient, although not always necessary, to restrict $l$ to be continuous in the ranges of interest and to choose it as a convex function [39]. A convex function on the interval [0,1] is defined by the inequality

$$l(p_1 q_1 + p_2 q_2) \leq p_1 l(q_1) + p_2 l(q_2) \tag{2–10}$$

where $p_1$ and $p_2$ are any constants such that

$$p_1, p_2 \geq 0$$

$$p_1 + p_2 = 1.$$

A geometrical representation of a convex function is one whose graph never lies above the line segment connecting two points.

Convex functions can be characterized by the fact that, if $l$ is twice differentiable, then $l(q)$ is convex in $q$ if, for all $q$,

$$\frac{d^2 l}{dq^2} \geq 0. \tag{2–11}$$

The class of loss functions, $L$, contains many desirable functions. These include, for constant $k > 0$,

$$
\begin{aligned}
&\text{a. } l(q) = kq^2; && \text{squared error} \\
&\text{b. } l(q) = kq^{2n}; && \text{even powers} \\
&\text{c. } l(q) = k\,|q|; && \text{magnitude of error} \\
&\text{d. } l(q) = \left[\frac{1}{b}(\hat{b} - b)\right]^2; && \text{fractional error} \\
&\text{e. } l(q) = k[1 - \exp(-q^2)]; && \\
&\text{f. } l(q) = \begin{cases} 0; & |q| < k \\ 1; & |q| \geq k \end{cases}; && \text{bounded error.}
\end{aligned} \tag{2–12}
$$

Although the general loss functions of class $L$ do not necessarily lead to the elegant and complete theoretical developments possible with the particular function $l(q) = q^2$, it is possible to obtain general fundamental properties of estimators employing convex loss functions of class $L$.

The *risk function* $R$ is defined as the expected value of the loss function over the range of admissable values of the error; i.e.,

$$
\begin{aligned}
R(b) &= \mathrm{E}\{l(b, \hat{b})\} \\
&= \mathrm{E}\{l(q)\}, \qquad \text{if } q = \hat{b} - b.
\end{aligned} \tag{2–13}
$$

More refined definitions of risk functions are used in decision theory and the theory of games; but for present purposes, the simple definition of (2–13) will suffice [25, 43, 67, 100, 150, 154]. For most of the following discussions the second form of (2–13) will be used or implied tacitly.

Notice that the risk function $R(b)$ is nothing more than a generalization of (2–3). If one is willing to assume that an a priori distribution of the errors $q$ exists, then an *optimum* estimator can be defined as the value of the estimated parameter $\hat{b}$ that minimizes the risk $R(b)$. Such an optimum procedure is called a *Bayes solution* corresponding to the a priori probability density of the error $q$. The resulting minimum of $R(b)$ is called the *Bayes risk* of $q$.

Although we shall develop the Bayes risk condition, it is necessary to point out that Bayes solutions have been seriously questioned by some statisticians. The fundamental argument is based upon the requirement of a priori probability densities for random variables observed during an experiment. In many statistical problems the existence of an a priori density function cannot be assumed; it is usually unknown to the observer, and thus the utility of a Bayes solution is doubtful. In spite of these valid objections, Bayes solutions will be employed in many instances because they allow us to develop a useful theory of optimal estimators in explicit form.

The minimization of the risk function $R(\hat{b})$ requires further assumptions than were necessary in the example of (2–3). Suppose that the loss function $l(q) \in L$ and is convex. Further, let us restrict the random variable $b$ to having a symmetric distribution function. That is, the distribution function of $b$ has the property

$$F_b(\beta) = \text{Prob}\,(b \leq \beta)$$
$$F_b(\beta + \bar{b}) = 1 - F_b(\bar{b} - \beta) \tag{2–14}$$
$$\bar{b} = \mathrm{E}\{b\}.$$

Although not strictly necessary to the arguments, we make the simplifying assumption that $F_b(\beta)$ is absolutely continuous and, therefore, has a derivative at every point. Then a probability density function $f(b)$ will exist and be related to the distribution function by the integral

$$F_b(\beta) = \int^{\beta} f(b)\, db. \tag{2–15}$$

Based upon the preceding assumptions, we shall now find the value of $\hat{b}$ that minimizes the risk $R(\hat{b})$. Consider the following sequence of manipulations:

$$\begin{aligned}
R(\hat{b}) &= \mathrm{E}\{l(\hat{b} - b)\}; && \text{(2–13) for } q = \hat{b} - b\\
&= \int l(\hat{b} - b) f(b - \bar{b})\, db; && \text{definition}\\
&= \int l(\hat{b} - x - \bar{b}) f(x)\, dx; && x = b - \bar{b}\\
&= \int l(\hat{b} + x - \bar{b}) f(-x)\, dx; && \text{replace } x \text{ by } -x\\
&= \int l(-\hat{b} - x + \bar{b}) f(-x)\, dx; && \text{symmetry of } l(q);\ \text{(2–9)}\\
&= \int l(-\hat{b} - x + \bar{b}) f(x)\, dx; && \text{symmetry of } F_x(\beta);\ \text{(2–14), (2–15)}\\
&= \int l(2\bar{b} - \hat{b} - b) f(b - \bar{b})\, db;\\
&= \mathrm{E}\{l(2\bar{b} - \hat{b} - b)\}.
\end{aligned} \tag{2–16}$$

Therefore, we can write

$$\mathrm{E}\{l(\hat{b} - b)\} = \tfrac{1}{2}\mathrm{E}\{l(\hat{b} - b)\} + \tfrac{1}{2}\mathrm{E}\{l(2\bar{b} - \hat{b} - b)\}. \tag{2–17}$$

Drawing upon the convex property of the loss function and the linearity of the expectation operator, it follows that

$$\begin{aligned}
&\mathrm{E}\{l[\tfrac{1}{2}(\hat{b} - b) + \tfrac{1}{2}(2\bar{b} - \hat{b} - b)]\}\\
&\qquad \leq \tfrac{1}{2}\mathrm{E}\{l(\hat{b} - b) + \tfrac{1}{2}\mathrm{E}\{l(2\bar{b} - \hat{b} - b)\},\\
&\mathrm{E}\{l(\bar{b} - b)\} \leq \mathrm{E}\{l(\hat{b} - b)\} = R(\hat{b}).
\end{aligned} \tag{2–18}$$

Hence, the minimum value of the risk is attained if the estimate $\hat{b}$ is chosen as [135]

$$\hat{b} = \bar{b} = \mathrm{E}\{b\}. \tag{2–19}$$

Notice that, even for the more general risk function of (2–13), the minimum value is attained when the estimate is equal to the mean value of the observables. This is the same result previously obtained for the least squares example of Section 2.1.

The result (2–19) can also be obtained if, instead of restricting the loss function to being convex, the distribution function is convex.

## 2.3
### *BEST ESTIMATES*

Frequently difficulties arise in estimating parameters in experiments for which the parameters themselves are not directly measureable. With this in mind, our immediate goal is to extend and generalize the results obtained in Section 2.2.

Let $x, y_1, y_2, \ldots, y_n$ be a set of $n + 1$ one-dimensional random variables. Further, assume that we are given the conditional distribution function of $x$ conditioned by the given set $\{y_i\}$,

$$F(\xi \,|\, \eta_1, \ldots, \eta_n) = Pr(x \leq \xi \,|\, y_1 = \eta_1, \ldots, y_n = \eta_n), \tag{2–20}$$

where $\{\eta_i\}$ are a set of values taken by the set of random variables $\{y_i\}$. If $F(\xi, \eta_1, \ldots, \eta_n)$ is the joint probability distribution function and if $F(\eta_1, \ldots, \eta_n)$ is the marginal distribution function, the three distribution functions are related in the following manner:

$$F(\xi, \eta_1, \ldots, \eta_n) = F(\eta_1, \ldots, \eta_n) F(\xi \,|\, \eta_1, \ldots, \eta_n), \tag{2–21}$$

$$\begin{aligned} &Pr(x \leq \xi, y_1 \leq \eta_1, \ldots, y_n \leq \eta_n) \\ &\quad = Pr(y_1 \leq \eta_1, \ldots, y_n \leq \eta_n)\, Pr(x \leq \xi \,|\, y_1 = \eta_1, \ldots, y_n = \eta_n). \end{aligned} \tag{2–22}$$

Further, if all these distribution functions are absolutely continuous, the corresponding density functions will exist. Then (2–22) can also be written in terms of integrals of the density functions,

$$\begin{aligned} &\int_{-\infty}^{\eta_n} \cdots \int_{-\infty}^{\eta_1} \int_{-\infty}^{\xi} f(x, y_1, \ldots, y_n)\, dx\, dy_1 \ldots dy_n \\ &\quad = \int_{-\infty}^{\eta_n} \cdots \int_{-\infty}^{\eta_1} f(y_1, \ldots, y_n)\, dy_1 \ldots dy_n \cdot \int_{-\infty}^{\xi} f(x \,|\, y_1, \ldots, y_n)\, dx. \end{aligned} \tag{2–23}$$

The conditional expectation of a function of $x$ is defined by analogy to the ordinary expectation (2–2). Thus, by definition,

$$\mathrm{E}_x\{g(x) \,|\, y_1, \ldots, y_n\} = \int_{-\infty}^{\infty} g(x) f(x \,|\, y_1, \ldots, y_n)\, dx. \tag{2–24}$$

From the given definitions, it follows that

$$\mathrm{E}_y\{\mathrm{E}_x\{g(x)\,|\,y_1, \ldots, y_n\}\} = \mathrm{E}_y\left\{\int_{-\infty}^{\infty} g(x) f(x\,|\,y_1, \ldots, y_n)\,dx\right\}$$

$$(2\text{–}25)\qquad = \int_{-\infty}^{\infty} \cdots \int_{-\infty}^{\infty} g(x) f(x\,|\,y_1, \ldots, y_n) f(y_1, \ldots, y_n)\,dx\,dy_1 \ldots dy_n$$

$$= \int_{-\infty}^{\infty} \cdots \int_{-\infty}^{\infty} g(x) f(x, y_1, \ldots, y_n)\,dx\,dy_1 \ldots dy_n,$$

or

$$(2\text{–}26)\qquad \mathrm{E}_y\{\mathrm{E}_x\{g(x)\,|\,y_1, \ldots, y_n\}\} = \mathrm{E}_x\{g(x)\}.$$

Consider an experiment designed to measure a parameter $x$. Because of inevitable experimental errors, the results will have the form

$$(2\text{–}27)\qquad \begin{aligned} &\text{Observable} = \text{parameter} + \text{error} \\ &y_i = x + \epsilon_i; \qquad i = 1, \ldots, n. \end{aligned}$$

Given the distribution functions of the random variables and a set of measured values, $y_1 = \eta_1, \ldots, y_n = \eta_n$, one can determine the probability for the simultaneous occurrence of a value $x = \xi$ for the unknown parameter $x$ which is to be estimated. The estimate of $x$ will, therefore, be some function of the conditional distribution function $F(\xi\,|\,y_1, \ldots, y_n)$ and as such will be a nonrandom function of the particular random variables $y_1, \ldots, y_n$. Let us denote this function as

$$(2\text{–}28)\qquad Y = u(y_1, \ldots, y_n).$$

$Y$ is a random variable whose value is known when a particular set of observables, $y_1, \ldots, y_n$, is given. We now define the optimal estimate as one which minimizes the risk function,

$$(2\text{–}29)\qquad R(x) = \mathrm{E}\{l(x - Y)\}.$$

Using the property of conditional expectations given in (2–26), (2–29) can also be written as

$$(2\text{–}30)\qquad R(x) = \mathrm{E}_y\{\mathrm{E}\{l(x - Y)\,|\,y_1, \ldots, y_n\}\}.$$

The reason for applying this transformation is apparent when one notes that the first expectation does not depend upon the choice of $Y$, but only depends upon the values of $y_1, \ldots, y_n$. Hence, the minimizing problem is equivalent to minimizing the conditional expectation

$$(2\text{–}31)\qquad R'(x) = \mathrm{E}\{l(x - Y)\,|\,y_1, \ldots, y_n\}.$$

The required minimizing condition can be obtained from the following theorem by Sherman [77,136] (stated without proof), which is related to a theorem given by Anderson [2,135].

THEOREM 2.1: Assume that the loss function $l \in L$ and the conditional distribution function $F_x(\xi\,|\,\mathscr{Y})$, $\mathscr{Y} = (y_1, \ldots, y_n)$ is

(i) symmetric about the mean $\bar{\xi} = \mathrm{E}\{x \mid \mathscr{Y}\}$

$$F_x[(\xi - \bar{\xi}) \mid \mathscr{Y}] = 1 - F_x[(\bar{\xi} - \xi) \mid \mathscr{Y}],$$

(ii) convex for $\xi \leq \bar{\xi}$

$$F_x[\lambda\xi_1 + (1 - \lambda)\xi_2 \mid \mathscr{Y}] \leq \lambda F_x(\xi_1 \mid \mathscr{Y}) + (1 - \lambda)F_x(\xi_2 \mid \mathscr{Y}),$$

for all $\xi_1$, $\xi_2 \leq \bar{\xi}$, and $0 \leq \lambda \leq 1$. Then the random variable $\hat{x}$, which minimizes the risk function

$$R(x) = \mathrm{E}\{l(x - Y) \mid \mathscr{Y}\}, \tag{2–32}$$

is the conditional expectation

$$\hat{x} = \mathrm{E}\{x \mid \mathscr{Y}\}. \tag{2–33}$$

A heuristic verification of this theorem can be made using analogous arguments leading from (2–16) to (2–19).

Applying Theorem 2.1 yields the result that the optimum estimate that minimizes the risk function (2–31), and hence (2–29), is

$$\hat{x} = \mathrm{E}\{x \mid y_1, \ldots, y_n\}. \tag{2–34}$$

Once more we perceive that, even for the very general risk function (2–29), the optimum estimate is given by an expected value in which only the random variable appears explicitly and not as an argument of a loss function.

It should be pointed out that condition (ii) in Theorem 2.1 can be replaced by the condition that the loss function be convex.

## 2.4
## *MINIMUM MEAN-SQUARED ESTIMATOR*

Although the theory of least squares estimators is the subject of Chapter 5, a short section is appropriate at this point to imbed the least squares risk function into the general theory of optimal estimators. In particular, we shall show that, for the loss function

$$l(q) = q^2, \tag{2–35}$$

the minimizing theorem of Section 2.3 is valid without imposing the restrictions that the conditional distribution function be both symmetric and convex.

The proof of this conjecture depends upon a theorem concerning conditional expectations [42, p.22].

THEOREM 2.2 If $x$ and $y$ are random variables such that

$$\mathrm{E}\{|y|\} < \infty, \qquad \mathrm{E}\{|xy|\} < \infty, \tag{2–36}$$

and $x = x(z_1, z_2, \ldots, z_n)$, then

$$\mathrm{E}\{xy\,|\,z_1, \ldots, z_n\} = x\mathrm{E}\{y\,|\,z_1, \ldots, z_n\} \tag{2–37}$$

with probability 1, and

$$\mathrm{E}\{[y - \mathrm{E}\{y\,|\,z_1, \ldots, z_n\}]x\} = 0. \tag{2–38}$$

The risk function (2–29) corresponding to the squared-error-loss function (2–35) is

$$R(\xi) = \mathrm{E}\{(\xi - Y)^2\}. \tag{2–39}$$

Let $y_1, \ldots, y_n$ be a sequence of experimental observations. Apply (2–26) to (2–39). Then

$$R(\xi) = \mathrm{E}_y\{\mathrm{E}\{(\xi - Y)^2\,|\,y_1, \ldots, y_n\}\}. \tag{2–40}$$

Again, our minimizing problem is equivalent to finding an estimate which minimizes

$$R'(\xi) = \mathrm{E}\{(\xi - Y)^2\,|\,y_1, \ldots, y_n\}. \tag{2–41}$$

Assume, for the moment, that

$$\hat{\xi} = \mathrm{E}\{\xi\,|\,y_1, \ldots, y_n\}. \tag{2–42}$$

Further, by property (2–26),

$$\mathrm{E}\{|\xi|^2\} = \mathrm{E}\{\mathrm{E}\{|\xi|^2\,|\,y_1, \ldots, y_n\}\}. \tag{2–43}$$

But because of Jensen's inequality (Section 2.5),

$$\mathrm{E}\{|\hat{\xi}|^2\} \le \mathrm{E}\{|\xi|^2\}, \tag{2–44}$$

$$\mathrm{E}\{|\hat{\xi}|^2\} \le \mathrm{E}\{\mathrm{E}\{|\xi|^2\,|\,y_1, \ldots, y_n\}\} = \mathrm{E}\{|\xi|^2\}. \tag{2–45}$$

Assuming that $\mathrm{E}\{|\xi Y|\} < \infty$, we can use Theorem 2.2 to show that

$$\mathrm{E}\{[\xi - \mathrm{E}\{\xi\,|\,y_1, \ldots, y_n\}]Y\} = 0. \tag{2–46}$$

Equations (2–46) and (2–42) together state that $\xi - \hat{\xi}$ is a random variable which is orthogonal to $Y$. It is also orthogonal to $(\hat{\xi} - Y)$, which is also a function of the set $\{y_i\}$. With this fact established, consider the expansion

$$\begin{aligned} \mathrm{E}\{(\xi - Y)^2\} &= \mathrm{E}\{[(\xi - \hat{\xi}) + (\hat{\xi} - Y)]^2\,|\,\mathscr{Y}\} \\ &= \mathrm{E}\{(\xi - \hat{\xi})^2\,|\,\mathscr{Y}\} + \mathrm{E}\{(\hat{\xi} - Y)^2\,|\,\mathscr{Y}\} \\ &\quad + 2\mathrm{E}\{(\xi - \hat{\xi})(\hat{\xi} - Y)\,|\,\mathscr{Y}\}; \qquad \mathscr{Y} = y_1, \ldots, y_n. \end{aligned} \tag{2–47}$$

The last term vanishes because of the orthogonality property, (2–46). Since each remaining term is positive, it follows that the right side of (2–47) attains an absolute minimum for the choice

$$Y = \hat{\xi} = \mathrm{E}\{\xi\,|\,y_1, \ldots, y_n\}. \tag{2–48}$$

This statement concludes the demonstration of the fact that a squared-loss function leads to our optimal estimator without the distribution function being either symmetric or convex.

Directly related to the preceding result is the principal reason why minimum mean-squared-error risk functions are almost universally employed for estimation problems.

## 2.5
## *AN INEQUALITY FOR FUNCTIONS OF EXPECTED VALUES*

Equation (2–45) in the preceding section is a special case of Jensen's inequality. This inequality can readily be proved in a restrictive form by using properties of optimal estimators. Let $y$ be a real random variable, and let the function $g(\cdot)$ be a convex function of its argument. Further, let $\mathrm{E}\{g(y)\}$ and the first two derivatives $g' = dg/dy$ and $g'' = d^2g/dy^2$ exist. Expand $g(y)$ into a Taylor series about some constant value $a$, keeping only two terms and a remainder. Thus,

$$g(y) = g(a) + g'(a)(y - a) + \tfrac{1}{2}g''(a)(y - a)^2 + \tfrac{1}{2}g''(\bar{y})(y - \bar{y})^2; \qquad y \leq \bar{y} \leq a. \tag{2–49}$$

Taking expected values of each side of (2–49) yields

$$\mathrm{E}\{g(y)\} = g(a) + g'(a)\mathrm{E}\{(y - a)\} + \tfrac{1}{2}g''(a)\mathrm{E}\{(y - a)^2\} + \tfrac{1}{2}g''(\bar{y})\mathrm{E}\{(y - \bar{y})^2\}. \tag{2–50}$$

Because $g$ is a convex function, $g''(\bar{y}) \geq 0$. Therefore, the last term on the right side of (2–50) is positive. Similarly, the third term is also positive. Moreover, we have already shown that the minimum value of this term is attained when $a = \mathrm{E}\{y\}$. It then follows that for $a = \mathrm{E}\{y\}$,

$$\mathrm{E}\{g(y)\} \geq g(\mathrm{E}\{y\}). \tag{2–51}$$

This result is called *Jensen's inequality*. Either by extending the arguments to conditional expectations or by referring to Doob [23, p.33], one finds the conditional version of the inequality to be

$$\mathrm{E}\{g(y)\,|\,\mathscr{Y}\} \geq g(\mathrm{E}\{y|\mathscr{Y}\}). \tag{2–52}$$

## 2.6
## *NORMAL DISTRIBUTIONS*

All too frequently, data analysts have jumped to the conclusion that only error-squared-loss functions can be handled in estimation problems. This, as has been demonstrated in the previous sections, is an erroneous conclusion. Nearly as prevalent as the belief in error-squared-loss functions is the almost inbred belief that a normal distribution must be postulated for the measurement or estimation errors in order to obtain *closed-form* expressions for optimal estimators. Again, such concepts are not founded upon fact and the present state of knowledge of estimation theory. It is true that the explicit knowledge that the random variables are normally distributed can frequently be exploited in the formulation of estimators. The fact that many estimators have been explicitly formulated for normal variates has led to an almost overemphasis of this distribution coupled with a false impression that normality assumptions are an essential ingredient in the theory of estimators.

Analogous to the lifting of restrictive conditions in the limited theory of mean-squared errors, similar generalizations can be obtained from the additional information that is available if one postulates that the random variables are normally distributed.

First, we remark that the normal distribution function is both convex and symmetric about the mean value. In one dimension, the normal distribution function is

$$F(\xi) = \int_{-\infty}^{\xi} (2\pi\sigma^2)^{-1/2} \exp\left(-\frac{1}{2}\frac{x^2}{\sigma^2}\right) dx. \tag{2–53}$$

Thus, $F(\xi)$ satisfies conditions (i) and (ii) of Theorem 2.1.

The interesting point is that, if the random variables have a normal distribution, then the theorems on best estimates can be extended to a class of asymmetric loss functions [9, 18]. Brown [18] considered the class of loss functions $l(q)$, which are nonnegative, nondecreasing for $q \geq 0$ and nonincreasing for $q < 0$. Therefore, an element of this class of functions, $L'$, can be written as

Class $L'$:

$$l(q) = l(\hat{b} - b) = l_1(q) + l_2(q), \tag{2–54}$$

where

$$\begin{aligned} l_1(q) &= 0, & q &\leq 0 \\ 0 \leq q_1 &\leq q_2 & &\text{implies } 0 \leq l_1(q_1) \leq l_1(q_2) \\ l_2(q) &= 0, & q &\geq 0 \\ q_1 \leq q_2 &\leq 0 & &\text{implies } 0 \leq l_2(q_2) \leq l_2(q_1). \end{aligned} \tag{2–55}$$

Notice that loss functions satisfying (2–54) and (2–55) include the loss functions of class $L$ defined by (2–9). Examples of asymmetric and symmetric loss functions are shown in Figure 2–1.

The risk function corresponding to a loss function $l(q)$ of class $L'$ is

$$R(b) = \mathrm{E}\{l(\hat{b} - b)\} = \mathrm{E}\{l(q)\}. \tag{2–56}$$

Suppose $q$ is postulated to have a normal distribution, then (2–56) becomes

$$R(b) = \int_{-\infty}^{\infty} l(q) f(q)\, dq, \tag{2–57}$$

where the probability density function in the expected value operation is

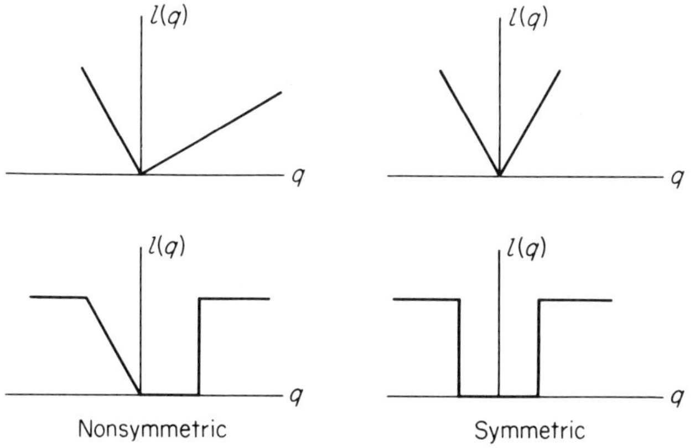


**Fig. 2-1** Examples of loss functions.

$$f(q) = (2\pi\sigma^2)^{-1/2} \exp\left(-\frac{1}{2}\frac{q^2}{\sigma^2}\right). \tag{2-58}$$

Hence, (2–57) can be explicitly written as

$$R(b) = (2\pi\sigma^2)^{-1/2} \int_{-\infty}^{\infty} l(q) \exp\left(-\frac{1}{2}\frac{q^2}{\sigma^2}\right) dq. \tag{2-59}$$

Using a change of variables, $q^2 = \sigma^2 u^2$,

$$R(b) = (2\pi)^{-1/2} \int_{-\infty}^{\infty} l(u\sigma) \exp(-\tfrac{1}{2}u^2)\, du. \tag{2-60}$$

Substitute the decomposition (2–54) into (2–60) to obtain

$$\begin{aligned} R(b) &= (2\pi)^{-1/2} \int_0^{\infty} l_1(u\sigma) \exp(-\tfrac{1}{2}u^2)\, du \\ &\quad + (2\pi)^{-1/2} \int_{-\infty}^{0} l_2(u\sigma) \exp(-\tfrac{1}{2}u^2)\, du. \end{aligned} \tag{2-61}$$

Next consider $\sigma_1$ and $\sigma_2$ such that $0 \leq \sigma_1 \leq \sigma_2$. From the definition of class $L'$, it follows that

$$\begin{aligned} l_1(u\sigma_1) &\leq l_1(u\sigma_2); \qquad u \geq 0 \\ l_2(u\sigma_1) &\leq l_2(u\sigma_2); \qquad u < 0. \end{aligned} \tag{2-62}$$

Hence, if $0 \leq \sigma_1 \leq \sigma_2$, (2–61) yields

$$\begin{aligned} &\frac{1}{\sqrt{2\pi}} \int_{-\infty}^{\infty} l(\sigma_1 u) e^{-u^2/2}\, du \\ &\qquad = \frac{1}{\sqrt{2\pi}} \int_0^{\infty} l_1(\sigma_1 u) e^{-u^2/2}\, du + \frac{1}{\sqrt{2\pi}} \int_{-\infty}^{0} l_2(\sigma_1 u) e^{-u^2/2}\, du, \\ &\frac{1}{\sqrt{2\pi}} \int_{-\infty}^{\infty} l(\sigma_1 u) e^{-u^2/2}\, du \\ &\qquad \leq \frac{1}{\sqrt{2\pi}} \int_0^{\infty} l_1(\sigma_2 u) e^{-u^2/2}\, du + \frac{1}{\sqrt{2\pi}} \int_{-\infty}^{0} l_2(\sigma_2 u) e^{-u^2/2}\, du, \end{aligned} \tag{2-63}$$

or

$$\frac{1}{\sqrt{2\pi}} \int_{-\infty}^{\infty} l(\sigma_1 u) e^{-u^2/2}\, du \le \frac{1}{\sqrt{2\pi}} \int_{-\infty}^{\infty} l(\sigma_2 u) e^{-u^2/2}\, du. \tag{2–64}$$

Equation (2–64) implies that $R(b)$ in (2–56), considered as a function of $\sigma$, is a nondecreasing function of $\sigma$. That is, $\mathrm{E}\{l(q)\}$, where $l(q)$ is a member of class $L'$, varies monotonically with $\mathrm{E}\{q^2\} = \sigma^2$; or the value of $\hat{b}$ which minimizes $\mathrm{E}\{q^2\}$ also minimizes $\mathrm{E}\{l(q)\}$.

Zakai has shown that the fact that the random variables are normally distributed can be exploited further for even more general loss functions [168]. Although Zakai's demonstrations were for random processes, we shall exhibit a simplified version for random sequences. Let $b$ be a normally distributed random variable with zero mean value and variance $\sigma_b^2$. Let $y_1, \ldots, y_n$ be a sequence of observations. The estimate $\hat{b}$ is a function of the observations, or

$$\hat{b} = H(y_1, \ldots, y_n); \tag{2–65}$$

$b$ and $\{y_n\}$ are assumed to be jointly normally distributed with zero mean value. The loss and risk functions are solely restricted by the existence condition

$$\begin{aligned} R(a) &= \mathrm{E}\{|\, l(b-a)\,|\} \\ &= (2\pi\sigma_b^2)^{-1/2} \int_{-\infty}^{\infty} |\, l(b-a)\,| \exp\left\{-\frac{1}{2}\frac{b^2}{\sigma_b^2}\right\} db < \infty. \end{aligned} \tag{2–66}$$

Equation (2–66) defines a new class $L''$ of loss functions. Define $\hat{H}_{ls}$ as the least squares estimate of $b$ based upon the observed samples $y_1, \ldots, y_n$. That is $\hat{H}_{ls}$ is the value of $H$ which minimizes the risk

$$R_{ls}(H) = \mathrm{E}\{(b-H)^2 \,|\, y_1, \ldots, y_n\}. \tag{2–67}$$

We can now write [31, Section 24.6]

$$\begin{aligned} R(H) &= \mathrm{E}\{l(b-H) \,|\, y_1, \ldots, y_n\} \\ &= \int_{-\infty}^{\infty} l(b-H) \frac{1}{(2\pi\sigma^2)^{1/2}} \exp\left\{-\frac{1}{2\sigma^2}(b-\hat{H}_{ls})^2\right\} db \\ &= \int_{-\infty}^{\infty} l(b) \frac{1}{(2\pi\sigma^2)^{1/2}} \exp\left\{-\frac{1}{2\sigma^2}[b-(\hat{H}_{ls}-H)]^2\right\} db, \end{aligned} \tag{2–68}$$

where

$$\sigma^2 = \mathrm{E}\{(b-\hat{H}_{ls})^2\}. \tag{2–69}$$

Observe that the form of (2–68) indicates that the minimizing estimate $\hat{H}_l$ of $H$ will be a function only of $\hat{H}_{ls}$ and $\sigma^2$. Let

$$K = \min_{-\infty < z < \infty} \int_{-\infty}^{\infty} l(x) \exp\left\{-\frac{1}{2\sigma^2}(x-z)^2\right\} dx, \tag{2–70}$$

and let $-C$ be the value of $z$ which minimizes $K$. Comparison of (2–68) and (2–70) produces the desired result, i.e.,

$$\hat{H}_{ls} - \hat{H}_l = -C. \tag{2–71}$$

The *minimum* in (2–70) must be replaced by *inf* for those cases in which $C$ may not exist. In these situations there can exist a sequence $\{C_n\}$ such that the mean error can be made as close as desired to the lower-bound $K$. It is important to remark that $C$ is permitted to have the values $\pm\infty$. The value of $C$ will in general depend upon the particular form of the loss function, but not upon the observations. For example, if the loss function is of class $L$, as in (2–9), then one can show that $C = 0$. On the other hand, consider the loss function

$$\begin{aligned} l(q) = l(b - \hat{b}) &= q^2, \qquad & q \geq 0 \\ &= 0, & q < 0. \end{aligned} \tag{2–72}$$

If we let $\hat{b} \rightarrow +\infty$, the loss function will tend toward a negative value so that $\mathrm{E}\{l(q)\} = 0$. This implies that $C \rightarrow +\infty$.

## 2.7
## *GOOD ESTIMATES*

By definition an optimal estimate is a judgment based upon all available information. In particular, we have shown that for the general case and a large class of loss functions, the optimal estimator is a conditional expectation. Because the optimal estimator is a conditional expectation, estimation theory has developed along two broad avenues. One line of approach deals with normal variates which have the convenient attribute of being amenable to the calculation of the required conditional expectations. The other approach includes both normal and nonnormal variates. However, we are willing to accept *good estimators* instead of restricting ourselves to the ideal optimal estimator and terminating developments with a conditional expectation which can only be expressed as an implicit function.

A suitable definition must be formulated for a good estimator. Intuitively one feels that a good estimator has the desirable characteristic that, if a series of judgments are made from a sequence of observed data, the estimated values of the system parameters will cluster *near* the true values of these parameters. If the estimated values are all clustered in a small neighborhood about the true values, it is highly probable that the estimated values differ by only a small amount from the true parameter values. From this viewpoint, estimates can be classified as being *better* the closer they concentrate about the true values. In this sense, good estimates are closely related to measures of statistical concentration, such as variance. Some properties and definitions of some common types of estimators follow.

(i) *Unbiased estimate:* Let $\hat{x} = g(x_1, x_2, \ldots, x_n)$ be an estimate of a parameter $\xi$ based upon a set of observed values $\{x_i\}$. If $\mathrm{E}\{\hat{x}\} = \xi$, then $\hat{x}$ is called an unbiased estimate of $\xi$. If $\mathrm{E}\{\hat{x}\} < \xi$, the estimator is said to have *negative bias;* if $\mathrm{E}\{\hat{x}\} > \xi$, it is said to have *positive bias.*

(ii) *Consistent estimate:* If the estimate $\hat{x} = g(x_1, x_2, \ldots, x_n)$ converges in probability to $\xi$ as $n \to \infty$, then $\hat{x}$ is called a consistent estimate of $\xi$; $\hat{x}$ converges in probability to $\xi$ if

$$\lim_{n\to\infty} [\text{Prob}\,(\hat{x} - \xi) = 0] = 1.$$

A consistent estimator is always unbiased for sufficiently large $n$. However, the converse statement may not be true; an unbiased estimator need not be consistent.

(iii) *Efficiency:* Again, let $\hat{x}_i = g(x_1, x_2, \ldots, x_n)$, $i = 1, 2$ be two estimates of a parameter $\xi$ based upon a set of observed values $\{x_j\}$. The efficiency of the estimate $\hat{x}_2$ relative to $\hat{x}_1$ is defined as the ratio

$$\eta = \frac{\mathrm{E}\{(\xi - \hat{x}_1)^2\}}{\mathrm{E}\{(\xi - \hat{x}_2)^2\}} = \frac{a_1}{a_2}.$$

Notice that we did not restrict $\hat{x}_i$ to be unbiased estimates. Therefore, $a_i$ are not necessarily variances of the errors.

(iv) *Efficient estimate:* If in (iii) $\hat{x}_1$ and $\hat{x}_2$ are restricted to be unbiased estimates, then $a_1$ and $a_2$ are variances. $\hat{x}_1$ is called an efficient estimate of $\xi$ if for any other unbiased estimate, such as $\hat{x}_2$, $a_2 \geq a_1$. That is, no other unbiased estimator has a smaller variance than $\mathrm{E}\{(\xi - \hat{x}_1)^2\}$.

(v) *Sufficient estimate:* An estimator is called sufficient if it contains all the information in the set of observed values regarding the parameter to be estimated. Suppose $x_1, \ldots, x_n$ is a sample sequence selected from a population having the probability density function $f(x; \xi)$. If $\hat{x} = g(x_1, \ldots, x_n)$ is an estimate of $\xi$ such that the conditional expectation $\mathrm{E}\{\hat{x} | x_1, \ldots, x_n\}$ does not depend upon $\xi$, then $\hat{x}$ is a sufficient estimate.

While sufficient estimates are very desirable, they can only be expected to exist for very special classes of random variables.

Further properties and extensions of the concepts of consistent, sufficient, and efficient estimates can be found in statistical reference books [31,154]. These ideas were first introduced by Fisher [10,47] and are the focal point for much of the modern progress in statistical estimation theory.

## Problems

**2.1** The $n$th moment of a random variable $x$ is defined as

$$\mu_n = \mathrm{E}\{x^n\}.$$

Assuming that all the following moments exist, prove the inequality

$$(\mu_{2n+1})^2 \leq \mu_{2n}\mu_{2n+2}.$$

**2.2** For the random variable $x > 0$, show that

$$\mathrm{E}\left\{\frac{1}{x}\right\} \geq \frac{1}{\mathrm{E}\{x\}}.$$

**2.3** Sketch the loss functions defined in Eq. (2–12). Discuss physical problems in which such loss functions might have advantages not shared by the squared-error function.

**2.4** Show that the result in Eq. (2–19) follows if the probability density function is convex and the loss function is of class $L$, (2–9).

**2.5** Given the joint normal probability density function

$$f(x_1, x_2) = \frac{1}{2\pi(1-\rho^2)^{1/2}} \exp\left\{-\frac{1}{2(1-\rho^2)}[x_1^2 - 2\rho x_1 x_2 + x_2^2]\right\},$$

compute the conditional density function $f(x_1 \mid x_2)$.

**2.6** The joint distribution function of two normal variates is

$$F(x_1, x_2) = \int_{-\infty}^{x_2} \int_{-\infty}^{x_1} f(\xi_1, \xi_2)\, d\xi_1\, d\xi_2,$$

where $f(x_1, x_2)$ is defined in Problem 2.5. By direct calculation show that for normal variates

$$F(x_1, x_2) \leq [F(x_1)F(x_2)]^{1/2}.$$

Extend the result to arbitrary distributions, and in general show that

$$F(x_1, x_2, \ldots, x_n) \leq [F(x_1)F(x_2)\ldots F(x_n)]^{1/n}.$$

**2.7** Using the result of Problem 2.5, verify Eqs. (2–36) and (2–37).

**2.8** Give a formal proof of Theorem 2.2 for real-valued random variables assuming the existence of appropriate density functions.

**2.9** From the normal population having the probability density function

$$f(x) = (2\pi\sigma^2)^{-1/2} \exp\left(-\frac{(x-a)^2}{2\sigma^2}\right),$$

select three samples, and arrange them in magnitude order, $x_1 \leq x_2 \leq x_3$. One method of estimating the mean of the three samples would be

$$z = bx_1 + (1 - 2b)x_2 + bx_3.$$

The simple arithmetic mean of $x_1$, $x_2$, $x_3$ corresponds to $b = \frac{1}{3}$. The question to be answered is whether any other value of $b$ would give a *better* estimate of the mean $a$. Compute $\mathrm{E}\{z\}$ and the variance

$$\sigma_z^2 = \mathrm{E}\{(z - \mathrm{E}\{z\})^2\},$$

and show that $\sigma_z^2$ has an absolute minimum when $b = \frac{1}{3}$ [31, p.483].

**2.10** Verify the inequality

$$\mathrm{E}\{\hat{x}^2\} \leq \mathrm{E}\{x_1^2\}$$

if

$$\hat{x} = \mathrm{E}\{x_1 \mid x_2\}$$

and $x_1$, $x_2$ are normal variates. Extend the proof to verify (2–45).

# Chapter 3

# GEOMETRICAL PROPERTIES OF OPTIMAL ESTIMATORS

Based upon all the available data and information, it has been established that the optimal estimator for a system parameter is a conditional expectation, which is itself a random variable. As a general rule, except for normally distributed random variables, conditional expectations cannot be calculated explicitly. The principal objective of this chapter is to examine the properties of conditional expectations of normally distributed random variables and to exhibit the manner in which these properties can be employed to formulate a geometrical interpretation applicable to optimal estimators. Although many of the most elegant features of the geometrical concept are strictly valid only for normal variates, many of these features can be retained as *wide-sense* properties.

Because most of the theoretical developments are required for $n$-dimensional sets of parameters, it is extremely convenient to use matrix formulations. Instead of first introducing a concept in one dimension, extending it to two dimensions, and then, finally, generalizing the concept to $n$ dimensions, it is frequently far more satisfactory to use matrix equations at the outset and immediately treat the general $n$-dimensional cases. The next section contains a brief review of some properties of matrix calculus that will be employed in the $n$-dimensional treatments.

## 3.1
## *MATRIX CALCULUS*

A column matrix $\boldsymbol{x}$ will be called a *vector* (it may not be a *true* vector in the physical sense), and in component display form this is written as

(3–1)
$$\boldsymbol{x}^{[n\times 1]} = \begin{bmatrix} x_1 \\ x_2 \\ \vdots \\ x_n \end{bmatrix}.$$

Square brackets are used to enclose the elements of a matrix. Row (column) matrices (vectors), are printed in italic boldface or in boldface lowercase Greek letters. Wherever it is necessary, or desirable, to define the order of a matrix, the order will be written as a superscript enclosed in square brackets as illustrated in (3–1). A rectangular matrix is printed in boldface. Thus, if $a_{ij}$ are the elements of a matrix $\mathbf{A}$ of order $m \times n$, we write

(3–2)
$$\mathbf{A}^{[m\times n]} = [a_{ij}].$$

Superscripts are used to denote matrix operations. Thus,

| | |
|---|---|
| $\mathbf{A}^{T[n\times m]}$, | transpose of $\mathbf{A}$ having order $n \times m$ |
| $\mathbf{A}^{-1[m\times m]}$, | inverse of $\mathbf{A}$ |
| $\mathbf{A}^{\dagger[m\times n]}$, | pseudoinverse of $\mathbf{A}$ (Chapter 7). |

The derivative of a matrix $\mathbf{A}$, whose elements are scalar functions of the variable $t$, is defined as the matrix whose elements are the derivatives of the elements of the original matrix $\mathbf{A}$. For example, the derivative of a matrix is written as $d\mathbf{A}/dt$ and is defined as

(3–3)
$$\frac{d\mathbf{A}^{[m\times n]}}{dt} = \begin{bmatrix} \dfrac{da_{11}}{dt} & \dfrac{da_{12}}{dt} \cdots & \dfrac{da_{1n}}{dt} \\ \cdots & \cdots & \cdots \\ \dfrac{da_{m1}}{dt} & \dfrac{da_{m2}}{dt} \cdots & \dfrac{da_{mn}}{dt} \end{bmatrix}.$$

It can be demonstrated that this definition leads to the properties

(3–4)
$$\frac{d}{dt}(\mathbf{A} + \mathbf{B}) = \frac{d\mathbf{A}}{dt} + \frac{d\mathbf{B}}{dt},$$
$$\frac{d}{dt}(\mathbf{AB}) = \frac{d\mathbf{A}}{dt}\mathbf{B} + \mathbf{A}\frac{d\mathbf{B}}{dt},$$
$$\frac{d\mathbf{A}^2}{dt} = \frac{d}{dt}(\mathbf{AA}) = \frac{d\mathbf{A}}{dt}\mathbf{A} + \mathbf{A}\frac{d\mathbf{A}}{dt} \qquad \text{if } \mathbf{A} \text{ is square,}$$
$$\frac{d\mathbf{A}^{-1}}{dt} = -\mathbf{A}^{-1}\frac{d\mathbf{A}}{dt}\mathbf{A}^{-1}.$$

Frequently the elements of a matrix $\mathbf{A}$ are functions of $q$ variables $q_1, q_2, \ldots, q_n$, and we shall be interested in the matrix which results from considering the $n$ partial derivatives. For this purpose we introduce a matrix partial derivative operator defined formally as the vector

$$\nabla_q = \nabla_q^{[n\times 1]} = \begin{bmatrix} \dfrac{\partial}{\partial q_1} \\ \vdots \\ \dfrac{\partial}{\partial q_n} \end{bmatrix}. \tag{3-5}$$

Because it is defined as a vector, the operator $\nabla_q$ can only be applied to the transpose of a vector. Thus

$$\begin{aligned} \nabla_q^{[n\times 1]} \boldsymbol{x}^{T[1\times p]} &= \begin{bmatrix} \dfrac{\partial}{\partial q_1} \\ \vdots \\ \dfrac{\partial}{\partial q_n} \end{bmatrix} [x_1 \cdots x_p] \stackrel{d}{=} \mathbf{B}^{[n\times p]} \\ &= \begin{bmatrix} \dfrac{\partial x_1}{\partial q_1} & \dfrac{\partial x_2}{\partial q_1} \cdots & \dfrac{\partial x_p}{\partial q_1} \\ \cdots & \cdots & \cdots \\ \dfrac{\partial x_1}{\partial q_n} & \dfrac{\partial x_2}{\partial q_n} \cdots & \dfrac{\partial x_p}{\partial q_n} \end{bmatrix}. \end{aligned} \tag{3-6}$$

Unless $\nabla_q$ is of order $1 \times 1$, the ordinary rules of differentiation similar to (3–4) are simply not valid. For example,

$$\nabla_q^{[n\times 1]} (\mathbf{A}^{[1\times n]} \mathbf{B}^{[n\times p]})$$

cannot be expressed in a form corresponding to the second line of (3–4). The differential operator matrix has no meaning when applied to the individual matrices of the product **AB**. However, there is a special case in which the product rule holds. Consider the differential operator matrix acting upon the special case of a product $\boldsymbol{A}^{[1\times n]}\boldsymbol{B}^{[n\times 1]}$; then

$$\nabla_q^{[n\times 1]} (\boldsymbol{A}^{[1\times n]} \boldsymbol{B}^{[n\times 1]}) = (\nabla_q \boldsymbol{A})\boldsymbol{B} + (\nabla_q \boldsymbol{B}^T)\boldsymbol{A}^T. \tag{3-7}$$

If $\boldsymbol{B}^{[n\times 1]}$ is a vector whose elements are not functions of $q$, then

$$\nabla_q^{[n\times 1]} (\boldsymbol{B}^{T[1\times n]} \boldsymbol{q}^{[n\times 1]}) = \boldsymbol{B}^{[n\times 1]}. \tag{3-8}$$

Similarly,

$$\nabla_q^{[n\times 1]} (\boldsymbol{q}^{T[1\times n]} \mathbf{D}^{[n\times m]}) = \mathbf{D}^{[n\times m]}. \tag{3-9}$$

We shall have several occasions to apply the differential-operator matrix to a quadratic form. Consider a quadratic form which is typical of those occurring in estimation problems,

$$Q = \boldsymbol{A}^{T[1\times n]}(\boldsymbol{q})\, \boldsymbol{\Phi}^{[n\times n]}\, \boldsymbol{A}^{[n\times 1]}(\boldsymbol{q}), \tag{3-10}$$

where $\boldsymbol{\Phi}$ is a symmetric positive semidefinite matrix. Thus, $\boldsymbol{\Phi}$ can be written as the product

$$\boldsymbol{\Phi} = \boldsymbol{\Phi}^{1/2}\boldsymbol{\Phi}^{1/2}. \tag{3-11}$$

Apply (3–7), (3–9), and (3–11) to (3–10) to obtain

$$\nabla_q^{[n\times 1]} Q = \nabla_q \left[(\boldsymbol{A}^T \boldsymbol{\Phi}^{1/2})(\boldsymbol{\Phi}^{1/2}\boldsymbol{A})\right]$$
$$= 2[\nabla_q (\boldsymbol{A}^T\boldsymbol{\Phi}^{1/2})]\boldsymbol{\Phi}^{1/2}\boldsymbol{A} \tag{3–12}$$
$$= 2(\nabla_q \boldsymbol{A}^T)\boldsymbol{\Phi}\boldsymbol{A}.$$

Often one encounters a special case of (3–10) in which

$$\boldsymbol{A}^{[m\times 1]} = \mathbf{B}^{[m\times n]}\boldsymbol{q}^{[n\times 1]}. \tag{3–13}$$

For this situation, substitute (3–13) into (3–12), and apply (3–9) to find

$$\nabla_q Q = 2(\nabla_q \boldsymbol{q}^T\mathbf{B}^T)\boldsymbol{\Phi}\mathbf{B}\boldsymbol{q}$$
$$= 2\mathbf{B}^T\boldsymbol{\Phi}\mathbf{B}\boldsymbol{q}. \tag{3–14}$$

The integral of a matrix is defined in a manner analogous to the total differential, (3–3). We write

$$\int \mathbf{A}^{[m\times n]}\, dt = \begin{bmatrix} \int a_{11}(t)\,dt & \cdots & \int a_{1n}(t)\,dt \\ \cdots & \cdots & \cdots \\ \int a_{m1}(t)\,dt & \cdots & \int a_{mn}(t)\,dt \end{bmatrix}. \tag{3–15}$$

By definition the expected value is an integral operator; thus it follows that

$$\mathrm{E}\{\boldsymbol{x}^{[n\times 1]}\} = \begin{bmatrix} \mathrm{E}\{x_1\} \\ \vdots \\ \mathrm{E}\{x_n\} \end{bmatrix} = \begin{bmatrix} \int x_1 f(x_1)\,dx_1 \\ \vdots \\ \int x_n f(x_n)\,dx_n \end{bmatrix}. \tag{3–16}$$

As an illustration of the definition for the expected value of a matrix, let $\boldsymbol{x}^{[n\times 1]}$ be a random variable. If it is assumed that $\mathrm{E}\{\boldsymbol{x}\} = \boldsymbol{0}$, the covariance matrix of the random variable is

$$\boldsymbol{\Psi}^{[n\times n]} = \mathrm{E}\{\boldsymbol{x}\boldsymbol{x}^T\} = \mathrm{E}\left\{\begin{bmatrix} x_1 \\ \vdots \\ x_n \end{bmatrix}[x_1 \cdots x_n]\right\}$$

$$= \begin{bmatrix} \mathrm{E}\{x_1x_1\} & \mathrm{E}\{x_1x_2\} & \cdots & \mathrm{E}\{x_1x_n\} \\ \mathrm{E}\{x_2x_1\} & \mathrm{E}\{x_2x_2\} & \cdots & \mathrm{E}\{x_2x_n\} \\ \cdots & \cdots & \cdots & \cdots \\ \mathrm{E}\{x_nx_1\} & \mathrm{E}\{x_nx_2\} & \cdots & \mathrm{E}\{x_nx_n\} \end{bmatrix} \tag{3–17}$$

$$= \begin{bmatrix} \mu_{11} & \mu_{12} & \cdots & \mu_{1n} \\ \mu_{21} & \mu_{22} & \cdots & \mu_{2n} \\ \cdots & \cdots & \cdots & \cdots \\ \mu_{n1} & \mu_{n2} & \cdots & \mu_{nn} \end{bmatrix},$$

where the moments $\mu$ are

$$\mu_{ij} = \mathrm{E}\{x_i x_j\}. \tag{3–18}$$

We shall on occasion wish to consider linear combinations of the random variable $\boldsymbol{x}$ and to determine the new covariance matrix. Suppose

$$\boldsymbol{y}^{[m\times 1]} = \mathbf{H}^{[m\times n]}\boldsymbol{x}^{[n\times 1]}. \tag{3–19}$$

The covariance matrix of the new random variable $\boldsymbol{y}$ is

$$\begin{aligned}\boldsymbol{\Theta}^{[m\times m]} &= \mathrm{E}\{\boldsymbol{y}\boldsymbol{y}^T\}\\ &= \mathrm{E}\{\mathbf{H}\boldsymbol{x}\boldsymbol{x}^T\mathbf{H}^T\}.\end{aligned} \tag{3–20}$$

Let $\boldsymbol{x}\boldsymbol{x}^T = \mathbf{D}^{[n\times n]}$, then

$$\begin{aligned}\boldsymbol{\Theta} &= \mathrm{E}\{\mathbf{H}\mathbf{D}\mathbf{H}^T\}\\ &= \mathrm{E}\left\{\left[\sum_{j=1}^{n}\sum_{k=1}^{n} h_{ij}d_{jk}h_{lk}\right]\right\},\end{aligned} \tag{3–21}$$

where

$$\begin{aligned}\mathbf{H} &= [h_{ij}]\\ \mathbf{D} &= [d_{ij}]\\ \mathbf{H}^T &= [h_{ji}].\end{aligned} \tag{3–22}$$

Using the linearity property of the expectation,

$$\mathrm{E}\{ax_1 + bx_2\} = a\mathrm{E}\{x_1\} + b\mathrm{E}\{x_2\}, \tag{3–23}$$

(3–21) becomes

$$\begin{aligned}\boldsymbol{\Theta} &= \left[\sum_{j=1}^{n}\sum_{k=1}^{n} h_{ij}\mathrm{E}\{d_{jk}\}h_{lk}\right]\\ &= \mathbf{H}\mathrm{E}\{\mathbf{D}\}\mathbf{H}^T\\ &= \mathbf{H}\mathrm{E}\{\boldsymbol{x}\boldsymbol{x}^T\}\mathbf{H}^T\\ &= \mathbf{H}\boldsymbol{\Psi}\mathbf{H}^T.\end{aligned} \tag{3–24}$$

If $\mathrm{E}\{\boldsymbol{x}\} \neq \boldsymbol{0}$, the covariance matrix $\boldsymbol{\Theta}$ can be shown to have exactly the same form as (3–24).

## 3.2 CONDITIONAL EXPECTATIONS

$\boldsymbol{x}^{[n\times 1]}$ is called a *normal vector*, or a random vector having a normal distribution, with a nonsingular distribution if the quadratic form represented by the covariance matrix $\boldsymbol{\Psi}$ is positive definite and if the probability density corresponding to $\boldsymbol{x}$ has the normal form

$$f_x(\boldsymbol{\xi}) = (2\pi)^{-n/2}\,|\,\boldsymbol{\Psi}\,|^{-1/2}\exp\{-\tfrac{1}{2}(\boldsymbol{\xi} - \boldsymbol{m})^T\boldsymbol{\Psi}^{-1}(\boldsymbol{\xi} - \boldsymbol{m})\}, \tag{3–25}$$

where $\det \boldsymbol{\Psi} \overset{d}{=} |\,\boldsymbol{\Psi}\,|$.

A quadratic form $Q = \boldsymbol{x}^{T[1\times n]}\boldsymbol{\Psi}^{-1[n\times n]}\boldsymbol{x}^{[n\times 1]}$ is positive definite if and only if $Q > 0$ for all $\boldsymbol{x} \neq \boldsymbol{O}$. It may well happen that $\boldsymbol{\Psi}$ is positive semi-definite, and the inverse matrix $\boldsymbol{\Psi}^{-1}$ does not exist. This situation could result in a singular normal distribution for which the probability density function (3–25) is not defined. One method of circumventing the difficulty caused by a singular distribution is to introduce a new random variable defined by the transformation

$$\boldsymbol{x}^{[n\times 1]} = \mathbf{A}^{[n\times \nu]}\boldsymbol{y}^{[\nu\times 1]} + \boldsymbol{m}^{[n\times 1]}, \tag{3–26}$$

where $\nu$ is the rank of the singular matrix $\boldsymbol{\Psi}$. The covariance matrix of $\boldsymbol{y}$ will not be singular, and a density function similar to (3–25) can be written for the random variable $\boldsymbol{y}$.

The problem of the existence of the inverse of the covariance matrix can be avoided by defining a normal distribution by means of the characteristic function

$$\begin{aligned} \phi_x(\boldsymbol{z}) &= \mathrm{E}\{\exp(i\boldsymbol{z}^T\boldsymbol{x})\} \\ &= \exp(i\boldsymbol{z}^T\boldsymbol{m} - \tfrac{1}{2}\boldsymbol{z}^T\boldsymbol{\Psi}\boldsymbol{z}), \\ \boldsymbol{m} &= \mathrm{E}\{\boldsymbol{x}\}. \end{aligned} \tag{3–27}$$

Suppose that $\boldsymbol{x}_1^{[n\times 1]}$ and $\boldsymbol{x}_2^{[n\times 1]}$ are two normal vectors having mean values

$$\mathrm{E}\{\boldsymbol{x}_i\} = \boldsymbol{m}_i; \qquad i = 1, 2 \tag{3–28}$$

and covariance matrix

$$\begin{aligned} \Lambda &= \mathrm{E}\left\{\begin{bmatrix} \boldsymbol{x}_1 - \boldsymbol{m}_1 \\ \boldsymbol{x}_2 - \boldsymbol{m}_2 \end{bmatrix} [(\boldsymbol{x}_1 - \boldsymbol{m}_1)^T \quad (\boldsymbol{x}_2 - \boldsymbol{m}_2)^T]\right\} \\ &= \begin{bmatrix} \boldsymbol{\Psi}_1 & \boldsymbol{\Psi}_{12} \\ \boldsymbol{\Psi}_{12} & \boldsymbol{\Psi}_2 \end{bmatrix}, \end{aligned} \tag{3–29}$$

where

$$\begin{aligned} \boldsymbol{\Psi}_{ij} &= \mathrm{E}\{(\boldsymbol{x}_i - \boldsymbol{m}_i)(\boldsymbol{x}_j - \boldsymbol{m}_j)^T\} = \boldsymbol{\Psi}_{ji} = \boldsymbol{\Psi}_{ij}^T \\ \boldsymbol{\Psi}_{11} &= \boldsymbol{\Psi}_1 \\ \boldsymbol{\Psi}_{22} &= \boldsymbol{\Psi}_2. \end{aligned} \tag{3–30}$$

Analogous to (3–27), the joint characteristic function for the vectors $\boldsymbol{x}_1$ and $\boldsymbol{x}_2$ is

$$\begin{aligned} \phi_{x_1x_2}(\boldsymbol{z}_1, \boldsymbol{z}_2) &= \mathrm{E}\{\exp[i(\boldsymbol{z}_1^T\boldsymbol{x}_1 + \boldsymbol{z}_2^T\boldsymbol{x}_2)]\} \\ &= \exp[i(\boldsymbol{z}_1^T\boldsymbol{m}_1 + \boldsymbol{z}_2^T\boldsymbol{m}_2) \\ &\quad -\tfrac{1}{2}(\boldsymbol{z}_1^T\boldsymbol{\Psi}_1\boldsymbol{z}_1 + 2\boldsymbol{z}_1^T\boldsymbol{\Psi}_{12}\boldsymbol{z}_2 + \boldsymbol{z}_2^T\boldsymbol{\Psi}_2\boldsymbol{z}_2)]. \end{aligned} \tag{3–31}$$

The conditional expectation $\mathrm{E}\{\boldsymbol{x}_1 | \boldsymbol{x}_2\}$ could be calculated from (3–31) by making use of the moment-generating properties of the characteristic function. However, the following theorem will enable us to treat a general class of random variates which includes the normal variates [3,79].

THEOREM 3.1: The conditional expectation of two random vectors has the linear form

(3–32) $$\mathrm{E}\{\boldsymbol{x}_1^{[n\times 1]} \mid \boldsymbol{x}_2^{[n\times 1]}\} = \boldsymbol{m}_{12}^{[n\times 1]} + \mathbf{A}^{[n\times n]}\boldsymbol{x}_2^{[n\times 1]}$$

if and only if

(3–33) $$\nabla_{iz_1}^{[n\times 1]} \phi_{x_1x_2}(\boldsymbol{z}_1, \boldsymbol{z}_2)\,|_{\boldsymbol{z}_1=\boldsymbol{o}} = [\boldsymbol{m}_{12} + \mathbf{A}\,\nabla_{iz_2}]\phi_{x_2}(\boldsymbol{z}_2).$$

*Proof:* Consider the left side of (3–33), and interchange the order of differentiation and integration to obtain

(3–34) $$\begin{aligned} K = \nabla_{iz_1} \phi_{x_1x_2}(\boldsymbol{z}_1, \boldsymbol{z}_2)\,|_{\boldsymbol{z}_1=\boldsymbol{o}} &= \nabla_{iz_1} \mathrm{E}_{x_1,x_2}\{\exp i(\boldsymbol{z}_1^T\boldsymbol{x}_1 + \boldsymbol{z}_2^T\boldsymbol{x}_2)\}\,|_{\boldsymbol{z}_1=\boldsymbol{o}} \\ &= \mathrm{E}_{x_1,x_2}\{\boldsymbol{x}_1 \exp(i\boldsymbol{z}_2^T\boldsymbol{x}_2)\}. \end{aligned}$$

Using the characteristic property of the conditional expectation (2–26), we can write

(3–35) $$K = \mathrm{E}_{x_2}\{\mathrm{E}_{x_1,x_2}\{\boldsymbol{x}_1 \exp(i\boldsymbol{z}_2^T\boldsymbol{x}_2) \mid \boldsymbol{x}_2\}\}.$$

Next apply (2–37) of Theorem 2.2 to reduce (3–35) to the form

(3–36) $$K = \mathrm{E}_{x_2}\{\exp(i\boldsymbol{z}_2^T\boldsymbol{x}_2)\,\mathrm{E}_{x_1}\{\boldsymbol{x}_1 \mid \boldsymbol{x}_2\}\}.$$

If we assume that the theorem statement (3–32) is valid, then (3–36) becomes

(3–37) $$K = \mathrm{E}_{x_2}\{(\boldsymbol{m}_{12} + \mathbf{A}\boldsymbol{x}_2)\exp(i\boldsymbol{z}_2^T\boldsymbol{x}_2)\}.$$

Interchanging the order of differentiation and expectation in (3–37) yields

(3–38) $$K = \nabla_{iz_1} \phi_{x_1x_2}(\boldsymbol{z}_1, \boldsymbol{z}_2)\,|_{\boldsymbol{z}_1=\boldsymbol{o}} = [\boldsymbol{m}_{12} + \mathbf{A}\,\nabla_{iz_2}]\phi_{x_2}(\boldsymbol{z}_2).$$

Hence the sufficiency statement of the theorem is verified. The necessity of the hypothesis must next be validated.

Suppose that (3–33) is true; then we must show that acceptance of (3–33) is equivalent to (3–32). Proceeding as before, we can obtain (3–36) and (3–37). Combine these equations in the form

(3–39) $$\mathrm{E}_{x_2}\{[\boldsymbol{m}_{12} + \mathbf{A}\boldsymbol{x}_2 - \mathrm{E}_{x_1}\{\boldsymbol{x}_1 \mid \boldsymbol{x}_2\}]\exp(i\boldsymbol{z}_2^T\boldsymbol{x}_2)\} = 0.$$

Since (3–39) holds for every $\boldsymbol{z}_2$, the truth of (3–32) follows from the uniqueness theorem for Fourier-Stieltjes transforms [31].

Theorem 3.1 is extremely useful because it establishes both necessary and sufficient conditions that the conditional expectation of two random vectors be expressible as a linear function of the conditioning random vector. These conditions are fulfilled by normal vectors. For normal vectors a less general form of Theorem 3.1 can be stated [79].

THEOREM 3.2: If $\boldsymbol{x}_1$ and $\boldsymbol{x}_2$ are normal random vectors, then

(3–40) $$\mathrm{E}\{\boldsymbol{x}_1 \mid \boldsymbol{x}_2\} = \boldsymbol{m}_1 + \boldsymbol{\Psi}_{12}\boldsymbol{\Psi}_2^{-1}(\boldsymbol{x}_2 - \boldsymbol{m}_2).$$

*Proof:* Apply (3–33) to (3–31). The result is

(3–41) $$\nabla_{iz_1} \phi_{x_1x_2}(\boldsymbol{z}_1, \boldsymbol{z}_2)\,|_{\boldsymbol{z}_1=\boldsymbol{o}} = (\boldsymbol{m}_1 + \boldsymbol{\Psi}_{12}i\boldsymbol{z}_2)\phi_{x_2}(\boldsymbol{z}_2).$$

From (3–27),

$$\nabla_{iz_2}\phi_{x_2}(\boldsymbol{z}_2) = (\boldsymbol{m}_2 + \boldsymbol{\Psi}_2 i\boldsymbol{z}_2)\phi_{x_2}(\boldsymbol{z}_2). \tag{3–42}$$

Insert (3–41) and (3–42) into (3–33). This yields

$$\begin{aligned}&[\boldsymbol{m}_1 + \boldsymbol{\Psi}_{12} i\boldsymbol{z}_2]\phi_{x_2}(\boldsymbol{z}_2)\\ &\qquad = \boldsymbol{m}_{12}\phi_{x_2}(\boldsymbol{z}_2) + \mathbf{A}[\boldsymbol{m}_2 + \boldsymbol{\Psi}_2 i\boldsymbol{z}_2]\phi_{x_2}(\boldsymbol{z}_2).\end{aligned} \tag{3–43}$$

Since (3–43) must hold identically in $\boldsymbol{z}_2$, $\mathbf{A}$ must be restricted such that

$$\boldsymbol{\Psi}_{12} = \mathbf{A}\boldsymbol{\Psi}_2. \tag{3–44}$$

If $\boldsymbol{\Psi}_2^{-1}$ exists, then

$$\mathbf{A} = \boldsymbol{\Psi}_{12}\boldsymbol{\Psi}_2^{-1}. \tag{3–45}$$

Note that (3–43) and (3–45) form the required sufficiency conditions for Theorem 3.1. Therefore, combining (3–43) and (3–45)

$$\boldsymbol{m}_{12} = \boldsymbol{m}_1 - \boldsymbol{\Psi}_{12}\boldsymbol{\Psi}_2^{-1}\boldsymbol{m}_2. \tag{3–46}$$

Substitute (3–46) and (3–45) into (3–32) to obtain (3–40). This completes the proof under the additional assumption that $\boldsymbol{\Psi}_2^{-1}$ exists.

Two properties of conditional expectations for normal random vectors can be demonstrated using the results already obtained.

(i) If $\boldsymbol{x}_1$ and $\boldsymbol{x}_2$ are normal random vectors, then $\boldsymbol{x}_2$ is independent of $\boldsymbol{x}_1 - \mathrm{E}\{\boldsymbol{x}_1 \mid \boldsymbol{x}_2\}$.

The statement follows if we can show that $\boldsymbol{x}_2$ is orthogonal to $\boldsymbol{x}_1 - \mathrm{E}\{\boldsymbol{x}_1 \mid \boldsymbol{x}_2\}$. Theorem 3.2 shows that the conditional expectation is the sum of a random vector and a constant vector, hence $\boldsymbol{x}_1 - \mathrm{E}\{\boldsymbol{x}_1 \mid \boldsymbol{x}_2\}$ is also a normal vector. For such vectors, orthogonality is equivalent to independence. Consider the covariance matrix

$$\boldsymbol{\phi} = \mathrm{E}\{(\boldsymbol{x}_1 - \mathrm{E}\{\boldsymbol{x}_1 \mid \boldsymbol{x}_2\})(\boldsymbol{x}_2 - \boldsymbol{m}_2)^T\}. \tag{3–47}$$

Insert (3–40) into (3–47) to obtain

$$\begin{aligned}\boldsymbol{\phi} &= \mathrm{E}\{[\boldsymbol{x}_1 - \boldsymbol{m}_1 - \boldsymbol{\Psi}_{12}\boldsymbol{\Psi}_2^{-1}(\boldsymbol{x}_2 - \boldsymbol{m}_2)][\boldsymbol{x}_2 - \boldsymbol{m}_2]^T\}\\ &= \boldsymbol{\Psi}_{12} - \boldsymbol{\Psi}_{12}\boldsymbol{\Psi}_2^{-1}\boldsymbol{\Psi}_2\\ &= \mathbf{0}.\end{aligned} \tag{3–48}$$

Because the covariance matrix for the normally distributed vectors vanishes, we conclude that the vectors must be independent. This result is a special case of Theorem 2.2.

(ii) Let $\boldsymbol{x}_1$ and $\boldsymbol{x}_2$ be normal random vectors. Define the covariance matrix of the conditional expectation $\mathrm{E}\{\boldsymbol{x}_1 \mid \boldsymbol{x}_2\}$ to be

$$\begin{aligned}\boldsymbol{\Theta} &= \mathrm{E}_{x_2}\{(\mathrm{E}_{x_1}\{\boldsymbol{x}_1 \mid \boldsymbol{x}_2\} - \boldsymbol{\mu})(\mathrm{E}_{x_1}\{\boldsymbol{x}_1 \mid \boldsymbol{x}_2\} - \boldsymbol{\mu})^T\},\\ \boldsymbol{\mu} &= \mathrm{E}_{x_2}\{\mathrm{E}_{x_1}\{\boldsymbol{x}_1 \mid \boldsymbol{x}_2\}\}.\end{aligned} \tag{3–49}$$

From (2–26), we can write

$$\boldsymbol{\mu} = \mathrm{E}\{\boldsymbol{x}_1\} = \boldsymbol{m}_1. \tag{3–50}$$

Insert (3–50) and the theorem statement (3–40) into (3–49), which then becomes

$$\boldsymbol{\Theta} = \mathrm{E}_{x_2}\{\boldsymbol{\Psi}_{12}\boldsymbol{\Psi}_2^{-1}(\boldsymbol{x}_2 - \boldsymbol{m}_2)(\boldsymbol{x}_2 - \boldsymbol{m}_2)^T\boldsymbol{\Psi}_2^{-1}\boldsymbol{\Psi}_{12}\}. \tag{3–51}$$

Use has been made of the fact that the covariance matrices $\boldsymbol{\Psi}_2$ and $\boldsymbol{\Psi}_{12}$ are symmetrical. Expand (3–51), using (3–24), to find

$$\begin{aligned}\boldsymbol{\Theta} &= \boldsymbol{\Psi}_{12}\boldsymbol{\Psi}_2^{-1}\boldsymbol{\Psi}_2\boldsymbol{\Psi}_2^{-1}\boldsymbol{\Psi}_{12}\\ &= \boldsymbol{\Psi}_{12}\boldsymbol{\Psi}_2^{-1}\boldsymbol{\Psi}_{12}.\end{aligned} \tag{3–52}$$

## 3.3
## *PROJECTIONS IN A SPACE OF RANDOM VECTORS*

In this section, we shall develop a particular linear space of random vectors and then demonstrate that the linear forms for conditional expectations for distributions satisfying Theorem 3.1 can be geometrically interpreted as orthogonal projections of random vectors on a subspace of this space. Because the optimal estimator has been shown to be a conditional expectation, it will follow that optimal estimates can be pictured as orthogonal projections of random vectors on an appropriate linear space.

The first step will be to generate a suitable linear space, or a linear manifold [126,42 Chapter IV]. Let $\boldsymbol{x}$ and $\boldsymbol{y}$ be random vectors of the same order (not necessarily normal vectors) such that

$$\begin{aligned}\mathrm{E}\{\boldsymbol{x}^T\boldsymbol{x}\} &< \infty\\ \mathrm{E}\{\boldsymbol{y}^T\boldsymbol{y}\} &< \infty.\end{aligned} \tag{3–53}$$

These vectors are called *uncorrelated* if

$$\mathrm{E}\{\boldsymbol{x}^T\boldsymbol{y}\} = \mathrm{E}\{\boldsymbol{x}^T\}\mathrm{E}\{\boldsymbol{y}\}. \tag{3–54}$$

If, in addition, $\mathrm{E}\{\boldsymbol{x}^T\boldsymbol{y}\} = 0$, the vectors are called *orthogonal*. Notice that it follows that, if $\boldsymbol{x}$ and $\boldsymbol{y}$ are uncorrelated, then the vectors

$$\begin{aligned}\boldsymbol{\xi} &= \boldsymbol{x} - \mathrm{E}\{\boldsymbol{x}\}\\ \boldsymbol{\eta} &= \boldsymbol{y} - \mathrm{E}\{\boldsymbol{y}\}\end{aligned} \tag{3–55}$$

are orthogonal.

To those readers familiar with the conventional, nonprobabilistic treatment of linear-normed complete spaces, it should be remarked that the only essential difference is that the inner product upon which the norm of the space is defined will in our case be defined as an expected value of two random vectors. This is at best only a formal difference, and, as such, it is perhaps unjustified to imply that any real difference exists between our use of probability measures and the conventional approach to Hilbert space theory, which uses general measure theory.

We form a linear manifold, or space, from a collection of a finite number of random vectors $\boldsymbol{x}_1, \ldots, \boldsymbol{x}_n$ by requiring that any finite linear combination of these vectors be a vector which is also a member of our space. That is, for a set of constants $\{a_i\}$,

$$\boldsymbol{y} = \sum_{i=1}^{n} a_i \boldsymbol{x}_i \tag{3–56}$$

is also a member of the space.

The inner product of two vectors in this space is defined as

$$(\boldsymbol{x}, \boldsymbol{y}) = \mathrm{E}\{\boldsymbol{x}^T \boldsymbol{y}\}. \tag{3–57}$$

Therefore, the norm of a vector $\boldsymbol{x}$ is

$$\begin{aligned} \|\boldsymbol{x}\| &\stackrel{d}{=} [\mathrm{E}\{\boldsymbol{x}^T \boldsymbol{x}\}]^{1/2} \stackrel{d}{=} \mathrm{E}^{1/2}\{\boldsymbol{x}^T \boldsymbol{x}\} \\ &= [\mathrm{tr}\,\mathrm{E}\{\boldsymbol{x}\boldsymbol{x}^T\}]^{1/2}, \end{aligned} \tag{3–58}$$

where tr denotes the trace of a matrix.

The distance between two vectors in the space is defined in the usual way from the norm of a vector. Thus the distance between two vectors $\boldsymbol{x}$ and $\boldsymbol{y}$ is

$$\rho_{xy} = \mathrm{E}^{1/2}\{(\boldsymbol{x} - \boldsymbol{y})^T (\boldsymbol{x} - \boldsymbol{y})\} = \|\boldsymbol{x} - \boldsymbol{y}\|. \tag{3–59}$$

The linear space is closed by adding to the space the limit of every sequence of random vectors. Because the elements of the space are random vectors, the limits are to be limits in the mean. Thus

$$\underset{n \to \infty}{\mathrm{l.i.m.}}\ \boldsymbol{x}_n = \boldsymbol{x} \tag{3–60}$$

is an abbreviated expression for

$$\lim_{n \to \infty} [\mathrm{E}\{(\boldsymbol{x}_n - \boldsymbol{x})^T (\boldsymbol{x}_n - \boldsymbol{x})\}]^{1/2} = 0. \tag{3–61}$$

Consider the set of vectors $\boldsymbol{x}_1, \ldots, \boldsymbol{x}_n$ and all finite linear combinations of these vectors. The resulting collection will be a linear manifold and will be the smallest linear manifold containing the original set of vectors. This space is called the linear manifold generated by the set of vectors $\boldsymbol{x}_1, \ldots, \boldsymbol{x}_n$. If all the limit points defined by (3–61) are adjoined to the manifold, the result will be the closed linear manifold generated by the given set of vectors.

Let the linear manifold generated by (3–56) be denoted as $M$. If a random vector $\boldsymbol{x}$ is orthogonal to every random vector in $M$, then we say that $\boldsymbol{x}$ is orthogonal to $M$. Two linear manifolds $M$ and $N$ are called orthogonal if every random vector in one manifold is orthogonal to every random vector in the other manifold.

A sequence of random vectors $\boldsymbol{z}_1, \ldots, \boldsymbol{z}_n$ is called an *orthonormal sequence* if

$$\mathrm{E}\{\boldsymbol{z}_j^T \boldsymbol{z}_k\} = \delta_{jk}, \tag{3–62}$$

where

$$\delta_{jk} = \begin{cases} 0, & j \neq k \\ 1, & j = k. \end{cases}$$

Orthonormal sequences are extremely useful in forming linear series representations for random vectors in our linear space.

Suppose that from the set of random vectors $\boldsymbol{x}_1, \ldots, \boldsymbol{x}_n$ that were used to generate our linear space, we wish to find a sequence of orthonormal vectors $\boldsymbol{\eta}_1, \boldsymbol{\eta}_2, \ldots$ such that each $\boldsymbol{\eta}$ is a linear combination of the $\boldsymbol{x}$'s, and conversely. Then the linear space generated by the set $\{\boldsymbol{\eta}\}$ will be the same as that generated by the $\{\boldsymbol{x}\}$. Thus, we still have the same space, but will have the added convenience of an orthonormal sequence of generating vectors. The selection of the $\boldsymbol{\eta}_j$ from the set $\{\boldsymbol{x}\}$ is accomplished by applying the Gram-Schmidt orthogonalization procedure.

From the set $\boldsymbol{x}_1, \ldots, \boldsymbol{x}_n$, select a set of $N$ linearly independent vectors, $\boldsymbol{x}^{(1)}, \ldots, \boldsymbol{x}^{(N)}$. That is, for the subset with superscripts, there exists no set of scalars $c_1, \ldots, c_N$ not all zero such that

$$c_1\boldsymbol{x}^{(1)} + c_2\boldsymbol{x}^{(2)} + \cdots + c_N\boldsymbol{x}^{(N)} = \boldsymbol{0}; \qquad N \leq n. \tag{3–63}$$

Select any member $\boldsymbol{x}^{(j)}$ of the linearly independent set, and let

$$\boldsymbol{\eta}_1 = \frac{\boldsymbol{x}^{(j)}}{\|\boldsymbol{x}^{(j)}\|} = \frac{\boldsymbol{\xi}_1}{\|\boldsymbol{\xi}_1\|}. \tag{3–64}$$

Choose any other $\boldsymbol{x}^{(k)}$, call it $\boldsymbol{\xi}_2$, and consider the linear combination

$$\boldsymbol{y}_2 = \boldsymbol{\xi}_2 - b_{21}\boldsymbol{\eta}_1. \tag{3–65}$$

The orthogonality condition is that

$$\mathrm{E}\{\boldsymbol{\eta}_1^T\boldsymbol{y}_2\} = 0 = \mathrm{E}\{\boldsymbol{\eta}_1^T(\boldsymbol{\xi}_2 - b_{21}\boldsymbol{\eta}_1)\}. \tag{3–66}$$

This condition is satisfied if

$$b_{21} = \mathrm{E}\{\boldsymbol{\eta}_1^T\boldsymbol{\xi}_2\}. \tag{3–67}$$

By construction, the set $\{\boldsymbol{x}^{(i)}\}$ is linearly independent. This implies that $\boldsymbol{\xi}_2$ is not a scalar multiple of $\boldsymbol{\xi}_1$ and, in turn, $\boldsymbol{\xi}_2$ is not linearly dependent upon $\boldsymbol{\eta}_1$. Further, $\boldsymbol{\xi}_2 - b_{21}\boldsymbol{\eta}_1$ does not vanish, so we can choose as our second element of the orthonormal set

$$\boldsymbol{\eta}_2 = \frac{\boldsymbol{y}_2}{\|\boldsymbol{y}_2\|}. \tag{3–68}$$

The preceding steps can readily be iterated to generate each element $\boldsymbol{\eta}_j$ of the desired orthonormal set of random vectors. At any stage $k$, the constants are determined by extension of (3–65) and (3–66);

$$\boldsymbol{y}_k = \boldsymbol{\xi}_k - b_{k1}\boldsymbol{\eta}_1 - b_{k2}\boldsymbol{\eta}_2 - \cdots - b_{k(k-1)}\boldsymbol{\eta}_{k-1}. \tag{3–69}$$

The constants $b_{ki}$ are determined by imposing the condition that $\mathrm{E}\{\boldsymbol{\eta}_i^T\boldsymbol{y}_k\} = 0$. One can verify that this condition yields the coefficients

$$b_{ki} = \mathrm{E}\{\boldsymbol{\eta}_i^T\boldsymbol{\xi}_k\}. \tag{3–70}$$

The set of orthonormal random vectors $\boldsymbol{\eta}_1, \ldots, \boldsymbol{\eta}_N$ is not unique. By selecting the $\boldsymbol{x}^{(i)}$ in another order, a different set of orthonormal vectors would be generated. The importance of the orthonormal set of vectors is that it forms a *basis for*, or *spans*, the manifold $M$ generated from the vectors $\boldsymbol{x}_1, \ldots, \boldsymbol{x}_n$. In other words, any vector $\boldsymbol{x}$ in $M$ can be expressed as a linear combination of the basis vectors in the form

$$\boldsymbol{x} = \sum_{i=1}^{N} a_i \boldsymbol{\eta}_i, \tag{3–71}$$

where $N$ is the number of elements in the basis; i.e., $N$ is the dimension of $M$. The constant $a_i$ is called the $i$th coordinate of $\boldsymbol{x}$ with respect to the basis. The $a_i$ constants are also called the *Fourier coefficients* of $\boldsymbol{x}$ and can be readily calculated because of the orthonormal properties of the basis vectors. Thus, from (3–71),

$$\begin{aligned} \mathrm{E}\left\{\sum_{i=1}^{N} a_i \boldsymbol{\eta}_i^T \boldsymbol{\eta}_j\right\} &= \mathrm{E}\{\boldsymbol{x}^T \boldsymbol{\eta}_j\} \\ \sum_{i=1}^{N} a_i \mathrm{E}\{\boldsymbol{\eta}_i^T \boldsymbol{\eta}_j\} &= \mathrm{E}\{\boldsymbol{x}^T \boldsymbol{\eta}_j\} \\ a_j &= \mathrm{E}\{\boldsymbol{x}^T \boldsymbol{\eta}_j\}. \end{aligned} \tag{3–72}$$

Because of the manner in which the orthonormal random vectors $\boldsymbol{\eta}_1, \ldots, \boldsymbol{\eta}_N$ were constructed, they correspond to the unit coordinate vectors in the space. For example, neglecting any significance of the subscripts,

$$\begin{aligned} \boldsymbol{\eta}_1^T &= [1 \ 0 \ 0 \cdots 0] \\ \boldsymbol{\eta}_2^T &= [0 \ 1 \ 0 \cdots 0] \\ &\cdots\cdots\cdots\cdots\cdots \\ \boldsymbol{\eta}_N^T &= [0 \ 0 \ 0 \cdots 1]. \end{aligned} \tag{3–73}$$

The distance between two random variables was defined in (3–59). Using the representation (3–71), an expression for this distance can be found in terms of the Fourier coefficients. Let $\boldsymbol{x}'$ be a second random vector in $M$ having the representation

$$\boldsymbol{x}' = \sum_{i=1}^{N} a_i' \boldsymbol{\eta}_i. \tag{3–74}$$

Then the square of the distance between $\boldsymbol{x}$ and $\boldsymbol{x}'$ is

$$\begin{aligned} \rho_{xx'}^2 &= \mathrm{E}\{(\boldsymbol{x} - \boldsymbol{x}')^T(\boldsymbol{x} - \boldsymbol{x}')\} = \|\boldsymbol{x} - \boldsymbol{x}'\|^2 \\ &= \mathrm{E}\left\{\sum_{j=1}^{N}\sum_{i=1}^{N} (a_i - a_i')\boldsymbol{\eta}_i^T \boldsymbol{\eta}_j (a_j - a_j')\right\} \\ &= \sum_{j=1}^{N} (a_j - a_j')^2 = \|\boldsymbol{x} - \boldsymbol{x}'\|^2. \end{aligned} \tag{3–75}$$

Hence, in $M$, the distance between two random variables is the ordinary Euclidean distance corresponding to the endpoints of the vectors. The scalar product of $\boldsymbol{x}$ with any coordinate vector is by definition the projection of $\boldsymbol{x}$ on that coordinate, or the component of $\boldsymbol{x}$ along the coordinate vector. The scalar product of $\boldsymbol{x}$ and $\boldsymbol{\eta}_i$ is defined as $\mathrm{E}\{\boldsymbol{x}^T\boldsymbol{\eta}_i\}$, but by (3–72) this component is $a_i$. In other words, if $M_1$ is the linear manifold spanned by $\boldsymbol{\eta}_1, \ldots, \boldsymbol{\eta}_k$; $k \leq N$, the Fourier series (3–71) of $\boldsymbol{x}$ in terms of the basis is the projection of $\boldsymbol{x}$ on the hyperplane corresponding to $M_1$.

(i) PARSEVAL'S FORMULA: Let $\boldsymbol{x}$ be an element of $M$ spanned by $\boldsymbol{\eta}_1, \ldots, \boldsymbol{\eta}_N$. Then from the representation (3–71) it follows that

$$\begin{aligned} \mathrm{E}\{\boldsymbol{x}^T\boldsymbol{x}\} &= \mathrm{E}\{\sum_i\sum_j a_i\boldsymbol{\eta}_i^T\boldsymbol{\eta}_j a_j\} \\ &= \sum_i a_i^2. \end{aligned} \tag{3–76}$$

This result is known as Parseval's formula.

(ii) BESSEL'S INEQUALITY: Suppose $\boldsymbol{x}_1$ is a random vector in $M$; then it can be expressed by a series of the form (3–71). Let $\boldsymbol{x}$ be any random vector, not necessarily in $M$. We wish to find the representation of $\boldsymbol{x}$ by a similar series such that the following norm is minimized:

$$\begin{aligned} \|\boldsymbol{x}-\boldsymbol{x}_1\|^2 &= \mathrm{E}\{(\boldsymbol{x}-\boldsymbol{x}_1)^T(\boldsymbol{x}-\boldsymbol{x}_1)\} \\ &= \mathrm{E}\{(\boldsymbol{x}-\sum_j a_j\boldsymbol{\eta}_j)^T(\boldsymbol{x}-\sum_j a_j\boldsymbol{\eta}_j)\} \\ &= \mathrm{E}\{\boldsymbol{x}^T\boldsymbol{x}\} - \sum_j a_j\mathrm{E}\{\boldsymbol{x}^T\boldsymbol{\eta}_j\} - \sum_j a_j\mathrm{E}\{\boldsymbol{\eta}_j^T\boldsymbol{x}\} \\ &\quad + \sum_j\sum_k a_j a_k\mathrm{E}\{\boldsymbol{\eta}_j^T\boldsymbol{\eta}_k\} \\ &= \|\boldsymbol{x}\|^2 - \sum_j \mathrm{E}^2\{\boldsymbol{x}^T\boldsymbol{\eta}_j\} + \sum_j [\mathrm{E}\{\boldsymbol{x}^T\boldsymbol{\eta}_j\} - a_j]^2. \end{aligned} \tag{3–77}$$

The minimum will be attained when $a_j = \mathrm{E}\{\boldsymbol{x}^T\boldsymbol{\eta}_j\}$. Then,

$$\mathrm{E}\{\boldsymbol{x}^T\boldsymbol{x}\} = \|\boldsymbol{x}\|^2 = \sum_j a_j^2 + \|\boldsymbol{x}-\boldsymbol{x}_1\|^2. \tag{3–78}$$

Equation (3–78) is often called the *n-dimensional Pythagorian theorem.* In particular, because each term is positive, (3–78) yields the Bessel inequality

$$\mathrm{E}\{\boldsymbol{x}^T\boldsymbol{x}\} \geq \sum_j a_j^2. \tag{3–79}$$

(iii) DECOMPOSITION THEOREM: Any random vector $\boldsymbol{x}$, not necessarily an element of the space $M$ spanned by the basis set $\boldsymbol{\eta}_1, \ldots, \boldsymbol{\eta}_n$, can be uniquely decomposed into the sum of a vector $\boldsymbol{z}$ which belongs to $M$ and a vector $\boldsymbol{z}_p$ which is orthogonal to $M$.

*Proof:* The uniqueness is readily demonstrated. Suppose that the decomposition was not unique; then there would exist two representations of $\boldsymbol{x}$, say,

$$\boldsymbol{x} = \boldsymbol{z} + \boldsymbol{z}_p \tag{3–80}$$

and

$$\boldsymbol{x} = \boldsymbol{z}' + \boldsymbol{z}_p'.$$

Because $M$ is a linear space and since both $\boldsymbol{z}$ and $\boldsymbol{z}'$ are elements of $M$, then necessarily $\boldsymbol{z} - \boldsymbol{z}' \in M$. Thus, (3–80) implies that

$$\boldsymbol{z} - \boldsymbol{z}' = \boldsymbol{z}_p' - \boldsymbol{z}_p. \tag{3–81}$$

But (3–81) shows that not only must $\boldsymbol{z} - \boldsymbol{z}' \in M$ but $\boldsymbol{z} - \boldsymbol{z}'$ must also be orthogonal to $M$; in particular, the difference must be orthogonal to itself, or

$$\mathrm{E}\{(\boldsymbol{z} - \boldsymbol{z}')^T(\boldsymbol{z} - \boldsymbol{z}')\} = 0. \tag{3–82}$$

However, for (3–82) to hold in general, we must have $\boldsymbol{z} = \boldsymbol{z}'$, which also implies $\boldsymbol{z}_p = \boldsymbol{z}_p'$. Thus, the uniqueness is established.

We must now show the existence of the decomposition. If $\boldsymbol{z} \in M$, then we can write

$$\begin{aligned} \boldsymbol{x} &= \sum_i a_i \boldsymbol{\eta}_i + \boldsymbol{z}_p \\ &= \sum_i \mathrm{E}\{\boldsymbol{x}^T \boldsymbol{\eta}_i\} \boldsymbol{\eta}_i + \boldsymbol{z}_p. \end{aligned} \tag{3–83}$$

$\boldsymbol{z}_p$ is determined by (3–83), and it remains to prove that $\boldsymbol{z}_p$ is orthogonal to $M$. Consider any vector $\boldsymbol{\eta}_j$ in the basis set. Then,

$$\begin{aligned} \mathrm{E}\{\boldsymbol{z}_p^T \boldsymbol{\eta}_j\} &= \mathrm{E}\{(\boldsymbol{x}^T - \sum_i \mathrm{E}\{\boldsymbol{x}^T \boldsymbol{\eta}_i\} \boldsymbol{\eta}_i^T) \boldsymbol{\eta}_j\} \\ &= \mathrm{E}\{\boldsymbol{x}^T \boldsymbol{\eta}_j\} - \mathrm{E}\{\boldsymbol{x}^T \boldsymbol{\eta}_j\} = 0. \end{aligned} \tag{3–84}$$

Thus $\boldsymbol{z}_p$ is orthogonal to $M$; $\boldsymbol{z}$ is called the *orthogonal projection* of $\boldsymbol{x}$ onto $M$, and $\boldsymbol{z}_p$ is the projection of $\boldsymbol{x}$ which is orthogonal to $M$.

(iv) PROJECTIONS: Let $M_1$ and $M_2$ be two orthogonal and complementary subspaces of $M$; $M_1 \cup M_2 = M$. Thus by the decomposition theorem, every random vector $\boldsymbol{x} \in M$ can be written as $\boldsymbol{x} = \boldsymbol{z} + \boldsymbol{z}_p$; $\boldsymbol{z} \in M_1$, $\boldsymbol{z}_p \in M_2$. We define an operator P such that

$$\mathrm{P} \circ \boldsymbol{x} = \boldsymbol{z} \in M_1. \tag{3–85}$$

P is called an *orthogonal projection*, or simply a *projection*, onto the subspace $M_1$. The projection has the following characteristic property:

$$\begin{aligned} \mathrm{P} \circ \boldsymbol{x} &= \boldsymbol{z} \\ \mathrm{P} \circ (\mathrm{P} \circ \boldsymbol{x}) &= \mathrm{P} \circ \boldsymbol{z} = \boldsymbol{z} = \mathrm{P} \circ \boldsymbol{x} \end{aligned} \tag{3–86}$$

or

$$\mathrm{P} \circ \mathrm{P} = \mathrm{P}^2 = \mathrm{P}.$$

Two properties of projections are readily proved.

(a) P is symmetric: Consider two random vectors $\boldsymbol{x}$ and $\boldsymbol{x}'$, which can be written in the component forms

$$\begin{aligned} \boldsymbol{x} &= \boldsymbol{z} + \boldsymbol{z}_p \\ \boldsymbol{x}' &= \boldsymbol{z}' + \boldsymbol{z}_p' \\ &\boldsymbol{z}, \boldsymbol{z}' \in M_1 \\ &\boldsymbol{z}_p, \boldsymbol{z}_p' \in M_2. \end{aligned} \tag{3–87}$$

Thus, from the definitions of the orthogonal subspaces,

$$\text{(3–88)} \qquad \begin{aligned} \mathrm{E}\{\boldsymbol{z}^T\boldsymbol{z}'_p\} &= 0 \\ \mathrm{E}\{\boldsymbol{z}_p^T\boldsymbol{z}'\} &= 0. \end{aligned}$$

Consider the following sequence of calculations:

$$\text{(3–89)} \qquad \begin{aligned} \mathrm{E}\{(\mathrm{P}\circ\boldsymbol{x})^T\boldsymbol{x}'\} &= \mathrm{E}\{\boldsymbol{z}^T\boldsymbol{x}'\} = \mathrm{E}\{\boldsymbol{z}^T\boldsymbol{x}'\} - \mathrm{E}\{\boldsymbol{z}^T\boldsymbol{z}'_p\} \\ &= \mathrm{E}\{\boldsymbol{z}^T(\boldsymbol{x}' - \boldsymbol{z}'_p)\} = \mathrm{E}\{\boldsymbol{z}^T\boldsymbol{z}'\} \\ &= \mathrm{E}\{\boldsymbol{z}^T\boldsymbol{z}'\} + \mathrm{E}\{\boldsymbol{z}_p^T\boldsymbol{z}'\} \\ &= \mathrm{E}\{(\boldsymbol{z} + \boldsymbol{z}_p)^T\boldsymbol{z}'\} = \mathrm{E}\{\boldsymbol{x}^T\boldsymbol{z}'\} \\ &= \mathrm{E}\{\boldsymbol{x}^T(\mathrm{P}\circ\boldsymbol{x}')\}. \end{aligned}$$

The final form exhibits the symmetry of the projection P for our form of the inner product of two random vectors.

(b) If P is a symmetric transformation, as defined in (3–89), such that $\mathrm{P}^2 = \mathrm{P}$, then P is a projection: We first remark that if P satisfies (3–85), then

$$\text{(3–90)} \qquad \begin{aligned} \boldsymbol{z}_p &= \boldsymbol{x} - \boldsymbol{z} = \boldsymbol{x} - \mathrm{P}\circ\boldsymbol{x} \\ &= (\mathrm{I} - \mathrm{P})\circ\boldsymbol{x} \in M_2. \end{aligned}$$

I is an identity operator which leaves $\boldsymbol{x}$ unchanged; it acts as a unit scalar. Equation (3–90) shows that $(\mathrm{I} - \mathrm{P})$ is the projection of $\boldsymbol{x}$ on the space $M_2$. The decomposition theorem can be written in terms of the projections

$$\text{(3–91)} \qquad \begin{aligned} \boldsymbol{x} &= \boldsymbol{z} + \boldsymbol{z}_P \\ \boldsymbol{x} &= \mathrm{P}\circ\boldsymbol{x} + (\mathrm{I} - \mathrm{P})\circ\boldsymbol{x}. \end{aligned}$$

Now let P be symmetric and such that $\mathrm{P}^2 = \mathrm{P}$. Then

$$\text{(3–92)} \qquad \begin{aligned} \mathrm{E}\{[(\mathrm{I} - \mathrm{P})\circ\boldsymbol{x}^T][\mathrm{P}\circ\boldsymbol{z}]\} &= \mathrm{E}\{[\mathrm{P}\circ(\mathrm{I} - \mathrm{P})\circ\boldsymbol{x}^T]\boldsymbol{z}\} \\ &= \mathrm{E}\{(\mathrm{P}\circ\boldsymbol{x}^T)\boldsymbol{z}\} - \mathrm{E}\{(\mathrm{P}^2\circ\boldsymbol{x}^T)\boldsymbol{z}\} = 0. \end{aligned}$$

However, because $(\mathrm{I} - \mathrm{P})\circ\boldsymbol{x}$ is orthogonal to $\boldsymbol{z}$ for all $\boldsymbol{z}$, (3–92) demonstrates that P is a projection.

(iv) Projection theorem: The importance of projections in estimation theory lies in the interpretation of the following theorem:

Theorem 3.3: Suppose that $\boldsymbol{x}$ is a random vector lying in the space $M$ spanned by the orthonormal basis set $\{\boldsymbol{\eta}\}$. Let $\boldsymbol{x}'$ be a vector in $M$ or any subspace $M' \subset M$, then the norm $\|\boldsymbol{x} - \boldsymbol{x}'\|$ has a minimum value. Further, the minimum of the norm is attained if and only if $\boldsymbol{x}'$ is the projection of $\boldsymbol{x}$ on $M'$.

*Proof:* By the decomposition theorem, we can write

$$\text{(3–93)} \qquad \boldsymbol{x} = \boldsymbol{z} + \boldsymbol{z}_p,$$

where $P \circ \boldsymbol{x} = \boldsymbol{z} \in M'$ and $\boldsymbol{z}_p$ is orthogonal to $M'$. The square of the norm is

$$\begin{aligned} \|\boldsymbol{x} - \boldsymbol{x}'\|^2 &= \mathrm{E}\{(\boldsymbol{x} - \boldsymbol{x}')^T(\boldsymbol{x} - \boldsymbol{x}')\} \\ &= \mathrm{E}\{[(\boldsymbol{x} - \boldsymbol{z}) + (\boldsymbol{z} - \boldsymbol{x}')]^T[(\boldsymbol{x} - \boldsymbol{z}) + (\boldsymbol{z} - \boldsymbol{x}')]\}. \end{aligned} \tag{3–94}$$

Now $\boldsymbol{x} - \boldsymbol{z}$ is orthogonal to $M'$, while $\boldsymbol{z}$, $\boldsymbol{x}'$, and $\boldsymbol{z} - \boldsymbol{x}'$ are all elements of $M'$. Using these facts, (3–94) reduces to

$$\begin{aligned} \|\boldsymbol{x} - \boldsymbol{x}'\|^2 &= \mathrm{E}\{(\boldsymbol{x} - \boldsymbol{z})^T(\boldsymbol{x} - \boldsymbol{z})\} + \mathrm{E}\{(\boldsymbol{z} - \boldsymbol{x}')^T(\boldsymbol{z} - \boldsymbol{x}')\} \\ &= \|\boldsymbol{x} - \boldsymbol{z}\|^2 + \|\boldsymbol{z} - \boldsymbol{x}'\|^2. \end{aligned} \tag{3–95}$$

Because each term on the right side is positive, we can write

$$\begin{aligned} \mathrm{E}\{(\boldsymbol{x} - \boldsymbol{x}')^T(\boldsymbol{x} - \boldsymbol{x}')\} &\geq \mathrm{E}\{(\boldsymbol{x} - \boldsymbol{z})^T(\boldsymbol{x} - \boldsymbol{z})\}, \\ \|\boldsymbol{x} - \boldsymbol{x}'\|^2 &\geq \|\boldsymbol{x} - \boldsymbol{z}\|^2. \end{aligned} \tag{3–96}$$

Thus, the required minimum has been formulated. Hence, if $\boldsymbol{x}'$ is to minimize the norm, equality in (3–96) holds if and only if $\boldsymbol{x}' = \boldsymbol{z} = P \circ \boldsymbol{x}$ with probability 1, (except possibly for a set of events having zero probability).

## 3.4
## *OPTIMAL ESTIMATE AS A PROJECTION*

The mean-square risk function defined in (2–39) can be written in the $n$-dimensional form

$$R(\boldsymbol{\xi}) = \mathrm{E}\{(\boldsymbol{\xi} - \boldsymbol{Y})^T(\boldsymbol{\xi} - \boldsymbol{Y})\}. \tag{3–97}$$

Thus, corresponding to (2–48), the minimum value of the risk occurs when $\boldsymbol{Y}$ is chosen such that

$$\boldsymbol{Y} = \bar{\boldsymbol{\xi}} = \mathrm{E}\{\boldsymbol{\xi} \mid \boldsymbol{y}_1, \ldots, \boldsymbol{y}_n\}. \tag{3–98}$$

Now compare (3–97) with (3–96). It is evident that $\bar{\boldsymbol{\xi}}$ corresponds to $\boldsymbol{z}$; i.e., the conditional expectation which minimizes the mean-squared risk function is the projection of $\boldsymbol{\xi}$ on the linear space generated by the random vectors $\boldsymbol{y}_1, \ldots, \boldsymbol{y}_n$. Let $\boldsymbol{\eta}_1, \ldots, \boldsymbol{\eta}_m$, $m \leq n$, be a set of orthonormal vectors which form a basis for the space $M$ generated by $\boldsymbol{y}_1, \ldots, \boldsymbol{y}_n$. Although we have shown that the absolute minimum of $R(\boldsymbol{\xi})$ is given by the projection of $\boldsymbol{\xi}$ on the space $M$, it does not follow that the conditional expectation $\bar{\boldsymbol{\xi}}$ is necessarily an element of the space $M$. Every random vector in the space $M$ must, by definition, be a finite linear sum of the basis $\boldsymbol{\eta}_1, \ldots, \boldsymbol{\eta}_m$. But, we have shown in Theorem 3.1 the necessary and sufficient conditions that a conditional expectation be expressible as a linear sum of the conditioning random vectors. Thus, unless the probability distribution of the random vectors satisfies Theorem 3.1, the absolute minimum of $R(\boldsymbol{\xi})$ cannot be attained as an element of the space $M$. Of course, the absolute minimum for normal variates is always an element of $M$, as implied by Theorem 3.2.

Even when the conditional expectation cannot be expressed as a linear sum of the base vectors $\boldsymbol{\eta}_1, \ldots, \boldsymbol{\eta}_m$, the minimum of $R(\boldsymbol{\xi})$ is still the projection of $\boldsymbol{\xi}$ on the space $M$. In this case, the value $\mathrm{P}\circ\boldsymbol{\xi} = \hat{\boldsymbol{\xi}}$ is called the *wide sense version* of the best least squares approximation and is customarily denoted by

$$\hat{\boldsymbol{\xi}} = \hat{\mathrm{E}}\{\boldsymbol{\xi} \,|\, \boldsymbol{y}_1, \ldots, \boldsymbol{y}_n\} \in M. \tag{3–99}$$

$\hat{\mathrm{E}}\{\boldsymbol{\xi} \,|\, M\}$ is called the wide sense conditional expectation of $\boldsymbol{\xi}$, relative to the set $M$, [42, p.153]. If $M$ contains no random variables or only random variables which vanish almost everywhere, we define

$$\hat{\mathrm{E}}\{\boldsymbol{\xi} \,|\, M\} = \boldsymbol{0}. \tag{3–100}$$

Using the fact that the wide sense conditional expectation is equivalent to a projection operator, we can readily demonstrate that this expectation satisfies the same combinatorial rules obeyed by conventional conditional expectations. These demonstrations can also be interpreted as proofs of the properties of either normal variates or distributions satisfying Theorem 3.1, because in these cases the wide sense conditional expectation is the conventional conditional expectation. The combination rules must be understood as equations valid with probability 1 and not as identities, because these are relations between random variables.

(i) If $c$ is a scalar constant, then

$$\hat{\mathrm{E}}\{c\boldsymbol{x} \,|\, M\} = c\hat{\mathrm{E}}\{\boldsymbol{x} \,|\, M\}. \tag{3–101}$$

Because $\hat{\mathrm{E}}\{\cdot \,|\, \cdot\}$ is a projection, we can write

$$\boldsymbol{y} = \hat{\mathrm{E}}\{\boldsymbol{x} \,|\, M\} = \mathrm{P}\circ\boldsymbol{x}.$$

Then,

$$\hat{\mathrm{E}}\{c\boldsymbol{x} \,|\, M\} = \mathrm{P}\circ(c\boldsymbol{x}) = c\boldsymbol{y} = c\hat{\mathrm{E}}\{\boldsymbol{x} \,|\, M\}.$$

(ii) $\mathrm{E}\{- \,|\, M\}$ is an additive function;

$$\hat{\mathrm{E}}\{\boldsymbol{x}_1 + \boldsymbol{x}_2 \,|\, M\} = \hat{\mathrm{E}}\{\boldsymbol{x}_1 \,|\, M\} + \hat{\mathrm{E}}\{\boldsymbol{x}_2 \,|\, M\}. \tag{3–102}$$

Using the linearity property of the projection,

$$\begin{aligned}\hat{\mathrm{E}}\{\boldsymbol{x}_1 + \boldsymbol{x}_2 \,|\, M\} &= \mathrm{P}\circ(\boldsymbol{x}_1 + \boldsymbol{x}_2) = \mathrm{P}\circ\boldsymbol{x}_1 + \mathrm{P}\circ\boldsymbol{x}_2 \\ &= \hat{\mathrm{E}}\{\boldsymbol{x}_1 \,|\, M\} + \hat{\mathrm{E}}\{\boldsymbol{x}_2 \,|\, M\}.\end{aligned}$$

(iii) If $M_1$ and $M_2$ are closed linear spaces such that $M_1 \subset M_2$, then

$$\hat{\mathrm{E}}_{M_1}\{\hat{\mathrm{E}}_x\{\boldsymbol{x} \,|\, M_2\} \,|\, M_1\} = \hat{\mathrm{E}}_x\{\boldsymbol{x} \,|\, M_1\}. \tag{3–103}$$

Consider the random vector

$$\boldsymbol{z}_p = \boldsymbol{x} - \hat{\mathrm{E}}\{\boldsymbol{x} \,|\, M_2\} = \boldsymbol{x} - \mathrm{P}_1\circ\boldsymbol{x} = (\mathrm{I} - \mathrm{P}_1)\circ\boldsymbol{x}. \tag{3–104}$$

From (3–91) it follows that $\boldsymbol{z}_p$ is the projection of $\boldsymbol{x}$ onto a space which is orthogonal to $M_2$. Now consider

$$\hat{E}\{x - \hat{E}_x\{x \mid M_2\} \mid M_1\} = P_2 \circ (x - \hat{E}\{x \mid M_2\}), \tag{3–105}$$

where, $P_2$ is the projection operator onto the space $M_1$. Therefore,

$$\hat{E}\{x - \hat{E}\{x \mid M_2\} \mid M_1\} = P_2 \circ (I - P_1) \circ x. \tag{3–106}$$

Because $(I - P_1)$ is the projection onto a space orthogonal to $M_2$ and since we did not restrict $M_1$ and $M_2$ to be orthogonal spaces, it follows that

$$P_2 \circ (I - P_1) \circ x = \boldsymbol{O}. \tag{3–107}$$

This last statement combined with (3–105) proves the relation (3–103), because, if (3–103) is valid, then, as we have proved,

$$\hat{E}\{x - \hat{E}\{x \mid M_2\} \mid M_1\} = 0. \tag{3–108}$$

(iv) If $M_1$ is orthogonal to $M_2$, then

$$\hat{E}\{x \mid M_1 \cup M_2\} = \hat{E}\{x \mid M_1\} + \hat{E}\{x \mid M_2\}. \tag{3–109}$$

Let

$$\begin{aligned} \hat{E}\{x \mid M_1\} &= P_1 \circ x = \xi_1 \in M_1 \\ \hat{E}\{x \mid M_2\} &= P_2 \circ x = \xi_2 \in M_2. \end{aligned} \tag{3–110}$$

Next we show that, using the symmetry of projections,

$$E\{\xi_1^T \xi_2\} = E\{(P_1 \circ x^T)(P_2 \circ x)\} = E\{(P_2 \circ P_1 \circ x^T) x\} = 0. \tag{3–111}$$

The first term vanishes because $\xi_1 \in M_1$, $\xi_2 \in M_2$, and $M_1$ is a space orthogonal to $M_2$. Hence, $P_2 P_1 = 0$, or the projections are mutually orthogonal. Note that $P_1 + P_2$ is also a projection which is the projection onto the sum space $M_1 \cup M_2$. Thus we can write

$$(P_1 + P_2) \circ x = \xi_1 + \xi_2 = \xi \in M_1 \cup M_2, \tag{3–112}$$

or, rewriting (3–112), the final result is

$$\hat{E}\{x \mid M_1 \cup M_2\} = \hat{E}\{x \mid M_1\} + \hat{E}\{x \mid M_2\}. \tag{3–113}$$

## Problems

**3.1** If the random vector $x$ has mean value $\boldsymbol{m} = E\{x\}$, compute the covariance function of the new random variable $y = \mathbf{A}x + z$, where $z$ and $\mathbf{A}$ are matrices with constant elements.

**3.2** Without using Theorem 3.1, calculate the conditional expectation $E\{x_1 \mid x_2\}$ for one-dimensional normal variates, using the moment-generating property of the joint characteristic function (3–31).

**3.3** If $x_1$, $x_2$, $x_3$ are normal random vectors such that $E\{x_2^T x_3\} = 0$, show that

$$E\{x_1 \mid x_2, x_3\} = E\{x_1 \mid x_2\} + E\{x_1 \mid x_3\}.$$

Do not use the projection-operator proof which was employed to establish (3–109). Assume zero mean values.

**3.4** What are the properties of a matrix $\mathbf{A}$ if the norm of $\boldsymbol{x}$ and the norm of $\mathbf{A}\boldsymbol{x}$ are the same? Has $\mathbf{A}^T$ the same property? Show that the columns of $\mathbf{A}$ are orthogonal scalar vectors.

**3.5** Given the following vectors:

$$\begin{aligned}
\boldsymbol{a}_1^T &= [\ \ 2\ -1\ -1\ \ \ 1\ \ \ 1\ \ \ 0]\\
\boldsymbol{a}_2^T &= [-1\ \ \ 2\ -1\ -1\ \ \ 0\ \ \ 1]\\
\boldsymbol{a}_3^T &= [-1\ -1\ \ \ 2\ \ \ 0\ -1\ -1]\\
\boldsymbol{a}_4^T &= [\ \ 1\ -1\ \ \ 0\ \ \ 2\ -1\ \ \ 1]\\
\boldsymbol{a}_5^T &= [\ \ 1\ \ \ 0\ -1\ -1\ \ \ 2\ -1]\\
\boldsymbol{a}_6^T &= [\ \ 0\ \ \ 1\ -1\ \ \ 1\ -1\ \ \ 2],
\end{aligned}$$

generate a basis set of orthonormal vectors using the inner product $(\boldsymbol{a}_i, \boldsymbol{a}_j) = \boldsymbol{a}_i^T \boldsymbol{a}_j$.

**3.6** Cameron [21] has presented the following algorithm based upon the Gram-Schmidt orthonormalization process, which carries out the process at the same time that an independent set of vectors is selected. Given a set of random vectors (the method is equally applicable to nonrandom vectors) $\boldsymbol{a}_1, \ldots, \boldsymbol{a}_n$, form the vectors

$$\begin{aligned}
\boldsymbol{b}_1 &= \boldsymbol{a}_1\\
\boldsymbol{b}_2 &= \mathrm{E}\{\boldsymbol{a}_1^T\boldsymbol{a}_1\}\boldsymbol{a}_2 - \mathrm{E}\{\boldsymbol{a}_1^T\boldsymbol{a}_2\}\boldsymbol{a}_1\\
\boldsymbol{b}_3 &= \mathrm{E}\{\boldsymbol{a}_1^T\boldsymbol{a}_1\}\boldsymbol{a}_3 - \mathrm{E}\{\boldsymbol{a}_1^T\boldsymbol{a}_3\}\boldsymbol{a}_1\\
&\vdots\\
\boldsymbol{b}_n &= \mathrm{E}\{\boldsymbol{a}_1^T\boldsymbol{a}_1\}\boldsymbol{a}_n - \mathrm{E}\{\boldsymbol{a}_1^T\boldsymbol{a}_n\}\boldsymbol{a}_1.
\end{aligned}$$

Next, form

$$\begin{aligned}
\boldsymbol{c}_1 &= \boldsymbol{b}_1\\
\boldsymbol{c}_2 &= \boldsymbol{b}_2\\
\boldsymbol{c}_3 &= \mathrm{E}\{\boldsymbol{b}_2^T\boldsymbol{b}_2\}\boldsymbol{b}_3 - \mathrm{E}\{\boldsymbol{b}_2^T\boldsymbol{b}_3\}\boldsymbol{b}_2\\
\boldsymbol{c}_4 &= \mathrm{E}\{\boldsymbol{b}_2^T\boldsymbol{b}_2\}\boldsymbol{b}_4 - \mathrm{E}\{\boldsymbol{b}_2^T\boldsymbol{b}_4\}\boldsymbol{b}_2\\
&\vdots\\
\boldsymbol{c}_n &= \mathrm{E}\{\boldsymbol{b}_2^T\boldsymbol{b}_2\}\boldsymbol{b}_n - \mathrm{E}\{\boldsymbol{b}_2^T\boldsymbol{b}_n\}\boldsymbol{b}_2.
\end{aligned}$$

Then,

$$\begin{aligned}
\boldsymbol{d}_1 &= \boldsymbol{c}_1\\
\boldsymbol{d}_2 &= \boldsymbol{c}_2\\
\boldsymbol{d}_3 &= \boldsymbol{c}_3\\
\boldsymbol{d}_4 &= \mathrm{E}\{\boldsymbol{c}_3^T\boldsymbol{c}_3\}\boldsymbol{c}_4 - \mathrm{E}\{\boldsymbol{c}_3^T\boldsymbol{c}_4\}\boldsymbol{c}_3\\
\boldsymbol{d}_5 &= \mathrm{E}\{\boldsymbol{c}_3^T\boldsymbol{c}_3\}\boldsymbol{c}_5 - \mathrm{E}\{\boldsymbol{c}_3^T\boldsymbol{c}_5\}\boldsymbol{c}_3\\
&\vdots
\end{aligned}$$

If in the process one of the vectors becomes zero, it should be transferred to the end and the vectors renumbered accordingly. This process is continued for $m$ steps, at which point the last $n - m$ will be zero vectors and the first $m$ will be the desired orthogonal set. It is a simple matter to normalize this set of vectors.

Verify that, at the $k$th stage, the first $(k - 1)$ vectors are mutually orthogonal and orthogonal to the remaining vectors.

**3.7** Use the preceding algorithm for the vectors in Problem 3.5. Explain the differences in the basis set.

**3.8** Let $M$ denote the space spanned by the basis set of vectors obtained in Problem 3.7. Decompose a vector

$$\boldsymbol{x}^T = [4 \ \ -2 \ \ 3 \ \ 0 \ \ -1 \ \ 1]$$

into

$$\boldsymbol{x} = \boldsymbol{z} + \boldsymbol{z}_p,$$

where $\boldsymbol{z} \in M$ and $\boldsymbol{z}_p$ is orthogonal to $M$. For a variable vector $\boldsymbol{w} \in M$, compute the minimum value of $||\boldsymbol{x} - \boldsymbol{w}||^2$.

**3.9** Projections are ordered by the definition that, if

$$\mathrm{P}_1 \circ \boldsymbol{x} = \boldsymbol{z}_1 \in M$$

$$\mathrm{P}_2 \circ \boldsymbol{x} = \boldsymbol{z}_2 \in M,$$

then $||\boldsymbol{z}_1|| \geq ||\boldsymbol{z}_2||$ implies that $\mathrm{P}_1 \geq \mathrm{P}_2$. Show that, for two projections, the relations $\mathrm{P}_1\mathrm{P}_2 = \mathrm{P}_2$ and $\mathrm{P}_1 \geq \mathrm{P}_2$ are equivalent.

**3.10** Prove the Schwarz inequality for the inner product defined for random variables. That is, prove that, if $x$ and $y$ are random vectors,

$$\mathrm{E}^2\{\boldsymbol{x}^T\boldsymbol{y}\} \leq \mathrm{E}\{\boldsymbol{x}^T\boldsymbol{x}\}\mathrm{E}\{\boldsymbol{y}^T\boldsymbol{y}\}.$$

From this inequality demonstrate the Minkowski inequality

$$\mathrm{E}\{(\boldsymbol{x} + \boldsymbol{y})^T(\boldsymbol{x} + \boldsymbol{y})\} \leq \mathrm{E}\{\boldsymbol{x}^T\boldsymbol{x}\} + \mathrm{E}\{\boldsymbol{y}^T\boldsymbol{y}\}.$$

**3.11** Restrict the random vectors in (3–95) to the 3-dimensional Euclidean space. Sketch (3–95), and show geometrically that the minimum value of $||\boldsymbol{x} - \boldsymbol{x}'||^2$ is attained if and only if $\boldsymbol{x}'$ is the projection of $\boldsymbol{x}$.

**3.12** Let $\boldsymbol{\Phi}^{[n\times n]}$ be a skew-symmetric matrix, and let $\boldsymbol{b}^{[n\times 1]}$ be a parameter vector. Show that

$$\nabla_b[\boldsymbol{b}^T\boldsymbol{\Phi}\boldsymbol{b}] = 0.$$

# Chapter 4

# GAUSS METHOD OF LEAST SQUARES

To a great many experimentalists, estimation is almost synonymous with minimum least squares fitting of data to predicted values. All too often, we are prone to neglect the original work on a subject in favor of recent abstracted and otherwise abbreviated versions. The first complete publication of the method of least squares was the exposition by Gauss in his famous paper *Theoria Motus* [24, 56]. Portions of his original work are reproduced here because these results form a practical motivation for many estimation theories that are in current use. Moreover, a survey of Gauss's arguments may be a sobering influence on those who believe that only recently developed mathematical theories are useful and the *classic*, or *old*, methods are passé or sterile.

Gauss made the following statement in 1809, which, with the proper interpretation for particular scientific disciplines using experimental data, has in essence been repeated many times as a preface to almost every discussion of the treatment of measured data [56, p. 249].

> If the astronomical observations and other quantities, on which the computation of orbits is based, were absolutely correct, the elements also, whether deduced from three or four observations, would be strictly accurate (so far indeed as the motion is supposed to take place exactly according to the laws of Kepler), and, therefore, if other observations were used, they might be confirmed, but not corrected. But since all our measurements and observations are nothing more than approximations to the truth, the same must be true of all calculations resting upon them, and the highest aim of

all computations made concerning concrete phenomena must be to approximate, as nearly as practicable, to the truth. But this can be accomplished in no other way than by a suitable combination of more observations than the number absolutely requisite for the determination of the unknown quantities. This problem can only be properly undertaken when an approximate knowledge of the orbit has been already attained, which is afterwards to be corrected so as to satisfy all the observations in the most accurate manner possible.

## 4.1
## *DISTRIBUTION OF ERRORS*

Suppose that an experiment is designed to measure, or estimate, a set of parameters $b_1, b_2, \ldots, b_q$. The set of parameters can be written as the matrix

$$\boldsymbol{b}^T = [b_1 \; b_2 \ldots b_q]. \tag{4–1}$$

The most general and most frequently encountered situation is that in which the desired parameters cannot be observed directly and must be indirectly measured as functions of the observables. Denote the observables as

$$\boldsymbol{W} = \boldsymbol{W}(\boldsymbol{b}) = \boldsymbol{W}(b_1, b_2, \ldots, b_q). \tag{4–2}$$

If the $b_i$ are the orbital elements of a space vehicle's trajectory, $\boldsymbol{W}$ might represent the data gathered by a tracking system at a given instant. For a radar system, the elements of $\boldsymbol{W}$ might be

$$\boldsymbol{W} = \begin{bmatrix} R \\ h \\ A \end{bmatrix}, \tag{4–3}$$

where $R$ is the slant range, $h$ is the elevation angle, and $A$ is the azimuth angle denoting the instantaneous position of the vehicle with respect to the radar.

The set of parameters for this experiment, as well as all those of this general class, are selected so that $\boldsymbol{W}$ can be computed at any time if the values of the parameters $\boldsymbol{b}$ are known. $\boldsymbol{w}(\boldsymbol{b})$ is called the *prediction function*, and it corresponds to $\boldsymbol{W}$ for the *true* values of the parameters. Therefore, the residuals, or observation errors, are defined as

$$\begin{gathered}\text{Residual} = \text{observations} - \text{prediction based upon true values} \\ \boldsymbol{d} = \boldsymbol{W} - \boldsymbol{w}(\boldsymbol{b}).\end{gathered} \tag{4–4}$$

If a sequence of observations are made at times $t_1, \ldots, t_n$, then a corresponding sequence of residuals can be calculated:

$$\begin{aligned} \boldsymbol{d}_1 &= \boldsymbol{W}_1 - \boldsymbol{w}(\boldsymbol{b}) \\ &\vdots \\ \boldsymbol{d}_n &= \boldsymbol{W}_n - \boldsymbol{w}(\boldsymbol{b}). \end{aligned} \tag{4–5}$$

In this example, we have implicitly imposed the same restriction used by Gauss. That is, the parameters to be estimated, $\boldsymbol{b}$, are not functions of time. It is this property that allows us to use a fixed value of the prediction function in the calculation of the residuals.

If the number of observables measured in the $n$ observations is equal to the number of parameters to be estimated $q$ (components of the matrix $\boldsymbol{b}^{[q\times 1]}$), then (4–4) can be written as

$$\boldsymbol{d}^{[q\times 1]} = \boldsymbol{W}^{[q\times 1]} - \boldsymbol{w}^{[q\times 1]}(\boldsymbol{b}^{[q\times 1]})$$

$$\begin{bmatrix} \boldsymbol{d}_1 \\ \boldsymbol{d}_2 \\ \vdots \\ \boldsymbol{d}_n \end{bmatrix} = \begin{bmatrix} \boldsymbol{W}_1^{[j\times 1]} \\ \boldsymbol{W}_2^{[j\times 1]} \\ \vdots \\ \boldsymbol{W}_n^{[j\times 1]} \end{bmatrix} - \begin{bmatrix} \boldsymbol{w}(\boldsymbol{b}) \\ \boldsymbol{w}(\boldsymbol{b}) \\ \vdots \\ \boldsymbol{w}(\boldsymbol{b}) \end{bmatrix}, \tag{4–6}$$

where $j$ is the number of observables measured at each observation and $q = nj$. Equation (4–6) is then a system of $q$ unknowns, which, at least in theory, would fully determine the values of the elements of $\boldsymbol{b}$. This is called the *deterministic case*, and the most probable values of the elements of $\boldsymbol{b}$ would be those that reduce each of the residuals in (4–5) to zero.

However, if $nj > q$, the number of observations exceeds the number of unknown parameters. Values of $\boldsymbol{b}$ obtained by solving any deterministic subset of order $q$ selected from (4–6) will not necessarily satisfy the remaining equations because of the existence of measurement errors which accompany the observations. This is the case for which the theory of least squares was studied by Gauss. The situation in which $nj < q$ can also be treated, but will be deferred to a later chapter because it was excluded by Gauss.

Gauss reasoned that, since all observations in a given experiment are made under the same conditions, then the residuals $\boldsymbol{d}$ would occur with equal probability. Let $f(\boldsymbol{d})$ be the probability density function associated with a residual. Then, if all the observations are statistically independent events, the joint probability density function of the $n$-residuals is

$$f_T(\boldsymbol{d}_1, \ldots, \boldsymbol{d}_n) = f_1(\boldsymbol{d}_1)f_2(\boldsymbol{d}_2)\ldots f_n(\boldsymbol{d}_n). \tag{4–7}$$

Gauss then argued that, because the residuals are a function of the parameters $\boldsymbol{b}$, the most probable system of values $\hat{\boldsymbol{b}}$ for the set $\boldsymbol{b}$ would be those that maximize the total density $f_T$ and thereby the total probability. Thus, $\hat{\boldsymbol{b}}$ can be obtained by the condition

$$\nabla_{\hat{b}}^{[q\times 1]} f_T^{[1\times 1]} = \boldsymbol{0} = \begin{bmatrix} \left.\dfrac{\partial f_T}{\partial b_1}\right|_{b_1=\hat{b}_1} \\ \vdots \\ \left.\dfrac{\partial f_T}{\partial b_q}\right|_{b_q=\hat{b}_q} \end{bmatrix}. \tag{4–8}$$

It is interesting to notice that Gauss introduced a technique that is still in common use. Because the logarithm is a monotonic function, the same values $b$ that maximize (4–7) will also maximize $\ln f_T$. We are then led to the following equations in place of (4–7) and (4–8):

$$\ln f_T = \ln f_1(\boldsymbol{d}_1) + \cdots + \ln f_n(\boldsymbol{d}_n), \tag{4–9}$$

$$\begin{aligned} \nabla_{\hat{b}} \ln f_T &= \boldsymbol{0} \\ &= \frac{1}{f_1(\boldsymbol{d}_1)} \nabla_{\hat{b}} f_1(\boldsymbol{d}_1) + \cdots + \frac{1}{f_n(\boldsymbol{d}_n)} \nabla_{\hat{b}} f_n(\boldsymbol{d}_n) \\ &= \frac{1}{f_1(\boldsymbol{d}_1)} [\nabla_{\hat{b}} \boldsymbol{d}_1^T][\nabla_{d_1} f_1(\boldsymbol{d}_1)] + \cdots + \frac{1}{f_n(\boldsymbol{d}_n)} [\nabla_{\hat{b}} \boldsymbol{d}_n^T][\nabla_{d_n} f_n(\boldsymbol{d}_n)] \\ &= \frac{1}{f_1(\boldsymbol{d}_1)} [\nabla_{\hat{b}} \boldsymbol{w}^T(\boldsymbol{b})][\nabla_{d_1} f_1(\boldsymbol{d}_1)] + \cdots + \frac{1}{f_n(\boldsymbol{d}_n)} [\nabla_{\hat{b}} \boldsymbol{w}^T(\boldsymbol{b})][\nabla_{d_n} f_n(\boldsymbol{d}_n)]. \end{aligned} \tag{4–10}$$

Equation (4–10) is a set of $q$ relations in the $q$ unknown components of $\boldsymbol{b}$. These equations can be solved for the unknown components as soon as an appropriate form is found, or selected, for the density functions $f_i$.

At this point Gauss made the following remarks which have been either explicitly or implicitly implanted into almost every argument concerning the reduction of physical measurements to the estimates of parameters, [56, p. 258].

> Since this (ed., the density functions $f_i$) cannot be defined *a priori*, we will, approaching the subject from another point of view, inquire upon what function, tacitly, as it were, assumed as a base, the common principle, the excellence of which is generally acknowledged, depends. It has been customary certainly to regard as an axiom the hypothesis that if any quantity has been determined by several direct observations, made under the same circumstances and with equal care, the arithmetical mean of the observed values affords the most probable value, if not rigorously, yet very nearly at least, so that it is always most safe to adhere to it.

Arguing that (4–10) must be true in general, Gauss considered a special case by first assuming that

$$\boldsymbol{w}(\boldsymbol{b}) = \frac{1}{n}(\boldsymbol{W}_1 + \cdots + \boldsymbol{W}_n), \tag{4–11}$$

where $n$ is the number of observations. Further, he *assumed* that observations yield the *fortuitous* result

$$\boldsymbol{W}_2 = \boldsymbol{W}_3 = \cdots = \boldsymbol{W}_n = \boldsymbol{W}_1 - n\boldsymbol{N}^{[q\times 1]}. \tag{4–12}$$

Combine (4–11) and (4–12) to find

$$\boldsymbol{w}(\boldsymbol{b}) = \boldsymbol{W}_1 - (n-1)\boldsymbol{N}, \tag{4–13}$$

and

$$\begin{aligned} \boldsymbol{d}_1 &= \boldsymbol{W}_1 - \boldsymbol{w}(\boldsymbol{b}) = (n-1)\boldsymbol{N} \\ \boldsymbol{d}_2 &= \boldsymbol{W}_2 - \boldsymbol{w}(\boldsymbol{b}) = \boldsymbol{W}_1 - n\boldsymbol{N} - [\boldsymbol{W}_1 - (n-1)\boldsymbol{N}] = -\boldsymbol{N} \\ &\vdots \\ \boldsymbol{d}_n &= -\boldsymbol{N}, \end{aligned} \tag{4–14}$$

$$\begin{aligned} \nabla_{d_1} &= \frac{1}{(n-1)}\nabla_N \\ \nabla_{d_j} &= -\nabla_N; \qquad 1 \neq j \leq n. \end{aligned} \tag{4–15}$$

Substitute (4–14) and (4–15) into (4–10) to obtain

$$\begin{aligned} \nabla_{\hat{b}}\boldsymbol{w}^T(\boldsymbol{b})\left\{\frac{1}{f(\boldsymbol{d}_1)}\nabla_{d_1}f(\boldsymbol{d}_1) - (n-1)\frac{1}{f(\boldsymbol{d}_j)}\nabla_{d_j}f(\boldsymbol{d}_j)\right\} = \boldsymbol{0}; \qquad 1 \neq j \leq n, \\ f_1 = f_2 = \cdots = f_n. \end{aligned} \tag{4–16}$$

Whence,

$$\frac{1}{f(\boldsymbol{d}_1)}\frac{1}{(n-1)}[\nabla_{d_1}f(\boldsymbol{d}_1)]\boldsymbol{N}^T = \frac{1}{f(\boldsymbol{d}_j)}[\nabla_{d_j}f(\boldsymbol{d}_j)]\boldsymbol{N}^T. \tag{4–17}$$

Because (4–17) must hold for all $n$ and arbitrary $\boldsymbol{N}$, it follows that each side must be equal to a constant matrix. Therefore, let

$$\frac{1}{f(\boldsymbol{d}_1)}[\nabla_{d_1}^{[q\times 1]}f(\boldsymbol{d}_1)]\boldsymbol{N}^{T[1\times q]} = -(n-1)\mathbf{A}^{[q\times q]} \tag{4–18}$$

and

$$\frac{1}{f(\boldsymbol{d}_j)}[\nabla_{d_j}f(\boldsymbol{d}_j)]\boldsymbol{N}^T = -\mathbf{A}. \tag{4–19}$$

Transform (4–18) in the following fashion:

$$\frac{1}{f(\boldsymbol{d}_1)}[\nabla_{d_1}f(\boldsymbol{d}_1)]\boldsymbol{N}^T\boldsymbol{N} = -\mathbf{A}(n-1)\boldsymbol{N} = -\mathbf{A}\boldsymbol{d}_1, \tag{4–20}$$

or

$$\frac{1}{f(\boldsymbol{d}_1)}\nabla_{d_1}f(\boldsymbol{d}_1) = -\mathbf{B}^{-1[q\times q]}\boldsymbol{d}_1, \tag{4–21}$$

where

$$\mathbf{B}^{-1[q\times q]} = \mathbf{A}[\boldsymbol{N}^T\boldsymbol{N}]^{-1}. \tag{4–22}$$

The indicated division is permissible because $\boldsymbol{N}^T\boldsymbol{N}$ is a constant, which we tacitly assume to be nonzero.

Next, integrate (4–21) with respect to $\boldsymbol{d}_1$; this yields

(4–23) $$\ln f(\boldsymbol{d}_1) = -\tfrac{1}{2}\boldsymbol{d}_1^T\mathbf{B}^{-1}\boldsymbol{d}_1 + \text{constant},$$

or

(4–24) $$f(\boldsymbol{d}_1) = D\exp\{-\tfrac{1}{2}\boldsymbol{d}_1^T\mathbf{B}^{-1}\boldsymbol{d}_1\}.$$

The constant $D$ is evaluated from the restriction that, since $f(\boldsymbol{d}_1)$ is a probability density function, its integral over the range of $\boldsymbol{d}_1$ must be unity. The constant can then be evaluated, and it is found that

(4–25) $$f(\boldsymbol{d}_1) = (2\pi)^{-q/2}\,|\mathbf{B}|^{-1/2}\exp\{-\tfrac{1}{2}\boldsymbol{d}_1^T\mathbf{B}^{-1}\boldsymbol{d}_1\}.$$

In exactly the same fashion, one can verify that (4–19) leads to

(4–26) $$f(\boldsymbol{d}_j) = (2\pi)^{-q/2}\,|\mathbf{B}|^{-1/2}\exp\{-\tfrac{1}{2}\boldsymbol{d}_j^T\mathbf{B}^{-1}\boldsymbol{d}_j\}; \qquad 1 \neq j \leq n.$$

Equations (4–25) and (4–26) for the density functions can be combined to find the joint density function for the $n$ residuals by introducing the total matrices defined as

$$\boldsymbol{d}^{T[q\times n]} = [\boldsymbol{d}_1^{T[q\times 1]}\ \boldsymbol{d}_2^{T[q\times 1]}\ \ldots\ \boldsymbol{d}_n^{T[q\times 1]}]$$

(4–27) $$\boldsymbol{\Psi}^{-1[nq\times nq]} = \begin{bmatrix} \mathbf{B}^{-1[q\times q]} & 0 & \ldots 0 \\ 0 & \mathbf{B}^{-1]q\times q]} & \ldots 0 \\ \cdots & \cdots & \cdots \\ 0\ \ldots & 0 & \mathbf{B}^{-1[q\times q]} \end{bmatrix}.$$

The joint probability density function for the residuals is then the normal function

(4–28) $$f(\boldsymbol{d}) = (2\pi)^{-nq/2}\,|\boldsymbol{\Psi}|^{-1/2}\exp\{-\tfrac{1}{2}\boldsymbol{d}^T\boldsymbol{\Psi}^{-1}\boldsymbol{d}\}.$$

This method of showing that the residuals have a normal distribution is, of course, not rigorous. All that has been shown is that for the special conditions (4–11) and (4–12), one obtains the normal form of (4–28). The fact that the desired form is obtained for a special case does not in itself imply any universal property. The tendency on the part of analysts today is to postulate that the residuals are either normally distributed or to show sufficient conditions to warrant an assumption that the residuals are at least asymptotically normal for sufficiently large sample sizes. The derivation of (4–28) is more of historical interest than of theoretical importance as an end in itself.

Gauss was concerned with the fact that his derivation of an equivalent form of (4–28) required an integration over an infinite range of the components of the residual $\boldsymbol{d}$. While this fiction of infinite values is mathematically convenient, in practice it is physically impossible to observe unbounded values of measured data [56, p. 259].

> The function just found cannot, it is true, express rigorously the probabilities of the errors: for since the possible errors are in all cases confined within certain limits, the probability of errors

exceeding those limits ought always to be zero; while our formula always gives some value. However, this defect, which every analytical function must, from its nature, labor under, is of no importance in practice, because the value of our function decreases so rapidly . . . (ed., when the exponent) has acquired a considerable magnitude, that it can safely be considered as vanishing. Besides, the nature of the subject never admits of assigning with absolute rigor the limits of error.

## 4.2
## *PRINCIPLE OF LEAST SQUARES*

Gauss observed, from a function equivalent to (4–28), that in order for $f(\boldsymbol{d})$ to be a maximum, implying a condition of maximum probability, the quadratic form

$$Q = \boldsymbol{d}^T \boldsymbol{\Psi}^{-1} \boldsymbol{d} \tag{4–29}$$

must be a minimum. Therefore, the most *probable* set of estimates $\hat{\boldsymbol{b}}$ for the parameters $\boldsymbol{b}$ will be those for which

$$\begin{aligned} Q &= [\boldsymbol{W} - \boldsymbol{w}'(\hat{\boldsymbol{b}})]^T \boldsymbol{\Psi}^{-1} [\boldsymbol{W} - \boldsymbol{w}'(\hat{\boldsymbol{b}})], \\ \boldsymbol{W}^T &= [\boldsymbol{W}_1^T \; \boldsymbol{W}_2^T \ldots \boldsymbol{W}_n^T] \\ \boldsymbol{w}'^T(\hat{\boldsymbol{b}}) &= [\boldsymbol{w}^T(\hat{\boldsymbol{b}}) \ldots \boldsymbol{w}^T(\hat{\boldsymbol{b}})], \end{aligned} \tag{4–30}$$

is a minimum. Equation (4–30) is the usual definition of a *weighted least squares* risk function.

It is remarkable that Gauss fully appreciated the arbitrariness in his arguments leading to the principle of least squares, [56, p. 260].

> This principle, which promises to be of most frequent use in all applications of the mathematics to natural philosophy, must, everywhere, be considered an axiom with the same propriety as the arithmetical mean of several observed values of the same quantity is adopted as the most probable value.

The original technique used by Gauss to find the minimizing values of $\hat{\boldsymbol{b}}$ in (4–30) will be omitted. Instead, this facet of the minimizing problem will be developed in greater detail in Chapters 5, 6, and 7.

## 4.3
## *SOME COMMENTS*

In many cases, as exemplified by the principle of least squares, we find that scarcely any perceptible progress has been made since the original conceptions. Although Gauss's approach, which has been modified in this chapter, can be readily omitted in a development of the foundations of estimation theory, his techniques and conclusions have made significant impacts on the theory and have motivated many recent developments.

Some items are listed which illustrate aspects of the Gauss development that are of almost equal importance with his final conclusion of the principle of least squares.

(i) The joint probability density function (4–7) can be expressed as a product of the density functions of the individual independent samples and is considered to be a function of the parameters $\boldsymbol{b}$ which are to be estimated. This is the basic concept of the likelihood function which plays a dominant role in recent extensions of estimation theory.

(ii) In (4–9), Gauss considered the maximum of the logarithm of the joint density function—a standard present day technique.

(iii) Gauss recognized and acknowledged that a certain arbitrariness must always exist in choosing a probability density function for the residuals resulting from physical experimental observations.

(iv) Gauss was aware of the arbitrariness of his development of the normal density function for the residuals. Although the principle of least squares was motivated by a mathematical argument, Gauss preferred to adopt the principle as an axiom rather than as a rigorous mathematical theorem.

# Chapter 5

# LINEAR ESTIMATES

## 5.1

## *LEAST SQUARES LINEAR REGRESSION*

The conditional expectation $\mathrm{E}\{\boldsymbol{x}_2 \,|\, \boldsymbol{x}_1\}$ was shown in Section 2.3 to be the random variable which minimizes the risk function

$$(5\text{–}1)\qquad \begin{aligned} R(\boldsymbol{x}_2) &= \mathrm{E}\{l(\boldsymbol{x}_2 - \mathbf{X}) \,|\, \boldsymbol{x}_1\} \\ \boldsymbol{X} &= \boldsymbol{X}(\boldsymbol{x}_1). \end{aligned}$$

In statistical literature the quantity $\mathrm{E}\{\boldsymbol{x}_2 \,|\, \boldsymbol{x}_1\}$, considered as a function of $\boldsymbol{x}_1$, is called the *regression function* of $\boldsymbol{x}_2$ on $\boldsymbol{x}_1$ [154]. If the conditions of Theorem 3.1 are satisfied so that one can write

$$(5\text{–}2)\qquad \mathrm{E}\{\boldsymbol{x}_2 \,|\, \boldsymbol{x}_1\} = \boldsymbol{a}_0^{[n\times 1]} + \mathbf{a}_1^{[n\times n]}\boldsymbol{x}_1^{[n\times 1]},$$

then we have a *linear regression function* of $\boldsymbol{x}_2$ on $\boldsymbol{x}_1$. $\boldsymbol{a}_0$ and $\mathbf{a}_1$ are called the *regression coefficients*. These definitions are readily extended to the general case $\mathrm{E}\{\boldsymbol{x}_n \,|\, \boldsymbol{x}_1, \boldsymbol{x}_2, \ldots, \boldsymbol{x}_{n-1}\}$.

The least squares linear regression problem is to determine the regression coefficients $\boldsymbol{a}_0$ and $\mathbf{a}_1$ which minimize the risk function

$$(5\text{–}3)\qquad R(\boldsymbol{a}_0, \mathbf{a}_1) = \mathrm{E}\{[\boldsymbol{x}_2 - \boldsymbol{u}(\boldsymbol{x}_1)]^T\,[\boldsymbol{x}_2 - \boldsymbol{u}(\boldsymbol{x}_1)]\}.$$

The minimim value of $R$ is attained from Theorem 2.1, for the choice

$$(5\text{–}4)\qquad u(\boldsymbol{x}_1) = \mathrm{E}\{\boldsymbol{x}_2 \,|\, \boldsymbol{x}_1\}.$$

Assume that the random variables satisfy Theorem 2.1, or that (5–2) is a sufficiently good approximation. In either case, (5–3) becomes

(5–5) $$R = \mathrm{E}\{[\boldsymbol{x}_2 - \boldsymbol{a}_0 - \mathbf{a}_1\boldsymbol{x}_1]^T[\boldsymbol{x}_2 - \boldsymbol{a}_0 - \mathbf{a}_1\boldsymbol{x}_1]\}.$$

Introduce

(5–6) $$\begin{aligned} \boldsymbol{m}_1 &= \mathrm{E}\{\boldsymbol{x}_1\} \\ \boldsymbol{m}_2 &= \mathrm{E}\{\boldsymbol{x}_2\} \end{aligned}$$

into (5–5) to find

(5–7) $$\begin{aligned} R = \mathrm{E}\{&[(\boldsymbol{x}_2 - \boldsymbol{m}_2) - (\boldsymbol{a}_0 - \boldsymbol{m}_2 + \mathbf{a}_1\boldsymbol{m}_1) - \mathbf{a}_1(\boldsymbol{x}_1 - \boldsymbol{m}_1)]^T \\ &\cdot [(\boldsymbol{x}_2 - \boldsymbol{m}_2) - (\boldsymbol{a}_0 - \boldsymbol{m}_2 + \mathbf{a}_1\boldsymbol{m}_1) - \mathbf{a}_1(\boldsymbol{x}_1 - \boldsymbol{m}_1)]\}. \end{aligned}$$

The regression coefficient $\boldsymbol{a}_0$ can be found by evaluating the condition

(5–8) $$\nabla_{a_0} R = 0.$$

The condition for which the derivative vanishes is

(5–9) $$\boldsymbol{a}_0 = \boldsymbol{m}_2 - \mathbf{a}_1\boldsymbol{m}_1.$$

The minimizing value of $\mathbf{a}_1$ requires a more sophisticated approach. Observe that

(5–10) $$\mathrm{tr}\, R = R.$$

We shall expand (5–7), and use the property for square matrices, which may be expressed as the product of two rectangular matrices **A** and **B**,

(5–11) $$\mathrm{tr}\, \mathbf{A}^T\mathbf{B} = \mathrm{tr}\, \mathbf{B}^T\mathbf{A} = \mathrm{tr}\, \mathbf{A}\mathbf{B}^T = \mathrm{tr}\, \mathbf{B}\mathbf{A}^T.$$

Further, introducing (5–6), we find that

(5–12) $$\begin{aligned} R = \mathrm{tr}\, [&\boldsymbol{\Psi}_2 - 2\mathbf{a}_1\boldsymbol{\Psi}_{12} + \mathbf{a}_1\boldsymbol{\Psi}_1\mathbf{a}_1^T \\ &+ (\boldsymbol{a}_0 - \boldsymbol{m}_2 + \mathbf{a}_1\boldsymbol{m}_1)^T(\boldsymbol{a}_0 - \boldsymbol{m}_2 + \mathbf{a}_1\boldsymbol{m}_1)], \end{aligned}$$

where

(5–13) $$\begin{aligned} \boldsymbol{\Psi}_1 &= \mathrm{E}\{(\boldsymbol{x}_1 - \boldsymbol{m}_1)(\boldsymbol{x}_1 - \boldsymbol{m}_1)^T\} \\ \boldsymbol{\Psi}_2 &= \mathrm{E}\{(\boldsymbol{x}_2 - \boldsymbol{m}_2)(\boldsymbol{x}_2 - \boldsymbol{m}_2)^T\} \\ \boldsymbol{\Psi}_{12} &= \mathrm{E}\{(\boldsymbol{x}_1 - \boldsymbol{m}_1)(\boldsymbol{x}_2 - \boldsymbol{m}_2)^T\} = \boldsymbol{\Psi}_{12}^T = \boldsymbol{\Psi}_{21}. \end{aligned}$$

Since the last two terms in the braces of (5–12) are positive, $R$ can be shown to have a minimum value when

(5–14) $$\mathbf{a}_1 = \boldsymbol{\Psi}_{12}\boldsymbol{\Psi}_1^{-1}.$$

It will be demonstrated that this is a minimum value. The risk function $R$, given in (5–7), with the aid of (5–11) can be written as

(5–15) $$\begin{aligned} R = \mathrm{tr}\, \mathrm{E}\{&[(\boldsymbol{x}_2 - \boldsymbol{m}_2) - \boldsymbol{K} - \mathbf{a}_1(\boldsymbol{x}_1 - \boldsymbol{m}_1)] \\ &\cdot [(\boldsymbol{x}_2 - \boldsymbol{m}_2) - \boldsymbol{K} - \mathbf{a}_1(\boldsymbol{x}_1 - \boldsymbol{m}_1)]^T\}, \end{aligned}$$

where

(5–16) $$\boldsymbol{K} = \boldsymbol{a}_0 - \boldsymbol{m}_2 + \mathbf{a}_1\boldsymbol{m}_1.$$

Introduce an estimate $\mathbf{a}_1'$ of $\mathbf{a}_1$ in the following fashion:

(5–17)

$$\begin{aligned} R &= \operatorname{tr} \mathrm{E}\{[\{\boldsymbol{x}_2 - \boldsymbol{m}_2 - \mathbf{a}_1'(\boldsymbol{x}_1 - \boldsymbol{m}_1)\} - \boldsymbol{K} + (\mathbf{a}_1' - \mathbf{a}_1)(\boldsymbol{x}_1 - \boldsymbol{m}_1)] \\ &\qquad \cdot [\{\boldsymbol{x}_2 - \boldsymbol{m}_2 - \mathbf{a}_1'(\boldsymbol{x}_1 - \boldsymbol{m}_1)\} - \boldsymbol{K} + (\mathbf{a}_1' - \mathbf{a}_1)(\boldsymbol{x}_1 - \boldsymbol{m}_1)]^T\} \\ &= \operatorname{tr} \boldsymbol{K}\boldsymbol{K}^T + \operatorname{tr} \mathrm{E}\{[(\boldsymbol{x}_2 - \boldsymbol{m}_2) - \mathbf{a}_1'(\boldsymbol{x}_1 - \boldsymbol{m}_1)][(\boldsymbol{x}_2 - \boldsymbol{m}_2) - \mathbf{a}_1'(\boldsymbol{x}_1 - \boldsymbol{m}_1)]^T\} \\ &\quad + \operatorname{tr} \mathrm{E}\{[(\mathbf{a}_1' - \mathbf{a}_1)(\boldsymbol{x}_1 - \boldsymbol{m}_1)][(\mathbf{a}_1' - \mathbf{a}_1)(\boldsymbol{x}_1 - \boldsymbol{m}_1)]^T\} \\ &\quad + \operatorname{tr} \mathrm{E}\{[(\boldsymbol{x}_2 - \boldsymbol{m}_2) - \mathbf{a}_1'(\boldsymbol{x}_1 - \boldsymbol{m}_1)][(\mathbf{a}_1' - \mathbf{a}_1)(\boldsymbol{x}_1 - \boldsymbol{m}_1)]^T\} \\ &\quad + \operatorname{tr} \mathrm{E}\{[(\mathbf{a}_1' - \mathbf{a}_1)(\boldsymbol{x}_1 - \boldsymbol{m}_1)][(\boldsymbol{x}_2 - \boldsymbol{m}_2) - \mathbf{a}_1'(\boldsymbol{x}_1 - \boldsymbol{m}_1)]^T\}. \end{aligned}$$

We shall next verify that the last two terms vanish if $\mathbf{a}_1' = \Psi_{12}\Psi_1^{-1}$. Consider the following sequence of manipulations:

(5–18)

$$\begin{aligned} R_4 &= \operatorname{tr} \mathrm{E}\{[(\boldsymbol{x}_2 - \boldsymbol{m}_2) - \mathbf{a}_1'(\boldsymbol{x}_1 - \boldsymbol{m}_1)][(\mathbf{a}_1' - \mathbf{a}_1)(\boldsymbol{x}_1 - \boldsymbol{m}_1)]^T\} \\ &= \operatorname{tr} [\Psi_{12}(\mathbf{a}_1' - \mathbf{a}_1)^T - \mathbf{a}_1'\Psi_1(\mathbf{a}_1' - \mathbf{a}_1)^T] \\ &= \operatorname{tr} [\Psi_{12}\Psi_1^{-1}\Psi_{12} - \Psi_{12}\mathbf{a}_1^T - \Psi_{12}\Psi_1^{-1}\Psi_1\Psi_1^{-1}\Psi_{12} + \Psi_{12}\Psi_1^{-1}\Psi_1\mathbf{a}_1^T] \\ &= 0. \end{aligned}$$

Similarly,

(5–19)

$$\begin{aligned} R_5 &= \operatorname{tr} \mathrm{E}\{[(\mathbf{a}_1' - \mathbf{a}_1)(\boldsymbol{x}_1 - \boldsymbol{m}_1)][(\boldsymbol{x}_2 - \boldsymbol{m}_2) - \mathbf{a}_1'(\boldsymbol{x}_1 - \boldsymbol{m}_1)]^T\} \\ &= \operatorname{tr} [(\mathbf{a}_1' - \mathbf{a}_1)\Psi_{12} - (\mathbf{a}_1' - \mathbf{a}_1)\Psi_1\mathbf{a}_1'^T] \\ &= \operatorname{tr} [\Psi_{12}\Psi_1^{-1}\Psi_{12} - \mathbf{a}_1\Psi_{12} - \Psi_{12}\Psi^{-1}\Psi_1\Psi_1^{-1}\Psi_{12} + \mathbf{a}_1\Psi_1\Psi_1^{-1}\Psi_{12}] \\ &= 0. \end{aligned}$$

Finally, notice that the first three, or nonzero, terms in (5–17) are all positive. Examination of the third term then indicates that $R$ is a minimum if $\mathbf{a}_1 = \mathbf{a}_1'$. Hence, (5–14) has been verified as the minimizing value of the regression coefficient. This proof depended upon judiciously guessing a value of $\mathbf{a}_1$, and then verifying the minimal property. The choice of $\mathbf{a}_1$ was motivated in this case, by considering one-dimensional random variables and finding the regression coefficient by evaluating the condition for which $dR/da = 0$.

The minimum regression coefficients are then

(5–20)

$$\begin{aligned} \boldsymbol{a}_0 &= \boldsymbol{m}_2 - \mathbf{a}_1\boldsymbol{m}_1 = \boldsymbol{m}_2 - \Psi_{12}\Psi_1^{-1}\boldsymbol{m}_1 \\ \mathbf{a}_1 &= \Psi_{12}\Psi_1^{-1}. \end{aligned}$$

The minimizing regression function is

(5–21)

$$\begin{aligned} u(\boldsymbol{x}_1) &= \mathrm{E}\{\boldsymbol{x}_2 \mid \boldsymbol{x}_1\} \\ &= \boldsymbol{a}_0 + \mathbf{a}_1\boldsymbol{x}_1 \\ &= \boldsymbol{m}_2 + \Psi_{12}\Psi_1^{\;1} \cdot (\boldsymbol{x}_1 - \boldsymbol{m}_1). \end{aligned}$$

It is significant that (5–21) has exactly the same form as (3–40), which was formulated for normal variates. The reason for this similarity stems from the arguments in Chapter 3. That is, for any distribution of random variables that satisfies the hypotheses of Theorem 3.1, the least squares regression functions are identical with the actual regression functions. Further, if (5–2) is a *sufficiently good* approximation, then (5–21) is a *wide sense* property of the distribution.

The line, in hyperspace,

$$\boldsymbol{x}_2 = \boldsymbol{m}_2 + \boldsymbol{\Psi}_{12}\boldsymbol{\Psi}_1^{-1}(\boldsymbol{x}_1 - \boldsymbol{m}_1) \tag{5–22}$$

is called the *least squares regression line* of $\boldsymbol{x}_2$ on $\boldsymbol{x}_1$.

Before discussing some applications of linear regression theory, the variance, or minimum value, of the risk function is needed. This minimum is found by inserting the coefficients given in (5–20) into (5–12). The result of this substitution is

$$\begin{aligned} R_{\min} = \sigma^2 &= \operatorname{tr}\{\boldsymbol{\Psi}_2 - 2\boldsymbol{\Psi}_{12}\boldsymbol{\Psi}_1^{-1}\boldsymbol{\Psi}_{12} + \boldsymbol{\Psi}_{12}\boldsymbol{\Psi}_1^{-1}\boldsymbol{\Psi}_{12}\} \\ &= \operatorname{tr}\{\boldsymbol{\Psi}_2 - \boldsymbol{\Psi}_{12}\boldsymbol{\Psi}_1^{-1}\boldsymbol{\Psi}_{12}\}. \end{aligned} \tag{5–23}$$

To illustrate some applications of regression theory, we shall restrict ourselves to two dimensions. Equation (5–22) becomes

$$x_2 = m_2 + \frac{\sigma_{12}^2}{\sigma_1^2}(x_1 - m_1), \tag{5–24}$$

and (5–23) reduces to

$$\sigma^2 = \sigma_2^2\left(1 - \frac{\sigma_{12}^4}{\sigma_1^2\sigma_2^2}\right). \tag{5–25}$$

Based upon a sequence of observations, one might wish to predict the number of red birds in a sampling of a given species which has $x_1$ red males. Thus, the predicted number of red babies based upon a linear assumption would be

$$\hat{x}_2 = \left(m_2 - m_1\frac{\sigma_{12}^2}{\sigma_1^2}\right) + \frac{\sigma_{12}^2}{\sigma_1^2}x_1. \tag{5–26}$$

Or again, a production run of camshafts in an automobile engine factory might show that the output of one department could be defective. The production engineer might try to predict the number of defective parts by keeping a record that indicates that machine $x_{1i}$ produces a defective camshaft when operated by operator $x_{2i}$. Then the predicted defective parts could be computed from a formula such as (5–26).

Related to the prediction interpretation of regression is the discrimination problem. In essence, discrimination is the converse of prediction. Prediction problems involve computing values of $x_2$ from a knowledge of $x_1$, given the values of the regression coefficients. Discrimination problems are those in which one estimates $x_1$ from observed values of $x_2$ and knowledge of the regression coefficients.

There has been some confusion between the meanings of theories associated with the names *analysis of variance*, *analysis of covariance*, and *regression analysis*. Scheffé has given a good working definition of these three closely related concepts [129, p. 5].

In $n$-dimensions, the linear regression function has the form

$$y_i = \beta_{0i} + \beta_{1i}x_1 + \beta_{2i}x_2 + \cdots + \beta_{ki}x_k; \qquad i = 1, 2, \ldots, n, \tag{5–27}$$

where $\{\beta_{ji}\}$ are the set of regression coefficients. The analysis of variance constitutes statistical methods of analyzing observations assumed to have the general form of (5–27) in which the coefficients $\beta_{ji}$ are usually chosen as 0 or 1. That is, the $\beta_{ji}$ are values of indicator variables which indicate the presence or absence of the effects $x_j$ under the given specified conditions of the observations. $\beta_{ji}$ can be interpreted as the number of times $x_j$ occurs in the $j$th observation, usually 0 or 1. If the $\beta_{ji}$ are independent continuous variables such as time, length, temperature, etc., and the observations $y_i$ are the dependent variables, then (5–27) represents a linear regression analysis. If the $\beta_{ji}$ are mixed and contain continuous as well as discrete values, then (5–27) represents the situation which has been called analysis of covariance.

## 5.2
## *LEAST SQUARES LINEAR ESTIMATOR*

Suppose that a sequence of observations $y_1, \ldots, y_n$ has been made as a result of a series of measurements. Since each observation may have $\nu$ elements, the total observation matrix is defined as

$$\begin{aligned} \boldsymbol{y}^{T[1\times n\nu]} &= [y_{11}\ y_{12} \cdots y_{1\nu}\ y_{21} \cdots y_{2\nu} \cdots y_{n1} \cdots y_{n\nu}] \\ &= [\boldsymbol{y}_1^T\ \boldsymbol{y}_2^T \cdots \boldsymbol{y}_n^T]. \end{aligned} \tag{5–28}$$

The observations can be represented as

$$\begin{gathered} \text{Observations} = \text{mean value} + \text{noise} \\ \boldsymbol{y}^{[n\nu\times 1]} = \boldsymbol{m}^{[n\nu\times 1]} + \boldsymbol{x}^{[n\nu\times 1]}, \end{gathered} \tag{5–29}$$

where

$$\mathrm{E}\{\boldsymbol{y}\} = \boldsymbol{m}. \tag{5–30}$$

Linear estimators are characterized by the hypothesis that the mean value $\boldsymbol{m}$ is expressible as a linear transformation of the $q$ unknown parameters $\boldsymbol{b}^{[q\times 1]}$ which are to be estimated. Accordingly, it is postulated that

$$\boldsymbol{m}^{[n\nu\times 1]} = \mathbf{A}^{[n\nu\times q]}\,\boldsymbol{b}^{[q\times 1]}. \tag{5–31}$$

Although not essential to the theory, it is almost universally agreed that the linear estimates be unbiased. This restriction is equivalent to postulating that

$$\text{(5–32)} \qquad \mathrm{E}\{\boldsymbol{x}\} = \boldsymbol{0}.$$

The *least squares linear unbiased* estimate of $\boldsymbol{b}$ is defined as the vector $\hat{\boldsymbol{b}}$ which minimizes the quadratic risk function

$$\text{(5–33)} \qquad R(\boldsymbol{b}) = (\boldsymbol{y} - \mathbf{A}\boldsymbol{b})^T(\boldsymbol{y} - \mathbf{A}\boldsymbol{b})$$

with respect to $\boldsymbol{b}$ considered as a parameter. It is convenient to restrict the theory so that $\mathbf{A}^T\mathbf{A}$ is a nonsingular matrix and has an inverse. This is not an essential assumption, and a parallel development is sketched in Chapter 7 for which the ordinary matrix inverse is generalized by introducing the concept of a pseudoinverse of a matrix.

Although (5–33) does not have the form of the expected value of a loss function, the methods of Chapters 2 and 3 can be employed to minimize $R$. Expand the right side of (5–33) into

$$\text{(5–34)} \qquad R = \boldsymbol{y}^T\boldsymbol{y} - \boldsymbol{b}^T\mathbf{A}^T\boldsymbol{y} - \boldsymbol{y}^T\mathbf{A}\boldsymbol{b} + \boldsymbol{b}^T\mathbf{A}^T\mathbf{A}\boldsymbol{b}.$$

Differentiate with respect to the parameters, and equate the result to zero to determine the conditions that minimize $R$ with respect to $\boldsymbol{b}$. Thus, using (3–9)

$\nabla_b (y^T A b) = A^T y$

$$\text{(5–35)} \qquad \begin{aligned} \nabla_b R(\hat{\boldsymbol{b}}) &= \nabla_b R(\boldsymbol{b})\,|_{\boldsymbol{b}=\hat{\boldsymbol{b}}} \\ &= -2\mathbf{A}^T\boldsymbol{y} + 2\mathbf{A}^T\mathbf{A}\hat{\boldsymbol{b}} = \boldsymbol{0}, \end{aligned}$$

or the least squares estimate is

$$\text{(5–36)} \qquad \hat{\boldsymbol{b}} = (\mathbf{A}^T\mathbf{A})^{-1}\mathbf{A}^T\boldsymbol{y}.$$

Because of the technique which was used to obtain the estimate $\hat{\boldsymbol{b}}$ given in (5–36), an argument must be presented to establish whether the result is merely a local extremum or indeed is the desired absolute minimal for the risk function.

Write the risk function $R$ in the form of the squared norm of a vector as follows:

$$\text{(5–37)} \qquad \begin{aligned} R &= \|\boldsymbol{y} - \mathbf{A}\boldsymbol{b}\|^2, \\ R &= \|\boldsymbol{y}\|^2 - \boldsymbol{y}^T\mathbf{A}\boldsymbol{b} - \boldsymbol{b}^T\mathbf{A}^T\boldsymbol{y} + \boldsymbol{b}^T\mathbf{A}^T\mathbf{A}\boldsymbol{b}. \end{aligned}$$

Suppose that

$$\text{(5–38)} \qquad \boldsymbol{y} = \mathbf{A}\hat{\boldsymbol{b}},$$

then (5–37) can be written as

$$\text{(5–39)} \qquad \begin{aligned} R &= \|\boldsymbol{y}\|^2 + (\boldsymbol{b} - \hat{\boldsymbol{b}})^T\mathbf{A}^T\mathbf{A}(\boldsymbol{b} - \hat{\boldsymbol{b}}) - \hat{\boldsymbol{b}}^T\mathbf{A}^T\mathbf{A}\hat{\boldsymbol{b}} \\ &= \|\boldsymbol{y}\|^2 + \|\mathbf{A}(\boldsymbol{b} - \hat{\boldsymbol{b}})\|^2 - \|\mathbf{A}\hat{\boldsymbol{b}}\|^2. \end{aligned}$$

Since each term in (5–39) is positive, it follows that

$$\text{(5–40)} \qquad R = \|\boldsymbol{y} - \mathbf{A}\boldsymbol{b}\|^2 \geq \|\boldsymbol{y}\|^2 - \|\mathbf{A}\hat{\boldsymbol{b}}\|^2.$$

Moreover, $R$ attains a minimum value if and only if $\boldsymbol{b} = \hat{\boldsymbol{b}}$, where $\hat{\boldsymbol{b}}$ is given in (5–38). Because (5–38) is another form of (5–36), it has been verified that (5–36) is the estimate that yields an absolute minimum of the quadratic risk function $R$, (5–33).

It is now a simple matter to demonstrate that $\hat{\boldsymbol{b}}$ is an unbiased estimate. Consider,

$$\begin{aligned} \mathrm{E}\{\hat{\boldsymbol{b}} - \boldsymbol{b}\} &= \mathrm{E}\{(\mathbf{A}^T\mathbf{A})^{-1}\mathbf{A}^T\boldsymbol{y}\} - \boldsymbol{b} \\ &= (\mathbf{A}^T\mathbf{A})^{-1}\mathbf{A}^T\mathrm{E}\{\boldsymbol{y}\} - \boldsymbol{b} \\ &= (\mathbf{A}^T\mathbf{A})^{-1}\mathbf{A}^T\mathbf{A}\boldsymbol{b} - \boldsymbol{b} = \boldsymbol{0}. \end{aligned} \tag{5–41}$$

Therefore, $\hat{\boldsymbol{b}}$ is an unbiased estimator.

The covariance matrix of our least squares linear estimates is

$$\begin{aligned} \boldsymbol{\Psi} &= \mathrm{E}\{(\hat{\boldsymbol{b}} - \boldsymbol{b})(\hat{\boldsymbol{b}} - \boldsymbol{b})^T\} \\ &= \mathrm{E}\{[(\mathbf{A}^T\mathbf{A})^{-1}\mathbf{A}^T\boldsymbol{y} - \boldsymbol{b}][(\mathbf{A}^T\mathbf{A})^{-1}\mathbf{A}^T\boldsymbol{y} - \boldsymbol{b}]^T\} \\ &= (\mathbf{A}^T\mathbf{A})^{-1}\mathbf{A}^T\mathrm{E}\{\boldsymbol{x}\boldsymbol{x}^T\}\mathbf{A}(\mathbf{A}^T\mathbf{A})^{-1}. \end{aligned} \tag{5–42}$$

Define the covariance matrix of the measurement errors to be

$$\boldsymbol{\Lambda} = \mathrm{E}\{\boldsymbol{x}\boldsymbol{x}^T\}, \tag{5–43}$$

and (5–42) reduces to

$$\boldsymbol{\Psi} = (\mathbf{A}^T\mathbf{A})^{-1}\mathbf{A}^T\boldsymbol{\Lambda}\mathbf{A}(\mathbf{A}^T\mathbf{A})^{-1}. \tag{5–44}$$

## 5.3
## *WEIGHTED LEAST SQUARES LINEAR ESTIMATOR*

A more general form of the quadratic risk function is one which permits assigning predetermined weights to the components. The general weighted quadratic risk function is of the form

$$R(\boldsymbol{b}) = (\boldsymbol{y} - \mathbf{A}\boldsymbol{b})^T\boldsymbol{\Phi}_a^{-1}(\boldsymbol{y} - \mathbf{A}\boldsymbol{b}) \overset{d}{=} \|\boldsymbol{y} - \mathbf{A}\boldsymbol{b}\|^2_{\boldsymbol{\Phi}_a^{-1}}. \tag{5–45}$$

In most expositions $\boldsymbol{\Phi}_a^{-1}$ is restricted to being both symmetric and positive definite. The symmetric condition is, in a sense, redundant because we can write the unique decomposition $\boldsymbol{\Phi}_a^{-1} = \boldsymbol{\Phi}^{-1} + \boldsymbol{\Phi}_s$, where $\boldsymbol{\Phi}^{-1}$ is symmetric and $\boldsymbol{\Phi}_s$ is skew-symmetric. But, since, for any nonzero column matrix $\boldsymbol{d}$, $\boldsymbol{d}^T\boldsymbol{\Phi}_s\boldsymbol{d} = 0$, it is apparent that only the symmetric component $\boldsymbol{\Phi}^{-1}$ of $\boldsymbol{\Phi}_a^{-1}$ contributes a nonzero value to the risk function. For this reason, it is common to state that the weighting matrix is symmetric for a quadratic form risk function rather than to restate the preceding decomposition arguments.

The estimate $\hat{\boldsymbol{b}}$, which produces a relative minimum of the risk function, can be established by operating on $R$ with the differential operator matrix $\boldsymbol{\nabla}_b$ and solving for the condition

$$\boldsymbol{\nabla}_b\, R(\hat{\boldsymbol{b}}) = \boldsymbol{0}. \tag{5–46}$$

Thus, one evaluates

$$(5\text{–}47)\quad \begin{aligned} 0 &= \nabla_b\,(\boldsymbol{y}^T\boldsymbol{\Phi}^{-1}\boldsymbol{y} - \boldsymbol{y}^T\boldsymbol{\Phi}^{-1}\mathbf{A}\boldsymbol{b} - \boldsymbol{b}^T\mathbf{A}^T\boldsymbol{\Phi}^{-1}\boldsymbol{y} + \boldsymbol{b}^T\mathbf{A}^T\boldsymbol{\Phi}^{-1}\mathbf{A}\boldsymbol{b})\big|_{b=\hat{b}} \\ &= -2\mathbf{A}^T\boldsymbol{\Phi}^{-1}\boldsymbol{y} + 2\mathbf{A}^T\boldsymbol{\Phi}^{-1}\mathbf{A}\hat{\boldsymbol{b}}. \end{aligned}$$

Therefore, the estimate for the relative minimum of the risk function is

$$(5\text{–}48)\quad \hat{\boldsymbol{b}} = (\mathbf{A}^T\boldsymbol{\Phi}^{-1}\mathbf{A})^{-1}\mathbf{A}^T\boldsymbol{\Phi}^{-1}\boldsymbol{y}.$$

Once again it must be verified that the value of the estimated parameters actually yields an absolute minimal value of the risk function rather than merely a relative minimum.

Because the effective component of the weighting matrix $\boldsymbol{\Phi}$ is symmetric and positive definite, it can be written as the product

$$(5\text{–}49)\quad \begin{aligned} \boldsymbol{\Phi} &= \boldsymbol{\Phi}^{1/2}(\boldsymbol{\Phi}^{1/2})^T \\ &= \boldsymbol{\Phi}^{1/2}\boldsymbol{\Phi}^{1/2}, \end{aligned}$$

and

$$(5\text{–}50)\quad \begin{aligned} \boldsymbol{\Phi}^{-1} &= (\boldsymbol{\Phi}^{-1/2})^T\boldsymbol{\Phi}^{-1/2} \\ &= \boldsymbol{\Phi}^{-1/2}\boldsymbol{\Phi}^{-1/2}. \end{aligned}$$

The proof of the absolute minimization property of $\hat{\boldsymbol{b}}$, as given in (5–48), starts with the observation that

$$(5\text{–}51)\quad \begin{aligned} (\boldsymbol{y} - \mathbf{A}\boldsymbol{b})^T\boldsymbol{\Phi}^{-1}(\boldsymbol{y} - \mathbf{A}\boldsymbol{b}) &= [\boldsymbol{\Phi}^{-1/2}(\boldsymbol{y} - \mathbf{A}\boldsymbol{b})]^T[\boldsymbol{\Phi}^{-1/2}(\boldsymbol{y} - \mathbf{A}\boldsymbol{b})] \\ &= \|\boldsymbol{\Phi}^{-1/2}(\boldsymbol{y} - \mathbf{A}\boldsymbol{b})\|^2. \end{aligned}$$

The remainder of the proof exactly parallels the steps in Section 5.2, starting with (5–51) replacing (5–37), and continuing through (5–41), to demonstrate the absolute minimal property as well as to establish that $\hat{\boldsymbol{b}}$ in (5–48) is an unbiased estimator of the parameter vector.

The covariance matrix corresponding to the estimate error $\hat{\boldsymbol{b}} - \boldsymbol{b}$ is

$$(5\text{–}52)\quad \begin{aligned} \boldsymbol{\Psi}_{LS} &= \mathrm{E}\{(\hat{\boldsymbol{b}} - \boldsymbol{b})(\hat{\boldsymbol{b}} - \boldsymbol{b})^T\} \\ &= \mathrm{E}\{(\mathbf{Q}\boldsymbol{y} - \boldsymbol{b})(\mathbf{Q}\boldsymbol{y} - \boldsymbol{b})^T\}, \end{aligned}$$

where

$$(5\text{–}53)\quad \begin{aligned} \mathbf{Q} &= (\mathbf{A}^T\boldsymbol{\Phi}^{-1}\mathbf{A})^{-1}\mathbf{A}^T\boldsymbol{\Phi}^{-1}, \\ \mathbf{QA} &= \mathbf{I}. \end{aligned}$$

Insert (5–29) and (5–31) into (5–52); the result is

$$(5\text{–}54)\quad \begin{aligned} \boldsymbol{\Psi}_{LS} &= \mathrm{E}\{\mathbf{Q}\boldsymbol{y}\boldsymbol{y}^T\mathbf{Q}^T - \mathbf{Q}\boldsymbol{y}\boldsymbol{b}^T - \boldsymbol{b}\boldsymbol{y}^T\mathbf{Q}^T + \boldsymbol{b}\boldsymbol{b}^T\} \\ &= \mathbf{Q}\mathrm{E}\{(\mathbf{A}\boldsymbol{b} + \boldsymbol{x})(\mathbf{A}\boldsymbol{b} + \boldsymbol{x})^T\}\mathbf{Q}^T \\ &\quad -\mathbf{QA}\boldsymbol{b}\boldsymbol{b}^T - \boldsymbol{b}\boldsymbol{b}^T\mathbf{A}^T\mathbf{Q}^T + \boldsymbol{b}\boldsymbol{b}^T \\ &= \mathbf{QA}\boldsymbol{b}\boldsymbol{b}^T\mathbf{A}^T\mathbf{Q}^T + \mathbf{Q}\mathrm{E}\{\boldsymbol{x}\boldsymbol{x}^T\}\mathbf{Q}^T - \mathbf{QA}\boldsymbol{b}\boldsymbol{b}^T \\ &\quad -\boldsymbol{b}\boldsymbol{b}^T\mathbf{A}^T\mathbf{Q}^T + \boldsymbol{b}\boldsymbol{b}^T. \end{aligned}$$

If the definition of $\mathbf{Q}$ is substituted in (5–54), it can be verified that

$$\begin{aligned}\boldsymbol{\Psi}_{LS} &= \mathbf{Q}\mathrm{E}\{\boldsymbol{x}\boldsymbol{x}^T\}\mathbf{Q}^T \\ &= \mathbf{Q}\boldsymbol{\Lambda}\mathbf{Q}^T \\ &= (\mathbf{A}^T\boldsymbol{\Phi}^{-1}\mathbf{A})^{-1}\mathbf{A}^T\boldsymbol{\Phi}^{-1}\boldsymbol{\Lambda}\boldsymbol{\Phi}^{-1}\mathbf{A}(\mathbf{A}^T\boldsymbol{\Phi}^{-1}\mathbf{A})^{-1}.\end{aligned} \tag{5–55}$$

An almost natural conjecture at this point is whether or not one can find a weighting function which will provide an absolute minimum of the weighted quadratic loss function. The existence of such a minimizing weighting function will be established.

Suppose the weighting function is chosen such that

$$\boldsymbol{\Phi} = \boldsymbol{\Lambda} = \mathrm{E}\{\boldsymbol{x}\boldsymbol{x}^T\}, \tag{5–56}$$

then the estimate $\hat{\boldsymbol{b}}$ given in (5–48) becomes

$$\hat{\boldsymbol{b}} = (\mathbf{A}^T\boldsymbol{\Lambda}^{-1}\mathbf{A})^{-1}\mathbf{A}^T\boldsymbol{\Lambda}^{-1}\boldsymbol{y}, \tag{5–57}$$

and the covariance matrix of the errors (5–55) reduces to

$$\boldsymbol{\Psi}_{MV} = (\mathbf{A}^T\boldsymbol{\Lambda}^{-1}\mathbf{A})^{-1}. \tag{5–58}$$

We shall now demonstrate that the choice (5–56) for the weighting matrix yields a minimum error covariance matrix. That is, for any choice of weighting matrices

$$\boldsymbol{\Psi}_{MV} \leq \boldsymbol{\Psi}_{LS}. \tag{5–59}$$

By definition, a positive definite matrix is less than or equal to a second positive definite matrix if the second matrix minus the first matrix is nonnegative definite.

While there are several methods for establishing (5–59), we shall use a technique of Grenander and Rosenblatt [62], which depends upon an inequality for matrices that is related to the Schwarz inequality for functions. The proof starts by considering the matrices

$$\begin{aligned}&\mathbf{F}^{[n\times q]} \\ &\mathbf{G}^{[n\times q]} \\ \boldsymbol{\lambda}^{[q\times 1]},\ \boldsymbol{\mu}^{[q\times 1]};\quad &\text{arbitrary vectors} \\ (\boldsymbol{G}^T\boldsymbol{G})^{[q\times q]};\quad &\text{symmetric, positive definite, } q \leq n; \\ &\text{rank } \mathbf{F} = q, \\ &\text{rank } \mathbf{G} = q;\end{aligned} \tag{5–60}$$

and forming the positive semidefinite quadratic form

$$(\mathbf{G}\boldsymbol{\lambda} + \mathbf{F}\boldsymbol{\mu})^T(\mathbf{G}\boldsymbol{\lambda} + \mathbf{F}\boldsymbol{\mu}) \geq 0. \tag{5–61}$$

Expand (5–61)

$$\boldsymbol{\lambda}^T\mathbf{G}^T\mathbf{G}\boldsymbol{\lambda} + \boldsymbol{\lambda}^T\mathbf{G}^T\mathbf{F}\boldsymbol{\mu} + \boldsymbol{\mu}^T\mathbf{F}^T\mathbf{G}\boldsymbol{\lambda} + \boldsymbol{\mu}^T\mathbf{F}^T\mathbf{F}\boldsymbol{\mu} \geq 0, \tag{5–62}$$

and introduce the definitions

$$\mathbf{a} = \mathbf{G}^T\mathbf{G}$$
$$\mathbf{b} = \mathbf{G}^T\mathbf{F} \tag{5-63}$$
$$\mathbf{c} = \mathbf{F}^T\mathbf{F}$$

to obtain

$$\boldsymbol{\lambda}^T\mathbf{a}\boldsymbol{\lambda} + \boldsymbol{\lambda}^T\mathbf{b}\boldsymbol{\mu} + \boldsymbol{\mu}^T\mathbf{b}^T\boldsymbol{\lambda} + \boldsymbol{\mu}^T\mathbf{c}\boldsymbol{\mu} \geq 0. \tag{5-64}$$

Because $\mathbf{a}$ was postulated to be a symmetric positive definite matrix, (5–64) can be written in the following form as the sum of positive terms:

$$(\boldsymbol{\lambda}^T\mathbf{a}^{1/2} + \boldsymbol{\mu}^T\mathbf{b}^T\mathbf{a}^{-1/2})(\boldsymbol{\lambda}^T\mathbf{a}^{1/2} + \boldsymbol{\mu}^T\mathbf{b}^T\mathbf{a}^{-1/2})^T + \boldsymbol{\mu}^T(\mathbf{c} - \mathbf{b}^T\mathbf{a}^{-1}\mathbf{b})\boldsymbol{\mu} \geq 0. \tag{5-65}$$

If

$$\boldsymbol{\lambda}^T = -\boldsymbol{\mu}^T\mathbf{b}^T\mathbf{a}^{-1}, \tag{5-66}$$

then (5–65) yields the desired inequality

$$\mathbf{c} \geq \mathbf{b}^T\mathbf{a}^{-1}\mathbf{b},$$
$$(\mathbf{F}^T\mathbf{F}) \geq (\mathbf{G}^T\mathbf{F})^T(\mathbf{G}^T\mathbf{G})^{-1}(\mathbf{G}^T\mathbf{F}). \tag{5-67}$$

Equality is attained in (5–67) if there exist vectors $\boldsymbol{\lambda}$ and $\boldsymbol{\mu}$, one of which does not vanish, such that

$$\mathbf{G}\boldsymbol{\lambda} + \mathbf{F}\boldsymbol{\mu} = \boldsymbol{0}. \tag{5-68}$$

We can now demonstrate that $\boldsymbol{\Psi}_{MV}$ is the minimum covariance matrix of the estimation errors. Assume an arbitrary unbiased linear estimator $\hat{\boldsymbol{b}}_0$ for our problem. This must have the form

$$\hat{\boldsymbol{b}}_0 = \mathbf{B}\boldsymbol{y},$$
$$\boldsymbol{y} = \mathbf{A}\boldsymbol{b} + \boldsymbol{x}. \tag{5-69}$$

Because of the restriction of unbiasedness, we must have

$$\begin{aligned} \mathrm{E}\{\hat{\boldsymbol{b}}_0 - \boldsymbol{b}\} = \boldsymbol{0} &= \mathrm{E}\{\mathbf{B}\boldsymbol{y} - \boldsymbol{b}\} \\ &= \mathbf{B}\mathrm{E}\{\boldsymbol{y}\} - \boldsymbol{b} \\ &= \mathbf{B}\mathbf{A}\boldsymbol{b} - \boldsymbol{b} \\ &= (\mathbf{B}\mathbf{A} - \mathbf{I})\boldsymbol{b} \end{aligned} \tag{5-70}$$

or

$$\mathbf{B}\mathbf{A} = \mathbf{I}. \tag{5-71}$$

The estimate error associated with $\hat{\boldsymbol{b}}_0$ is

$$\boldsymbol{q}_0 = \hat{\boldsymbol{b}}_0 - \boldsymbol{b}, \tag{5-72}$$

having the covariance matrix

$$\begin{aligned} \boldsymbol{\Psi}_{LS} &= \mathrm{E}\{\boldsymbol{q}_0\boldsymbol{q}_0^T\} = \mathrm{E}\{(\hat{\boldsymbol{b}}_0 - \boldsymbol{b})(\hat{\boldsymbol{b}}_0 - \boldsymbol{b})^T\} \\ &= \mathrm{E}\{(\mathbf{B}\boldsymbol{y} - \boldsymbol{b})(\mathbf{B}\boldsymbol{y} - \boldsymbol{b})^T\} \\ &= \mathbf{B}\mathrm{E}\{\boldsymbol{x}\boldsymbol{x}^T\}\mathbf{B}^T \\ &= \mathbf{B}\boldsymbol{\Lambda}\mathbf{B}^T. \end{aligned} \tag{5-73}$$

The final step is to apply the inequality (5–67) with the matrices identified as

$$\begin{aligned} \mathbf{F}^T &= \mathbf{B}\mathbf{\Lambda}^{1/2} \\ \mathbf{G} &= \mathbf{\Lambda}^{-1/2}\mathbf{A}, \end{aligned} \tag{5–74}$$

then

$$\begin{aligned} (\mathbf{F}^T\mathbf{F}) &\geq (\mathbf{G}^T\mathbf{F})^T(\mathbf{G}^T\mathbf{G})^{-1}(\mathbf{G}^T\mathbf{F}) \\ \mathbf{\Psi}_{LS} = \mathbf{B}\mathbf{\Lambda}\mathbf{B}^T &\geq [\mathbf{A}^T(\mathbf{\Lambda}^{-1/2})^T(\mathbf{\Lambda}^{1/2})^T\mathbf{B}^T]^T(\mathbf{A}^T\mathbf{\Lambda}^{-1}\mathbf{A})^{-1}(\mathbf{A}^T\mathbf{B}^T). \end{aligned} \tag{5–75}$$

Now use (5–58) and (5–71) in (5–75) to find

$$\mathbf{\Psi}_{LS} \geq (\mathbf{A}^T\mathbf{\Lambda}^{-1}\mathbf{A})^{-1} = \mathbf{\Psi}_{MV}. \tag{5–76}$$

Hence, it has been demonstrated that, if the quadratic loss function is weighted by the covariance matrix of the observation errors, the result is a minimum variance estimate. *Minimum variance* estimates are also called *Markov estimates.*

## 5.4
## *COMPARISON OF WEIGHTED LEAST SQUARES ESTIMATES*

Although it has been shown that the minimum variance, or Markov, estimator provides the *best* linear unbiased estimate of a set of parameters in the sense of yielding a minimum variance of the estimate errors, this characteristic may be of more theoretical than practical utility. For theoretical formulations it is fine to postulate the knowledge of the covariance matrix of the observation errors. Unfortunately, in practice the exact values of the elements of the error matrix are seldom known. Thus one is frequently faced with the practical necessity of performing calculations using some judicious estimate of the required covariance weighting function. The problem is then one of examining how *close* one must know the covariance elements to be, in some specified measure of closeness, to the minimum variance estimate.

The necessity of comparing approximations with minimum variance estimates has been recognized, and several papers have been published on this subject, for example, [1, 59, 62, 128, 129, 152, 154]. Grenander and Rosenblatt have examined the case in which the observations are stationary random processes and have derived asymptotic properties of the weighted least squares linear estimates of such processes [62, Chapter 7]. The results contained in this section were obtained by Magness and McGuire [97].

It is convenient to transform the linear form (5–29) into a canonical form. Multiply each side of (5–29) by a symmetric square weighting matrix $\mathbf{\Phi}^{-1/2}$, then

$$\mathbf{\Phi}^{-1/2}\boldsymbol{y} = \mathbf{\Phi}^{-1/2}\mathbf{A}\boldsymbol{b} + \mathbf{\Phi}^{-1/2}\boldsymbol{x}. \tag{5–77}$$

The covariance matrix of the transformed noise term is

$$\boldsymbol{\Omega} = \mathrm{E}\{\boldsymbol{\Phi}^{-1/2}\boldsymbol{x}\boldsymbol{x}^T(\boldsymbol{\Phi}^{-1/2})^T\} = \boldsymbol{\Phi}^{-1/2}\boldsymbol{\Lambda}(\boldsymbol{\Phi}^{-1/2})^T. \tag{5–78}$$

Define

$$\begin{aligned} \boldsymbol{\eta} &= \boldsymbol{\Phi}^{-1/2}\boldsymbol{y} \\ \boldsymbol{\xi} &= \boldsymbol{\Phi}^{-1/2}\boldsymbol{x}, \end{aligned} \tag{5–79}$$

and (5–77) becomes

$$\begin{gathered} \boldsymbol{\eta} = \boldsymbol{\Phi}^{-1/2}\mathbf{A}\boldsymbol{b} + \boldsymbol{\xi} \\ \text{New observation} = \text{signal} + \text{new noise}. \end{gathered} \tag{5–80}$$

By definition, it follows that $\boldsymbol{\Omega}$ is the covariance matrix of the new variable $\boldsymbol{\xi}$.

Next consider the matrix

$$\mathbf{Q} = \mathbf{A}^T\boldsymbol{\Phi}^{-1}\mathbf{A}, \tag{5–81}$$

which appears as a factor in the covariance matrix of the estimate errors for a weighted linear least squares estimator, (5–55). Because it has been hypothesized that $\mathbf{Q}$ is nonsingular, a matrix $\mathbf{B}$ can be formulated, which has the property

$$\mathbf{B}^T\mathbf{Q}\mathbf{B} = \mathbf{I} = \mathbf{B}^T\mathbf{A}^T\boldsymbol{\Phi}^{-1}\mathbf{A}\mathbf{B}. \tag{5–82}$$

Let

$$\begin{aligned} \mathbf{M} &= \boldsymbol{\Phi}^{-1/2}\mathbf{A}\mathbf{B} \\ \boldsymbol{\beta} &= \mathbf{B}^{-1}\boldsymbol{b}, \end{aligned} \tag{5–83}$$

then (5–80) reduces to the desired canonical form

$$\boldsymbol{\eta} = \mathbf{M}\boldsymbol{\beta} + \boldsymbol{\xi}, \tag{5–84}$$

where

$$\mathbf{M}^T\mathbf{M} = \mathbf{B}^T\mathbf{A}^T\boldsymbol{\Phi}^{-1/2}\boldsymbol{\Phi}^{-1/2}\mathbf{A}\mathbf{B} = \mathbf{I}. \tag{5–85}$$

The important point is to note that estimates of $\boldsymbol{\beta}$ in (5–84) are exactly equivalent in a statistical sense to estimating $\boldsymbol{b}$ in (5–29).

The general weighted least squares estimate error covariance matrix, (5–55), can be written in the equivalent form

$$\begin{aligned} \boldsymbol{\Psi}_{LS} &= (\mathbf{A}^T\boldsymbol{\Phi}^{-1}\mathbf{A})^{-1}\mathbf{A}^T\boldsymbol{\Phi}^{-1}\boldsymbol{\Lambda}\boldsymbol{\Phi}^{-1}\mathbf{A}(\mathbf{A}^T\boldsymbol{\Phi}^{-1}\mathbf{A})^{-1} \\ &= \mathbf{B}\mathbf{N}_{LS}\mathbf{B}^T, \end{aligned} \tag{5–86}$$

where

$$\mathbf{N}_{LS} = \mathbf{M}^T\boldsymbol{\Omega}\mathbf{M}. \tag{5–87}$$

Similarly, the covariance matrix for the minimum variance estimator, (5–58), can be written as

$$\boldsymbol{\Psi}_{MV} = \mathbf{B}\mathbf{N}_{MV}\mathbf{B}^T, \tag{5–88}$$

where

$$\mathbf{N}_{MV} = (\mathbf{M}^T \mathbf{\Omega}^{-1} \mathbf{M})^{-1}. \tag{5–89}$$

Using the preceding canonical forms for linear weighted least squares estimators, the following results obtained by Magness and McGuire are stated without proof:

(a) The *LS* and *MV* estimates of $\boldsymbol{\beta}$ have identical covariance matrices if and only if the subspace spanned by the $q$ columns of $\mathbf{M}$ coincide with the space spanned by $q$ of the eigenvectors of $\mathbf{\Omega}$, in which case both covariance matrices are similar to a diagonal matrix whose elements are the corresponding eigenvectors of $\mathbf{\Omega}$.

(b) If $\mathbf{N}_{LS}$ and $\mathbf{N}_{MV}$ denote the covariance matrices of the *LS* and *MV* estimates of $\boldsymbol{\beta}$, then

$$\lambda_{\min} \mathbf{I} \leq \mathbf{N}_{MV} \leq \mathbf{N}_{LS} \leq \lambda_{\max} \mathbf{I}, \tag{5–90}$$

where $\lambda_{\max}$ and $\lambda_{\min}$ are the maximum and minimum eigenvalues of the noise covariance matrix $\mathbf{\Omega}$. Because of the manner in which the matrices were introduced, it can be verified that $\mathbf{N}_{MV} \leq \mathbf{N}_{LS}$.

(c) If $\mathbf{\Psi}_{UC}$ is the covariance matrix for the special case in which the estimate errors in the noncanonical form (5–29), are uncorrelated, then

$$\lambda_{\min} \mathbf{\Psi}_{UC} \leq \mathbf{\Psi}_{MV} \leq \mathbf{\Psi}_{LS} \leq \lambda_{\max} \mathbf{\Psi}_{UC}, \tag{5–91}$$

where $\lambda_{\max}$ and $\lambda_{\min}$ are the maximum and minimum eigenvalues of the covariance matrix $\mathbf{\Lambda}$ for the observation noise. This result has very practical implications because, if one computes the covariance matrix $\mathbf{\Psi}_{UC}$ under the assumption of uncorrelated errors, then by multiplying by the maximum and minimum eigenvalues of $\mathbf{\Lambda}$, upper and lower bounds are established for both $\mathbf{\Psi}_{MV}$ and $\mathbf{\Psi}_{LS}$.

(d) With the same definitions of eigenvalues used in (c),

$$\mathbf{\Psi}_{LS} \leq \frac{1}{2} (\lambda_{\max} + \lambda_{\min}) \left( \frac{1}{\lambda_{\max}} + \frac{1}{\lambda_{\min}} \right) \mathbf{\Psi}_{MV}. \tag{5–92}$$

## 5.5 *PARAMETERS ARE RANDOM VARIABLES*

The most common application of linear least squares estimation is to situations in which the true values of the estimated parameters are a set of constants. However, closely related to linear regression is the situation in which the parameters to be estimated may themselves be random variates. Consider the linear form

$$\begin{aligned} &\text{Observation} = \text{signal} + \text{noise} \\ &\boldsymbol{y}^{[n\times 1]} = \mathbf{A}^{[n\times q]}\boldsymbol{b}^{[q\times 1]} + \boldsymbol{x}^{[n\times 1]}, \end{aligned} \tag{5–93}$$

where all the vectors are random variables having the statistical properties

$$\begin{aligned} \mathrm{E}\{\boldsymbol{x}\} &= \boldsymbol{0} \\ \mathrm{E}\{\boldsymbol{x}\boldsymbol{x}^T\} &= \boldsymbol{\Lambda}_x^{[n\times n]} \\ \mathrm{E}\{\boldsymbol{y}\boldsymbol{y}^T\} &= \boldsymbol{\Lambda}_y^{[n\times n]} \\ \mathrm{E}\{\boldsymbol{b}\boldsymbol{y}^T\} &= \boldsymbol{\Delta}_{by}^{[q\times n]} \\ \mathrm{E}\{\boldsymbol{x}\boldsymbol{y}^T\} &= \mathbf{0} \\ \mathrm{E}\{\boldsymbol{b}\boldsymbol{b}^T\} &= \boldsymbol{\Xi}_b^{[q\times q]}. \end{aligned} \tag{5–94}$$

Instead of searching for estimates $\hat{\boldsymbol{b}}$ which minimize a risk function, we consider the problem of a linear unbiased estimate of $\boldsymbol{b}$ having the general form

$$\hat{\boldsymbol{b}}^{[q\times 1]} = \mathbf{B}^{[q\times n]}\boldsymbol{y}^{[n\times 1]} \tag{5–95}$$

and find the matrix $\mathbf{B}$ which minimizes the quadratic risk function

$$R(\mathbf{B}) = \mathrm{E}\{(\hat{\boldsymbol{b}} - \boldsymbol{b})^T\mathbf{M}^{[q\times q]}(\hat{\boldsymbol{b}} - \boldsymbol{b})\}. \tag{5–96}$$

The weighting matrix $\mathbf{M}$ is arbitrary and is only restricted to being positive definite. If it is not symmetric, it can be written as the sum of a symmetric and a skew-symmetric matrix. The skew-symmetric component will not affect the minimization. Hence, one can in essence restrict the discussion entirely to symmetric weighting matrices. An interesting result will be that the minimization of $R$, subject to variations of $\mathbf{B}$, will not depend upon an explicit choice of the weighting matrix $\mathbf{M}$.

The minimizing matrix $\mathbf{B}$ is found by a technique exactly analogous to the method of finding the minimizing value of $\mathbf{a}_1$ in (5–15) for the linear regression problem. We start by writing (5–96) in the form of a trace of a matrix and expand the quadratic form in the following manner:

$$\begin{aligned} R(\mathbf{B}) &= \mathrm{tr}\,\mathrm{E}\{(\hat{\boldsymbol{b}} - \boldsymbol{b})^T\mathbf{M}(\hat{\boldsymbol{b}} - \boldsymbol{b})\} \\ &= \mathrm{tr}\,\mathrm{E}\{(\hat{\boldsymbol{b}} - \boldsymbol{b})(\hat{\boldsymbol{b}} - \boldsymbol{b})^T\mathbf{M}\} \\ &= \mathrm{tr}\,\mathrm{E}\{[\boldsymbol{b}\boldsymbol{b}^T - \boldsymbol{b}\hat{\boldsymbol{b}}^T - \hat{\boldsymbol{b}}\boldsymbol{b}^T + \hat{\boldsymbol{b}}\hat{\boldsymbol{b}}^T]\mathbf{M}\} \\ &= \mathrm{tr}\,\mathrm{E}\{[\boldsymbol{b}\boldsymbol{b}^T - \boldsymbol{b}\boldsymbol{y}^T\mathbf{B}^T - \mathbf{B}\boldsymbol{y}\boldsymbol{b}^T + \mathbf{B}\boldsymbol{y}\boldsymbol{y}^T\mathbf{B}^T]\mathbf{M}\}. \end{aligned} \tag{5–97}$$

Insert the statistical properties of (5–94) into (5–97), which then becomes

$$R(\mathbf{B}) = \mathrm{tr}\,[(\boldsymbol{\Xi}_b - 2\,\boldsymbol{\Delta}_{by}\mathbf{B}^T + \mathbf{B}\boldsymbol{\Lambda}_y\mathbf{B}^T)\mathbf{M}]. \tag{5–98}$$

The assertion is that the risk function is a minimum for the choice

$$\mathbf{B} = \mathbf{B}_0 = \boldsymbol{\Delta}_{by}\boldsymbol{\Lambda}_y^{-1}. \tag{5–99}$$

The verification of the asserted minimizing matrix can be made by writing the risk function as

$$
\begin{aligned}
R(\mathbf{B}) &= \operatorname{tr} \mathrm{E}\{(\boldsymbol{b} - \hat{\boldsymbol{b}})\mathbf{M}(\boldsymbol{b} - \hat{\boldsymbol{b}})^T\} \\
&= \operatorname{tr} \mathrm{E}\{(\boldsymbol{b} - \mathbf{B}\boldsymbol{y})(\boldsymbol{b} - \mathbf{B}\boldsymbol{y})^T\mathbf{M}\} \\
&= \operatorname{tr} \mathrm{E}\{[(\boldsymbol{b} - \mathbf{B}_0\boldsymbol{y}) + (\mathbf{B}_0 - \mathbf{B})\boldsymbol{y}][(\boldsymbol{b} - \mathbf{B}_0\boldsymbol{y}) + (\mathbf{B}_0 - \mathbf{B})\boldsymbol{y}]^T\mathbf{M}\} \\
&= \operatorname{tr} \mathrm{E}\{(\boldsymbol{b} - \mathbf{B}_0\boldsymbol{y})(\boldsymbol{b} - \mathbf{B}_0\boldsymbol{y})^T\mathbf{M}\} \\
&\quad + \operatorname{tr} \mathrm{E}\{[(\mathbf{B}_0 - \mathbf{B})\boldsymbol{y}][(\mathbf{B}_0 - \mathbf{B})\boldsymbol{y}]^T\mathbf{M}\} \\
&\quad + \operatorname{tr} \mathrm{E}\{(\boldsymbol{b} - \mathbf{B}_0\boldsymbol{y})[(\mathbf{B}_0 - \mathbf{B})\boldsymbol{y}]^T\mathbf{M}\} \\
&\quad + \operatorname{tr} \mathrm{E}\{[(\mathbf{B}_0 - \mathbf{B})\boldsymbol{y}][\boldsymbol{b} - \mathbf{B}_0\boldsymbol{y}]^T\mathbf{M}\}.
\end{aligned}
\tag{5–100}
$$

If $\mathbf{B}_0$ is chosen as (5–99), then the last two terms in (5–100) will vanish. The first two terms are nonnegative because they are the traces of quadratic forms. Hence, the conclusion is that the absolute minimum as a function of $\mathbf{B}$ is obtained when the second term vanishes, or $\mathbf{B} = \mathbf{B}_0$ as given in (5–99).

Other problems could be posed. For example, one might inquire about the value of the weighting matrix $\mathbf{M}$ which minimizes the risk function. The solution is simply that $\mathbf{M}^{-1}$ should be the covariance function $\mathbf{\Lambda}_x$ required for the minimum variance estimate.

Substituting (5–99) into (5–98) yields the minimum value of the risk function

$$
R_{\min} = \operatorname{tr} [(\mathbf{\Xi}_b - \mathbf{\Delta}_{by} \mathbf{\Lambda}_y^{-1} \mathbf{\Delta}_{by}^T)\mathbf{M}]. \tag{5–101}
$$

The problem of finding the minimizing linear transformation treated in this section is intimately related to the Wiener-Kolmogorov theory for the prediction and smoothing of time series. The theory is the central topic of Chapter 11, and the formulation of the simplified problem treated in this section serves the alternative objective of being an introduction to a more complete theoretical development.

## Problems

**5.1** Given the data

| | | | | | |
|---|---|---|---|---|---|
| $x_1$: | 3.4 | −0.1 | −1.9 | −1.1 | −1.0 |
| $x_2$: | 0.7 | 0.0 | −0.9 | −0.6 | 1.2 |

fit a regression line of $x_2$ on $x_1$.

**5.2** Suppose $x_1, x_2, x_3$ are jointly normally distributed random variables. Derive the regression function for $x_1$ given $x_2$ and $x_3$.

**5.3** Let $x_1$ and $x_2$ be jointly normally distributed; write the regression line of $x_1$ on $x_2$ and the regression line of $x_2$ on $x_1$. Compute the regression lines for the data in Problem 5.1. Explain any differences. Under what conditions are the lines identical?

**5.4** If $x = (x_1, \ldots, x_n)$ is a random variable such that

$$E\{x_i\} = \mu, \ E\{(x_i - \mu)^2\} = \sigma^2, \ E\{(x_i - \mu)(x_j - \mu)\} = \rho\sigma^2,$$

show that the Markov estimator for $\mu$ is the sample mean value of the $n$ elements of $x$.

**5.5** Demonstrate that, if $x_1, x_2, \ldots, x_n$ is a sample sequence selected from a population having mean value $m$ and variance $\sigma^2$, then the sample mean

$$\bar{x} = \frac{1}{n}\sum_{i=1}^{n} x_i$$

is the minimum variance linear estimator for the population mean $m$.

**5.6** Verify Eq. (5–55).

**5.7** Let $\boldsymbol{a}_0 = \boldsymbol{0}$ in (5–5). Under what conditions is the minimum variance estimator of the regression coefficient $\mathbf{a}_1$ the same as the least squares estimator of $\mathbf{a}_1$?

**5.8** The following example is due to Magness and McGuire [97]. Let

$$\boldsymbol{\eta} = \mathbf{M}\boldsymbol{\beta} + \boldsymbol{\xi},$$

where

$$\boldsymbol{\Omega} = E\{\boldsymbol{\xi}\boldsymbol{\xi}^T\} = \begin{bmatrix} 1 & \rho & 0 & 0 \\ \rho & 1 & 0 & 0 \\ 0 & 0 & 1 & \rho \\ 0 & 0 & \rho & 1 \end{bmatrix}; \qquad 0 < \rho < 1$$

$$\mathbf{M} = \begin{bmatrix} \frac{1}{2} & \frac{1}{2} \\ \frac{1}{2} & -\frac{1}{2} \\ \frac{1}{2} & \frac{1}{2} \\ -\frac{1}{2} & \frac{1}{2} \end{bmatrix}.$$

Show that $\mathbf{M}^T\mathbf{M} = \mathbf{I}$. Further, show that the covariance matrix for the least squares estimate error of $\boldsymbol{\beta}$ is $\mathbf{N}_{LS} = \mathbf{M}^T\boldsymbol{\Omega}\mathbf{M} = \mathbf{I}$. Compute the covariance matrix for the minimum variance estimate error of $\boldsymbol{\beta}$. Verify that the eigenvalues of $\boldsymbol{\Omega}$ satisfy

$$\lambda_{\max} = 1 + \rho$$
$$\lambda_{\min} = 1 - \rho,$$

and, therefore, the equality holds in Eq. (5–91).

**5.9** Show that the last two terms in Eq. (5–100) are identically zero.

**5.10** If the least squares linear estimate is permitted to have a bias, what is the equivalent form of the estimator corresponding to Eq. (5–36).

# Chapter 6

# NONLINEAR ESTIMATES

A natural extension to almost any discussion of linear operators is the companion problem of nonlinear operators. Throughout many branches of mathematics, as well as in estimation theory, the theory developed for linear operations is frequently characterized by completeness and mathematical elegance. Unfortunately one can seldom extend the elegant formulations and solution techniques from linear to nonlinear situations. Partly from the desire to emulate the niceties of linear theory and partly because frequently the nonlinearities are so *small*, a procedure has evolved which is called *linearization* of the problem. In a linearization method, for a variety of justifications or mere rationalizations, one replaces nonlinear operations by linear transformations. Such replacements of the original problem by a linear operation must be accompanied by arguments that demonstrate that, within the domains of interest, the linearized solution is *sufficiently close* in some defined sense to the true solution.

Other techniques for treating nonlinear estimation problems include those in which the given nonlinear functions are replaced by other functions, either linear or nonlinear, which have the admirable characteristic that they are amenable to the mathematical manipulations required in formulating an optimal estimator. The manipulative difficulties in formulating analytical expressions for nonlinear optimal estimators are frequently so severe, that in most situations one must usually be content with approximate solutions. Recently there has been a trend toward using numerical methods on automatic digital computers to solve nonlinear estimation problems rather than using approximate formulations.

Although it might seem to be a superfluous remark, experience has demonstrated the need to emphasize that a transformation, or function, is either linear or nonlinear. There is no intermediate state, and concepts such as *almost linear* and *approximately linear* by themselves are loose, meaningless statements without careful accompanying definitions. Moreover, if an approximation, such as a linearizing transformation, has been employed in the solution of a nonlinear problem, then it is incumbent upon the person formulating such solutions to indicate the regions for which the solution is valid as well as to exhibit the error produced by the linearization. Until such statements have been formulated, the problem has not been completely solved in the true sense of the word.

## 6.1
## *MATRIX FORM OF TAYLOR SERIES EXPANSION*

The use of Taylor series expansions of functions is a powerful operation in the development of higher-order perturbation expansions and in the treatment of nonlinear estimation problems. We shall have many occasions to write a series expansion for a function of $n$ variables. Such $n$-dimensional series are given in some advanced calculus texts, but not usually in a form convenient for a matrix formulation of $n$-dimensional estimators.

Consider the expansion of the function $f(b_1, \ldots, b_n)$ about the point $(\beta_1, \ldots, \beta_n)$. In component operator form, the Taylor series expansion can be written in the familiar form

$$\begin{aligned} f(b_1, \cdots, b_n) &= f(\beta_1, \cdots, \beta_n) \\ &+ \sum_{k=1}^{q} \frac{1}{k!}\left[(b_1 - \beta_1)\frac{\partial}{\partial b_1} + \cdots + (b_n - \beta_n)\frac{\partial}{\partial b_n}\right]^k f(b_1, \cdots, b_n)\big|_{b_i=\beta_i} + R_q, \end{aligned} \tag{6–1}$$

where $R_q$ is the remainder after $q$ terms. Care must be exercised in the interpretation of the powers, or products, of the differential operators appearing in the square bracket. These products are not ordinary multiplications and are defined by the operator multiplication

$$\begin{aligned} &\left[(b_i - \beta_i)\frac{\partial}{\partial b_i}\right] \circ \left[(b_j - \beta_j)\frac{\partial}{\partial b_j}\right] \\ &\qquad = (b_i - \beta_i)(b_j - \beta_j)\frac{\partial^2}{\partial b_i\, \partial b_j}. \end{aligned} \tag{6–2}$$

The preceding concepts motivate the following matrix formulations. Let $\boldsymbol{d}$ denote the matrix of the difference between the points $\boldsymbol{b}$ and $\boldsymbol{\beta}$. That is

$$\boldsymbol{d} = \boldsymbol{b} - \boldsymbol{\beta} = \begin{bmatrix} b_1 - \beta_1 \\ b_2 - \beta_2 \\ \cdots \\ b_n - \beta_n \end{bmatrix}. \tag{6–3}$$

Using the matrix differential operator, the desired Taylor series in matrix formulation is

$$f(\boldsymbol{b}) = f(\boldsymbol{\beta}) + \sum_{k=1}^{q} \frac{1}{k!} [\boldsymbol{d}^T \nabla_b]^k f(\boldsymbol{\beta}) + R_q, \tag{6–4}$$

where for notational convenience,

$$\nabla_b f(\boldsymbol{b})|_{\boldsymbol{b}=\boldsymbol{\beta}} \overset{d}{=} \nabla_b f(\boldsymbol{\beta}). \tag{6–5}$$

Again, it is necessary to interpret carefully the powers of the matrix operator which appears in the square brackets. We introduce a matrix operator multiplication, denoted by the symbol $\otimes$, having the following properties:

$$[\boldsymbol{d}^T \nabla_b] \otimes [\boldsymbol{d}^T \nabla_b] = \boldsymbol{d}^T [\nabla_b \otimes \boldsymbol{d}^T] \nabla_b, \tag{6–6}$$

where

$$[\nabla_b \otimes \boldsymbol{d}^T] = [\boldsymbol{d} (\nabla_b)^T]^T. \tag{6–7}$$

It is important that the matrix operator in the square bracket be computed as a conventional product before the transpose is performed. This rule is the matrix analogue to the operator component multiplication rule defined in (6–2).

If $k = 3$ in (6–4), the resulting matrix differential operator is

$$\begin{aligned} &[\boldsymbol{d}^T \nabla_b] \otimes [\boldsymbol{d}^T \nabla_b] \otimes [\boldsymbol{d}^T \nabla_b] \\ &\quad = \boldsymbol{d}^T [\nabla_b \otimes \boldsymbol{d}^T][\nabla_b \otimes \boldsymbol{d}^T] \nabla_b \\ &\quad = \boldsymbol{d}^T [\boldsymbol{d} (\nabla_b)^T]^T [\boldsymbol{d} (\nabla_b)^T]^T \nabla_b. \end{aligned} \tag{6–8}$$

When the elements of the two matrices in the square brackets in (6–8) are multiplied, the product rule (6–2) for component operators must be used.

The matrix formulation of the Taylor series is primarily intended for theoretical analyses wherein one desires a compact notation for the first few terms of a Taylor series expansion. On the other hand, if the problem requires the components of any specific term of a series expansion, the component form of (6–1) is the most convenient formulation. The expansion can be extended to a function $\boldsymbol{f}(\boldsymbol{b})$, which is itself a row matrix. For example:

$$\begin{aligned} \boldsymbol{f}^{[q\times 1]}(\boldsymbol{b}^{[n\times 1]}) &= \boldsymbol{f}(\boldsymbol{\beta}^{[n\times 1]}) + \sum_k \frac{1}{k!} \{[\boldsymbol{d}^T \nabla_b]^k \boldsymbol{f}^T(\boldsymbol{\beta})\}^T + \boldsymbol{R}_v \\ &= \boldsymbol{f}(\boldsymbol{\beta}) + [\nabla_b \boldsymbol{f}^T(\boldsymbol{\beta})]^T \cdot \boldsymbol{d} + \cdots . \end{aligned}$$

## 6.2
## *THE NONLINEAR PROBLEM*

A group of data is taken with the intent of estimating a set of parameters $\boldsymbol{b}^{[q\times 1]}$.

In general, the observables $\boldsymbol{W}^{[p\times 1]}$ at any instant are not the parameters themselves. Therefore, we assume that there exists a model, or a prediction function $\boldsymbol{w}^{[p\times 1]}(\boldsymbol{b})$, which predicts the observation $\boldsymbol{W}$ as a function of the parameter set; these constitute the set of exact values of the measurements. The observations can then be written as

$$\text{Observation} = \text{prediction} + \text{error}$$

$$\boldsymbol{W}_j = \boldsymbol{w}_j(\boldsymbol{b}) + \boldsymbol{a}_j, \tag{6–9}$$

where $\boldsymbol{a}_j$ is called the measurement error.

The general risk function is then

$$R(\boldsymbol{b}) = \mathrm{E}\{l[\boldsymbol{W}_j - \boldsymbol{w}_j(\boldsymbol{b})]\}. \tag{6–10}$$

The nonlinear estimation problem is to determine an estimate $\hat{\boldsymbol{b}}$ of $\boldsymbol{b}$ which minimizes the risk function. The general conditions and solutions for this problem were discussed in Chapter 2. However, instead of stopping with existence solutions in the form of conditional expectations, the objective in this chapter is to formulate approximate explicit solutions for nonlinear estimators.

## 6.3 *GAUSS-NEWTON METHOD*

The Gauss-Newton method is also called a linearization technique because the nonlinear prediction function is replaced by the first two terms of a Taylor series expansion. In order to exhibit explicit formulations, the loss function in the risk will be restricted to a quadratic loss so that the nonlinear estimator is limited to a least squares estimator. With this limitation, the risk function (6–10) assumes the form

$$\begin{aligned} R(\boldsymbol{b}) &= [\boldsymbol{W} - \boldsymbol{w}(\boldsymbol{b})]^T \boldsymbol{\Psi}^{-1}[\boldsymbol{W} - \boldsymbol{w}(\boldsymbol{b})] \\ &\stackrel{d}{=} \|\boldsymbol{W} - \boldsymbol{w}(\boldsymbol{b})\|^2_{\boldsymbol{\Psi}^{-1}}. \end{aligned} \tag{6–11}$$

$\boldsymbol{\Psi}$ is the weighting matrix and is selected so that its inverse exists, and it is symmetric positive definite. $\boldsymbol{W}$ is called the *total matrix of observations* and has the definition

$$\boldsymbol{W}^{[np\times 1]} = \begin{bmatrix} \boldsymbol{W}_1^{[p\times 1]} \\ \boldsymbol{W}_2^{[p\times 1]} \\ \cdots \\ \boldsymbol{W}_n^{[p\times 1]} \end{bmatrix}. \tag{6–12}$$

The total prediction matrix is defined analogously as

$$\boldsymbol{w}^{[np\times 1]}(\boldsymbol{b}) = \begin{bmatrix} \boldsymbol{w}_1^{[p\times 1]}(\boldsymbol{b}) \\ \cdots \\ \boldsymbol{w}_n^{[p\times 1]}(\boldsymbol{b}) \end{bmatrix}. \tag{6–13}$$

The minimizing conditions for the risk function can be found by differentiating (6–11) and solving for the estimate $\hat{\boldsymbol{b}}$ that causes the derivative to vanish. Using (3–12), the conditioning equation, or normal equations, can be shown to be

$$\nabla_b \boldsymbol{w}^T(\hat{\boldsymbol{b}}) \cdot \Psi^{-1}[\boldsymbol{W} - \boldsymbol{w}(\hat{\boldsymbol{b}})] = \boldsymbol{0}, \tag{6–14}$$

where, similar to (6–5), the abbreviated notation is

$$\nabla_b \boldsymbol{w}^T(\hat{\boldsymbol{b}}) \equiv \nabla_b \boldsymbol{w}^T(\boldsymbol{b})|_{\boldsymbol{b}=\hat{\boldsymbol{b}}}. \tag{6–15}$$

Because $\boldsymbol{w}(\hat{\boldsymbol{b}})$ is a nonlinear function, (6–14) frequently cannot be solved algebraically for the estimate $\hat{\boldsymbol{b}}$.

One method of solving the equations of condition is to employ a successive-perturbation solution technique. It is hypothesized that a *sufficiently good* estimate $\hat{\boldsymbol{b}}_0$ of $\boldsymbol{b}$ exists and, therefore, $\boldsymbol{w}(\hat{\boldsymbol{b}})$ can be expanded into a Taylor series with only the first two terms retained. Thus,

$$\boldsymbol{w}(\hat{\boldsymbol{b}}) = \boldsymbol{w}(\hat{\boldsymbol{b}}_0) + \mathbf{T}(\hat{\boldsymbol{b}}_0) \cdot (\hat{\boldsymbol{b}} - \hat{\boldsymbol{b}}_0), \tag{6–16}$$

where

$$\mathbf{T}^T(\hat{\boldsymbol{b}}_0) = \nabla_b \boldsymbol{w}^T(\hat{\boldsymbol{b}}_0). \tag{6–17}$$

Similarly, the first factor in (6–14) is approximately

$$\nabla_b \boldsymbol{w}^T(\hat{\boldsymbol{b}}) = \mathbf{T}^T(\hat{\boldsymbol{b}}) \approx \mathbf{T}^T(\hat{\boldsymbol{b}}_0). \tag{6–18}$$

Combine (6–14), (6–16), and (6–18) to find

$$\mathbf{T}^T(\hat{\boldsymbol{b}}_0)\Psi^{-1}\mathbf{T}(\hat{\boldsymbol{b}}_0)\cdot(\hat{\boldsymbol{b}} - \hat{\boldsymbol{b}}_0) - \mathbf{T}^T(\hat{\boldsymbol{b}}_0)\Psi^{-1} \cdot [\boldsymbol{W} - \boldsymbol{w}(\hat{\boldsymbol{b}}_0)] = \boldsymbol{0}. \tag{6–19}$$

This result can be placed in a more convenient form by introducing the definitions

$$\boldsymbol{q} = \hat{\boldsymbol{b}}_0 - \hat{\boldsymbol{b}} \tag{6–20}$$

and

$$\mathbf{N} = \mathbf{T}^T(\hat{\boldsymbol{b}}_0)\Psi^{-1}\mathbf{T}(\hat{\boldsymbol{b}}_0). \tag{6–21}$$

With these definitions, (6–19) becomes

$$\mathbf{N}\boldsymbol{q} = -\mathbf{T}^T(\hat{\boldsymbol{b}}_0)\Psi^{-1}\cdot[\boldsymbol{W} - \boldsymbol{w}(\hat{\boldsymbol{b}}_0)]. \tag{6–22}$$

Further, if $\mathbf{N}$ is a nonsingular matrix, the desired solution is approximately

$$\hat{\boldsymbol{b}} = \hat{\boldsymbol{b}}_0 + \mathbf{N}^{-1}\mathbf{T}^T(\hat{\boldsymbol{b}}_0)\Psi^{-1}\boldsymbol{a}. \tag{6–23}$$

In essence, the expansion of (6–16) is equivalent to replacing the original risk function by the corresponding linearized risk function

$$R_L(\boldsymbol{b}) = \|\boldsymbol{W} - [\boldsymbol{w}(\hat{\boldsymbol{b}}_0) + \mathbf{T}(\hat{\boldsymbol{b}}_0)\cdot(\boldsymbol{b} - \hat{\boldsymbol{b}}_0)]\|^2_{\Psi^{-1}}. \tag{6–24}$$

This is now a linear least squares estimate in $\boldsymbol{b}$, and, using the techniques of Chapter 5, it can be verified that (6–23) yields an absolute minimum of $R_L$.

The practical problem is to choose $\hat{\boldsymbol{b}}_0$ in the expansion (6–16) such that the first two terms in the series are an adequate representation. Write (6–23) in the following equivalent iterative form:

$$\hat{\boldsymbol{b}}_k = \hat{\boldsymbol{b}}_{k-1} + \mathbf{N}^{-1}(\hat{\boldsymbol{b}}_{k-1})\mathbf{T}^T(\hat{\boldsymbol{b}}_{k-1})\Psi^{-1}\boldsymbol{a}. \tag{6–25}$$

The iterative solution process starts by selecting some value $\hat{\boldsymbol{b}}_0$ and then evaluating the corresponding $\boldsymbol{q}_0$ from (6–22).

If $\boldsymbol{q}_0$ is not less than some preassigned number, the new estimate $\hat{\boldsymbol{b}}_1$ obtained from (6–25) is used to replace $\hat{\boldsymbol{b}}_0$. These steps are iterated until a value $\boldsymbol{q}_k$ is obtained which satisfies a smallness criterion. The unfortunate fact is that this iterative solution technique may not converge. It is an all-too-common occurrence that convergence is not found in practical problems [98]. One reason for the lack of convergence is that the initial estimate $\hat{\boldsymbol{b}}_0$ places the domain of the expansion of $\boldsymbol{w}(\hat{\boldsymbol{b}})$ beyond the region in which (6–16) is an adequate representation. If this is suspected, a different value of $\hat{\boldsymbol{b}}_0$ should be selected and the iteration steps repeated. An alternative is to reformulate the estimator using higher-order terms in the Taylor series expansion of the prediction function.

The Gauss-Newton method is plagued by a theoretical as well as a practical dilemma. While it is relatively easy to show that $\hat{\boldsymbol{b}}$ in (6–23) yields an absolute minimum of the linearized problem of the risk function $R_L$, there is no easy way of demonstrating that, in general, this same estimate yields an absolute minimum of the original risk function (6–11).

## 6.4
## *MINIMIZATION*

A serious theoretical and practical problem was illustrated in Section 6.3. The solution technique required the assumption that a minimum value of the risk function (6–11) existed for some suitable choice of an estimate $\hat{\boldsymbol{b}}$ for the parameters $\boldsymbol{b}$. In addition, we were *forced* to postulate that the iterative solution technique for the equivalent linearized least squares risk function converged and, in fact, converged to the value that yielded the desired absolute minimum of the original risk function. None of these conjectures is capable of a simple generalized proof.

For an insight into the true cause of these theoretical difficulties, it is desirable to turn to the theory of maxima and minima problems. A good summary of these problems appears in Reference 93. In particular, the following remarks are amplified in a paper of Edelbaum [93, Chapter 1].

Weierstrass [29] proved the existence of a solution to the minimization problem for continuous functions through the theorem:

> Every function which is continuous in a closed domain possesses a largest and a smallest value either in the interior or on the boundary of the domain.

The location of these extremes are provided by the theorem [142]:

> A continuous function $f(x_1, x_2, \ldots, x_n)$ of $n$ independent variables $x_1, \ldots, x_n$ attains a maximum or a minimum in the interior of a region $R$ only at those values of the variables $x_i$ for which the partial derivatives $f_{x_1}, \ldots, f_{x_n}$ either vanish simultaneously (a stationary point) or at which one or more of these derivatives cease to exist (are discontinuous).

The location of the stationary points are usually found by the elementary operation of forming the partial derivatives and finding the conditions that cause these derivatives to vanish. However, as we must constantly bear in mind, this simple technique only furnishes the stationary points and additional arguments are required to establish which, if any, of these stationary points are also extrema. Neither stationary points nor points of discontinuity need be extrema. The given function would have to be evaluated at all stationary points found from equating derivatives to zero in order to verify that any of these points were extrema and then to determine which points corresponded to local and absolute extremum. The required amount of calculation is frequently too large in practical work to permit a careful investigation of all possible extrema. Instead, the workable technique is to rely upon prior experience with analogous problems or upon a physical interpretation of the mathematical model in order to select judiciously the absolute extremum from amongst a collection of possible candidates.

The behavior of the risk function $R(\boldsymbol{b}^{[q\times 1]})$ in the neighborhood of an estimated point $\hat{\boldsymbol{b}}$ can be investigated by examination of the terms in the Taylor series expansion of the risk function about this point. Apply (6–4) to obtain

$$R(\boldsymbol{b}) = R(\hat{\boldsymbol{b}}) + (\boldsymbol{b} - \hat{\boldsymbol{b}})^T \nabla_b R(\hat{\boldsymbol{b}}) + \tfrac{1}{2}[(\boldsymbol{b} - \hat{\boldsymbol{b}})^T \nabla_b]^2 R(\hat{\boldsymbol{b}}) + \cdots. \tag{6–26}$$

Define the determinants

$$d_i = \begin{vmatrix} \dfrac{\partial^2 R}{\partial b_1\,\partial b_1} & \dfrac{\partial^2 R}{\partial b_1\,\partial b_2} & \cdots & \dfrac{\partial^2 R}{\partial b_1\,\partial b_i} \\ \dfrac{\partial^2 R}{\partial b_2\,\partial b_1} & \cdots & \cdots & \dfrac{\partial^2 R}{\partial b_2\,\partial b_i} \\ \cdots & \cdots & \cdots & \cdots \\ \dfrac{\partial^2 R}{\partial b_i\,\partial b_1} & \cdots & \cdots & \dfrac{\partial^2 R}{\partial b_i\,\partial b_i} \end{vmatrix}; \qquad i = 1, \ldots, q. \tag{6–27}$$

The necessary condition which must be satisfied if a stationary point is to be a minimum is that

$$d_i > 0, \qquad i = 1, \ldots, q \tag{6–28}$$

while the necessary condition that a stationary point be a local maximum is

$$\begin{aligned} d_i &> 0; \qquad i = 2, 4, 6, \ldots \\ d_i &< 0; \qquad i = 1, 3, 5, \ldots . \end{aligned} \tag{6–29}$$

## 6.5
## *POLYNOMIAL APPROXIMATIONS*

The general nonlinear estimation problem leads to a set of nonlinear equations of condition of the form given by (6–14). Instead of linearizing the problem by means of a Taylor series expansion, an alternate technique is to replace $\boldsymbol{w}(\boldsymbol{b})$ by an appropriate approximating function. The linear approximation is the most frequently employed substitution; however, in particular cases other functions may be found which provide a *better* approximation and lead to a solution with fewer iterations from an initial estimate of the parameters.

A natural step in complexity following linearization is to consider the best polynomial estimators of any specified degree [42, 102]. For example, suppose we consider a polynomial of the second degree,

$$P(\xi) = a_0 + \sum_{i=1}^{n} a_i \xi_i + \sum_{i=1}^{n} \sum_{j=1}^{n} a_{ij} \xi_i \xi_j. \tag{6–30}$$

Let $y = y_1, y_2, \ldots$ be a sequence of measurements, and let the problem be one of determining the polynomial coefficients $a_0, a_i, a_{ij}$ which minimize the risk function

$$R(a_0, a_i, a_{ij}) = \mathrm{E}\{[y - P(\xi)]^2\}. \tag{6–31}$$

This is an extension of the linear least squares regression problem. Although the minimization of (6–31) appears at first glance to be a more complex situation than minimization of a linear estimator, this is in fact not the true situation. The crux of the argument will be to demonstrate that finding the polynomial estimator is exactly equivalent to finding the best linear estimator in terms of the $[1 + n + n(n-1)/2]$ random variables $\xi_i$ and their products. Let these derived random variables be denoted by $x_i$ so that (6–31) can be replaced by the equivalent risk function

$$\begin{aligned} R(\beta_i) &= \mathrm{E}\left\{\left(y - \sum_{i=1}^{N} \beta_i x_i\right)^2\right\}, \\ N &= 1 + n + \tfrac{1}{2}n(n-1) = \tfrac{1}{2}(n^2 + n + 2). \end{aligned} \tag{6–32}$$

Thus, we have reduced the problem to one of determining the minimizing set of coefficients $\beta_i$.

Following the linear space theory concepts of Chapter 3, consider the set $\{x_i\}$ as the generating elements of a space and let $y$ be represented as

$$y = \sum_{i=1}^{N} \eta_i x_i, \tag{6–33}$$

where the expansion coefficients $\eta_i$ are found from

$$\mathrm{E}\{yx_j\} = \sum_{i=1}^{N} \eta_i \mathrm{E}\{x_i x_j\}. \tag{6–34}$$

Combine (6–34) with (6–32) to obtain the risk function

$$\begin{aligned} R(\beta_i) &= \mathrm{E}\{[y - \sum_i \eta_i x_i + \sum_i \eta_i x_i - \sum_i \beta_i x_i]^2\} \\ &= \mathrm{E}\{[y - \sum_i \eta_i x_i]^2\} + \mathrm{E}\{[\sum_i (\eta_i - \beta_i) x_i]^2\}. \end{aligned} \tag{6–35}$$

Because each term is positive, $R$ will be a minimum if $\eta_i = \beta_i$. With this substitution, the minimum risk is

$$\begin{aligned} R_{\min} &= \mathrm{E}\{[y - \sum_i \beta_i x_i]^2\} \\ &= \mathrm{E}\{y^2\} - 2 \sum_i \beta_i \mathrm{E}\{yx_i\} + \sum_i \sum_j \beta_i \beta_j \mathrm{E}\{x_i x_j\} \\ &= \mathrm{E}\{y^2\} - \sum_i \sum_j \beta_i \beta_j \mathrm{E}\{x_i x_j\} \\ &= \mathrm{E}\{y(y - \sum_i \beta_i x_i)\}. \end{aligned} \tag{6–36}$$

Notice that (6–32) has the same form as (3–97), so that the optimal estimate of $y$ must be the set of coefficients $\beta_i$ that makes $\sum \beta_i x_i$ the projection of $y$ on the linear space generated by the components $x_i$. These optimizing components are exhibited in (6–33) for $\beta_i = \eta_i$.

Instead of attempting directly to extend the problem in polynomial estimation to polynomials of arbitrary degree, it has been found convenient to introduce orthogonal polynomials. Expansions in orthogonal polynomials are extremely useful in analysis as a type of generalized Fourier series expansions. This same sort of theoretical and practical usefulness is shared by orthogonal polynomial expansions of random variates [153,40 Chapter 6].

Let $Q_i(\xi_1, \ldots, \xi_n)$ be a polynomial of degree $i$ in the random variates $\xi_1, \ldots, \xi_n$. We define a set of orthogonal polynomials relative to the probability density function of the $\{\xi_i\}$ by the relation

$$\begin{aligned} &\mathrm{E}\{Q_i Q_j\} = A_{ij}\,\delta_{ij} \\ &\int \cdots \int Q_i(\xi_1, \ldots, \xi_n) Q_j(\xi_1, \ldots, \xi_n) f_n(\xi_1, \cdots, \xi_n)\, d\xi_1 \cdots d\xi_n \\ &\qquad = A_{ij}\,\delta_{ij}. \end{aligned} \tag{6–37}$$

If we, in addition, normalize the polynomials by requiring that $A_{ij} = 1$, then the corresponding orthonormal polynomials $P_i$ satisfy the orthogonality condition

$$\mathrm{E}\{P_i(\xi_1, \ldots, \xi_n) P_j(\xi_1, \ldots, \xi_n)\} = \delta_{ij}. \tag{6–38}$$

Suppose that we now wish to replace our prediction function $w(b)$ by a *best* polynomial estimate of degree $k$. Let this polynomial be $g_k(\xi_1, \ldots, \xi_n)$, and represent the polynomial by the series expansion

$$g_k(\xi_1, \ldots, \xi_n) = \sum_{j=0}^{N} \alpha_j P_j(\xi_1, \ldots, \xi_n), \tag{6–39}$$

where, if $n > 1$, $N \neq k$. For this situation, the squared-loss risk function is

$$R(\alpha_j) = \mathrm{E}\{[y - g_k(\xi_1, \ldots, \xi_n)]^2\}. \tag{6–40}$$

The solution for the minimum risk can be written down immediately from the knowledge that the minimum is a projection of $y$ on the linear space spanned by the basis set of orthonormal polynomials, $P_j$. Instead of repeating the steps used previously for the second-degree polynomial, we shall proceed with a direct application of the theory developed in Section 3.3. The element $y$ can be written as

$$y = \sum_{i=0}^{N} \gamma_i P_i(\xi_1, \ldots, \xi_n). \tag{6–41}$$

From (3–83), the projection $\hat{g}$ of $y$ orthogonal to the space spanned by the orthogonal polynomials can be written as

$$\hat{g} = \sum_i \gamma_i P_i - \sum_i \mathrm{E}\{yP_i\} P_i. \tag{6–42}$$

Multiply (6–42) by $P_j$, and take the expected values to obtain

$$\begin{aligned} \mathrm{E}\{\hat{g} P_j\} &= \sum_i \gamma_i \mathrm{E}\{P_i P_j\} - \sum_i \mathrm{E}\{\mathrm{E}\{yP_i\} P_i P_j\} \\ 0 &= \gamma_j - \mathrm{E}\{yP_j\}. \end{aligned} \tag{6–43}$$

The left side vanishes because, by definition, $\hat{g}$ is a projection of $y$ orthogonal to the linear space generated by the orthonormal polynomials. Equation (6–43) provides the values of the coefficients, which, when one sets $\alpha_j = \gamma_j$ in (6–39), yield the optimum polynomial estimate. Although we have shown that the technique leads to the optimum polynomial estimate, it is not true that is the best estimate in the sense that we have proved the optimality of the conditional expectation. In reality, the assumption of the series expansion (6–39) is equivalent to accepting a wide sense conditional expectation as the optimal estimator (see Section 3.4).

While the concept of expansions in orthogonal polynomials generated by the probability density function leads to elegant theoretical results, the practical problems of generating these polynomials can be truly formidable. One should be careful that the improvement attained in the polynomial approximation to the prediction function beyond a second-degree polynomial is worth the added burden of computing the set of orthogonal polynomials. This burden has deterred most such approaches before the present availability of automatic digital computers. It may now be profitable to pursue numerically this technique of nonlinear estimation beyond the past confines which were artificially limited by the patience and perserverance of the analyst.

## 6.6
## *SYSTEMS REDUCIBLE TO LINEAR*

The common element of all the methods described in this chapter for treating nonlinear estimators is that all the prediction functions were either of a type that was reducible to linear or were assumed to be well approximated by a function that was reducible to linear.

Pugachev has given the following generalized definition for a system reducible to linear [119]. An operator $\mathcal{S}$ is said to be reducible to linear if it is of the form

$$\mathcal{S} \circ x(t) = \sum_{j=1}^{N} \mathcal{S}_j \circ \phi_j [x(t_1), \ldots, x(t_n), t_1, \ldots, t_n, s], \tag{6–44}$$

where $\mathcal{S}_j$ are any linear operators acting upon the functions of $n$ variables $t_1, \ldots, t_n$. A system is said to be reducible to linear if the relation between the input $x$ to the output $y$ is of the form

$$y(s) = \mathcal{S} \circ x(t). \tag{6–45}$$

If the loss function is quadratic and the risk function is chosen as the mean-squared error, then, because (6–45) is merely a generalization of the linear vector space representations of Chapter 3, the optimum estimator is known to be the projection on the space generated by the functions $\phi_j$. The projection cannot be immediately written without first extracting the set of linearly independent functions and then forming an orthogonal basis. Rather than go through the intermediate steps of generating the orthogonal functions, it is sometimes simpler to proceed directly with the minimization of the risk function.

The direct procedure depends upon being able to represent the random variable

$$U_r(t, s) = \phi_r [x(t_1), \ldots, x(t_n), t_1, \ldots, t_n, s] \tag{6–46}$$

as a function of $t$ for fixed $s$ by a generalized Fourier expansion in orthogonal random variates. Expansions of this type are one of the subjects of Chapter 13, and the minimization of systems reducible to linear can be treated more elegantly by means of the techniques therein.

## Problems

**6.1** For $\boldsymbol{b}^{[2\times 1]}$, evaluate the differential operator (6–8), and show that the result is the same as that obtained using (6–1). Write a matrix form for the remainder term in (6–4).

**6.2** Represent $\boldsymbol{w}^{[n\times 1]}(\boldsymbol{b}^{[q\times 1]})$ as a second-degree polynomial in $\boldsymbol{b} - \hat{\boldsymbol{b}}_0$, where $\hat{\boldsymbol{b}}_0$ is an initial estimate of the parameter vector. Using this representation, find the conditions that minimize the risk function.

**6.3** We wish to generate a set of orthonormal polynomials of degree $k$, $P_k(x)$, where $x$ is normally distributed. For simplicity let $f(x)$, the probability density function, have mean zero and unit variance. Derive these polynomials, and show their relation to the Hermite polynomials $H_n$, which can be defined by the generating function

$$\left(\frac{d}{dx}\right)^n e^{-x^2/2} = (-1)^n H_n(x)\, e^{-x^2/2}.$$

**6.4** Extend the polynomial generating problem of 6.3 to two dimensions. That is, find the polynomials $P_k(x_1, x_2)$ of degree $k$, where $x_1$ and $x_2$ are jointly normally distributed.

# Chapter 7

# SOLUTION PROBLEMS

There are a variety of practical difficulties that arise during the numerical solution of estimation problems. These difficulties have been the subject of many numerical analyses and have motivated a large number of studies in numerical methods that are directed toward the solution of statistical estimators. A few of the most troublesome topics have been chosen to illustrate the close relationship between estimation theory and other branches of mathematics including matrix theory, maxima and minima functional approximations, and numerical methods. It will be seen that, although estimation theory is based upon foundations of statistics and probability, the solutions of the estimator formulations depend strongly upon the application of techniques drawn from other fields of applied mathematics.

## 7.1
## *GENERALIZED INVERSE OF A MATRIX*

Frequently, during an analytical development, it is necessary to postulate that a square matrix is nonsingular and has an inverse. It is of both practical and theoretical interest to determine if the nonsingularity condition can be removed so that a single set of arguments can be used for the singular as well as the nonsingular situations.

A typical case in which the nonsingularity of a matrix is customarily imposed is in the solution of the normal equations for a linear least squares estimator. For example, (5–47) can be written in the form

$$\mathbf{A}^{[n\times q]}\hat{\boldsymbol{b}}^{[q\times 1]} = \mathbf{B}^{[n\times p]}\boldsymbol{y}^{[p\times 1]}. \tag{7–1}$$

The standard solution technique is to multiply (7–1) by $\mathbf{A}^T$ and postulate that $\mathbf{A}^T\mathbf{A}$ is nonsingular so that one can solve for

$$\hat{\boldsymbol{b}} = (\mathbf{A}^T\mathbf{A})^{-1}\mathbf{B}\boldsymbol{y}. \tag{7–2}$$

In theoretical work it is certainly not convenient to have to postulate that the inverse $(\mathbf{A}^T\mathbf{A})^{-1}$ exists; in a sense such a postulate is really not pertinent because a solution, not necessarily unique, can exist for $\hat{\boldsymbol{b}}$ in (7–1) even if this inverse does not exist. Moreover, when using numerical values for the elements, it is frequently cumbersome or extremely difficult to ascertain if a matrix is singular.

The concept of a *generalized inverse* or *semi-inverse* can be introduced to sidestep both the theoretical and practical problems of singular matrices. Various forms of generalized matrix inverses have been independently discovered by several authors, and no attempt is made to judge prior discovery [11, 51, 64, 65, 117, 123, 124].

For our purposes we shall require that the generalized inverse of a matrix must always exist and, when used in place of the true inverse (which may not exist), it must yield the correct answers to such questions as the solution of the normal equations.

The generalized inverse of a matrix $\mathbf{A}^{[m\times n]}$ of rank $r$ is an $[n \times m]$ matrix $\mathbf{A}^s$ of rank $r$ such that

$$\mathbf{A}\mathbf{A}^s\mathbf{A} = \mathbf{A}. \tag{7–3}$$

If $\mathbf{A} = \mathbf{0}$, define $\mathbf{0}^s = \mathbf{0}^T$. Both $\mathbf{A}^s\mathbf{A}$ and $\mathbf{A}\mathbf{A}^s$ are idempotent because they are equal to their squares

$$\begin{aligned}(\mathbf{A}^s\mathbf{A})^2 &= \mathbf{A}^s\mathbf{A}\mathbf{A}^s\mathbf{A} = \mathbf{A}^s\mathbf{A}\\ (\mathbf{A}\mathbf{A}^s)^2 &= \mathbf{A}\mathbf{A}^s\mathbf{A}\mathbf{A}^s = \mathbf{A}\mathbf{A}^s.\end{aligned} \tag{7–4}$$

If $\mathbf{A}^{[m\times n]}$ is of rank $r > 0$, then it has a rank factorization of the form

$$\mathbf{A}^{[m\times n]} = \mathbf{B}^{[m\times r]}\mathbf{C}^{[r\times n]}, \tag{7–5}$$

where both $\mathbf{B}$ and $\mathbf{C}$ are of rank $r$. This form follows by first selecting $\mathbf{B}$ such that its columns are the distinguished columns of $\mathbf{A}$ or such that the columns form a basis for the column space generated by the columns of $\mathbf{A}$. Because the rank of $\mathbf{A}$ is $r > 0$, it follows that the number of independent vectors generating the column space of $\mathbf{A}$ must be $r$ or, equivalently, $\mathbf{B}$ must be of order $[m \times r]$. $\mathbf{C}$ is chosen to satisfy (7–5). Both $\mathbf{B}$ and $\mathbf{C}$ are of rank $r$ because [15, p. 19]

$$\operatorname{rank}(\mathbf{A}) = r = \operatorname{rank}(\mathbf{BC}) \leq \min(\operatorname{rank}\mathbf{B}, \operatorname{rank}\mathbf{C}). \tag{7–6}$$

The pseudoinverse of a matrix, often called the *Moore-Penrose generalized inverse*, is defined as

$$\mathbf{A}^{\dagger} = \mathbf{C}^T(\mathbf{C}\mathbf{C}^T)^{-1}(\mathbf{B}^T\mathbf{B})^{-1}\mathbf{B}^T \tag{7-7}$$
$$\mathbf{0}^{\dagger} = \mathbf{0}^T.$$

A pseudoinverse is a generalized inverse because (7–7) can be shown to satisfy (7–3); i.e.,

$$\begin{aligned}\mathbf{A}\mathbf{A}^{\dagger}\mathbf{A} &= \mathbf{A}[\mathbf{C}^T(\mathbf{C}\mathbf{C}^T)^{-1}(\mathbf{B}^T\mathbf{B})^{-1}\mathbf{B}^T]\mathbf{A}\\ &= \mathbf{B}\mathbf{C}\mathbf{C}^T(\mathbf{C}\mathbf{C}^T)^{-1}(\mathbf{B}^T\mathbf{B})^{-1}\mathbf{B}^T\mathbf{B}\mathbf{C}\\ &= \mathbf{B}\mathbf{C}\\ &= \mathbf{A}.\end{aligned} \tag{7-8}$$

The important property is that, if $\mathbf{A}$ is nonsingular, then $\mathbf{A}^{\dagger} = \mathbf{A}^s = \mathbf{A}^{-1}$. This fact follows from the observation that

$$\begin{aligned}\mathbf{A}\mathbf{A}^s\mathbf{A} &= \mathbf{A}\\ \mathbf{A}^{-1}\mathbf{A}\mathbf{A}^s\mathbf{A} &= \mathbf{A}^{-1}\mathbf{A} = \mathbf{I},\end{aligned} \tag{7-9}$$

or $\mathbf{A}^s\mathbf{A} = \mathbf{I}_R$ is a right identity; moreover,

$$\begin{aligned}\mathbf{A}\mathbf{A}^s\mathbf{A}\mathbf{A}^{-1} &= \mathbf{I}\\ \mathbf{A}\mathbf{A}^s &= \mathbf{I}_L,\end{aligned} \tag{7-10}$$

or $\mathbf{A}\mathbf{A}^s$ is a left identity. $\mathbf{I}_R$ and $\mathbf{I}_L$ are the right and left identity matrices. But because $\mathbf{A}$ is nonsingular, $\mathbf{I}_R = \mathbf{I}_L$, which implies the property that $\mathbf{A}^s = \mathbf{A}^{-1}$.

There are several advantages for employing the pseudoinverse rather than the more inclusive generalized inverse. These stem from the following properties:

(i) The pseudoinverse of a pseudoinverse yields the original matrix. Write (7–7) in the form

$$\begin{aligned}\mathbf{A}^{\dagger} &= \mathbf{E}\mathbf{D}\\ \mathbf{E} &= \mathbf{C}^T(\mathbf{C}\mathbf{C}^T)^{-1} \qquad & \mathbf{D} &= (\mathbf{B}^T\mathbf{B})^{-1}\mathbf{B}^T\\ \mathbf{E}^T &= (\mathbf{C}\mathbf{C}^T)^{-1}\mathbf{C} \qquad & \mathbf{D}^T &= \mathbf{B}(\mathbf{B}^T\mathbf{B})^{-1}.\end{aligned} \tag{7-11}$$

Then, by definition,

$$\begin{aligned}(\mathbf{A}^{\dagger})^{\dagger} &= \mathbf{D}^T(\mathbf{D}\mathbf{D}^T)^{-1}(\mathbf{E}^T\mathbf{E})^{-1}\mathbf{E}^T\\ &= \mathbf{B}\mathbf{C},\end{aligned} \tag{7-12}$$

or

$$(\mathbf{A}^{\dagger})^{\dagger} = \mathbf{A}. \tag{7-13}$$

(ii) $(\mathbf{A}\mathbf{A}^{\dagger})$ and $(\mathbf{A}^{\dagger}\mathbf{A})$ are symmetric matrices. From (7–7),

$$\begin{aligned}\mathbf{A}\mathbf{A}^{\dagger} &= \mathbf{B}(\mathbf{B}^T\mathbf{B})^{-1}\mathbf{B}^T\\ \mathbf{A}^{\dagger}\mathbf{A} &= \mathbf{C}^T(\mathbf{C}\mathbf{C}^T)^{-1}\mathbf{C}.\end{aligned} \tag{7-14}$$

Hence, as required,

$$(\mathbf{AA}^{\dagger})^T = \mathbf{AA}^{\dagger} \qquad (7\text{–}15)$$
$$(\mathbf{A}^{\dagger}\mathbf{A})^T = \mathbf{A}^{\dagger}\mathbf{A}.$$

(iii) The pseudoinverse of a matrix is unique.
Greville [64] has shown that, for any matrix $\mathbf{A}$, there exists a unique pseudo-inverse $\mathbf{A}^{\dagger}$, which has its rows and columns in the row space and column space of $\mathbf{A}^T$ and satisfies the equations

$$\mathbf{AA}^{\dagger} = \mathbf{I}_L \qquad (7\text{–}16)$$
$$\mathbf{A}^{\dagger}\mathbf{A} = \mathbf{I}_R.$$

For the decomposition of $\mathbf{A}$ given in (7–5), we can easily form the pseudo-inverses of $\mathbf{B}$ and $\mathbf{C}$. Let $\mathbf{B}$ have rank $r$, then, by a similar decomposition, we can write

$$\mathbf{B}^{[m\times r]} = \mathbf{D}^{[m\times r]}\mathbf{I}^{[r\times r]}, \qquad (7\text{–}17)$$

where $\mathbf{I}$ is the ordinary identity matrix.

Formally apply the definition (7–7) to (7–17) to find

$$\begin{aligned}\mathbf{B}^{\dagger} &= \mathbf{I}^T(\mathbf{I}\,\mathbf{I}^T)^{-1}(\mathbf{D}^T\mathbf{D})^{-1}\mathbf{D}^T \\ &= (\mathbf{D}^T\mathbf{D})^{-1}\mathbf{D}^T \\ &= (\mathbf{B}^T\mathbf{B})^{-1}\mathbf{B}^T.\end{aligned} \qquad (7\text{–}18)$$

A parallel argument demonstrates that

$$\mathbf{C}^{\dagger} = \mathbf{C}^T(\mathbf{CC}^T)^{-1}. \qquad (7\text{–}19)$$

When (7–7), (7–18), and (7–19) are combined, one is led to the relation

$$\mathbf{A}^{\dagger} = \mathbf{C}^{\dagger}\mathbf{B}^{\dagger}. \qquad (7\text{–}20)$$

Thus, the pseudoinverse has the same property as ordinary inverses of products; viz.,

$$\mathbf{A}^{\dagger} = (\mathbf{BC})^{\dagger} = \mathbf{C}^{\dagger}\mathbf{B}^{\dagger}. \qquad (7\text{–}21)$$

To show the existence of the pseudoinverse for a general nonzero matrix of rank $r$, introduce a matrix $\mathbf{H}$ of order $r$ by the relation

$$\mathbf{H} = \mathbf{B}^{\dagger}\mathbf{AC}^{\dagger}. \qquad (7\text{–}22)$$

Insert (7–18) and (7–19) into (7–22) as indicated,

$$\mathbf{BHC} = \mathbf{B}(\mathbf{B}^T\mathbf{B})^{-1}\mathbf{B}^T\mathbf{AC}^T(\mathbf{CC}^T)^{-1}\mathbf{C}. \qquad (7\text{–}23)$$

For a left identity $\mathbf{I}_L\mathbf{B} = \mathbf{B}$, and necessarily $\mathbf{I}_L\mathbf{A} = \mathbf{A}$ because the rank factorization (7–5) implies that each column of $\mathbf{A}$ is a linear combination of the columns of $\mathbf{B}$. Suppose $\mathbf{I}_L$ is of the form $\mathbf{XB}^T$ and satisfies $\mathbf{I}_L\mathbf{A} = \mathbf{A}$, then it preserves every vector in the column space of $\mathbf{A}$ and thus $\mathbf{XB}^T\mathbf{B} = \mathbf{B}$. Therefore,

$$\mathbf{X} = \mathbf{B}(\mathbf{B}^T\mathbf{B})^{-1}$$

(7–24)
$$\begin{aligned}\mathbf{X}\mathbf{B}^T &= \mathbf{I}_L \\ &= \mathbf{B}(\mathbf{B}^T\mathbf{B})^{-1}\mathbf{B}^T \\ &= \mathbf{B}\mathbf{B}^{\dagger}.\end{aligned}$$

Similarly,

(7–25)
$$\mathbf{I}_R = \mathbf{C}^{\dagger}\mathbf{C}$$

is the only matrix with columns in the column space of $\mathbf{A}^T$ which satisfies $\mathbf{A}\,\mathbf{I}_R = \mathbf{A}$.

Hence, (7–23) becomes

(7–26)
$$\mathbf{BHC} = \mathbf{I}_L\mathbf{A}\mathbf{I}_R = \mathbf{A}.$$

Apply (7–6) to show that $\mathbf{H}$ must be of rank $r$, is nonsingular, and has an ordinary inverse. We can, therefore, invert (7–26) to obtain

(7–27)
$$\mathbf{A}^{\dagger} = \mathbf{C}^{\dagger}\mathbf{H}^{-1}\mathbf{B}^{\dagger}.$$

Because of the manner in which $\mathbf{A}^{\dagger}$ was formed, it has rows and columns in the row space of $\mathbf{B}^T$ and the column space of $\mathbf{C}^T$. Or, equivalently, $\mathbf{A}^{\dagger}$ has rows and columns in the row space and column space of $\mathbf{A}^T$. A substitution of relations demonstrates that (7–16) is satisfied, and the existence part of the theorem is verified.

The uniqueness of the pseudoinverse $\mathbf{A}^{\dagger}$ must now be proven. Suppose $\mathbf{A}^{\dagger}$ were not unique, then there must be at least two matrices $\mathbf{A}_1^{\dagger}$ and $\mathbf{A}_2^{\dagger}$ satisfying (7–16) and having their rows and columns in the row space and column space of $\mathbf{A}^T$. Hence,

(7–28)
$$\begin{aligned}\mathbf{A}\mathbf{A}_i^{\dagger} &= \mathbf{I}_L \\ \mathbf{A}_i^{\dagger}\mathbf{A} &= \mathbf{I}_R; \qquad i = 1, 2\end{aligned}$$

and

(7–29)
$$\mathbf{A}_1^{\dagger}\mathbf{A}\mathbf{A}_2^{\dagger} = \mathbf{I}_R\mathbf{A}_2^{\dagger}.$$

Equation (7–25) shows that $\mathbf{I}_R = \mathbf{C}^{\dagger}\mathbf{C}$, and, because the columns of $\mathbf{A}_2^{\dagger}$ are in the column space of $\mathbf{A}^T$ (which is also that of $\mathbf{C}^{\dagger}$), there must exist a matrix $\mathbf{X}$ such that

(7–30)
$$\mathbf{A}_2^{\dagger} = \mathbf{C}^{\dagger}\mathbf{X}.$$

This relation permits us to write (7–29) as

(7–31)
$$\mathbf{A}_1^{\dagger}\mathbf{A}\mathbf{A}_2^{\dagger} = \mathbf{C}^{\dagger}\mathbf{C}\mathbf{C}^{\dagger}\mathbf{X} = \mathbf{C}^{\dagger}\mathbf{X} = \mathbf{A}_2^{\dagger}.$$

In the same manner, we can write

(7–32)
$$\begin{aligned}\mathbf{A}_1^{\dagger}\mathbf{A}\mathbf{A}_2^{\dagger} &= \mathbf{A}_1^{\dagger}\mathbf{I}_L \\ &= \mathbf{A}_1^{\dagger}\mathbf{B}\mathbf{B}^{\dagger}.\end{aligned}$$

Let

$$\mathbf{A}_1^{\dagger} = \mathbf{E}\mathbf{B}^{\dagger}, \tag{7–33}$$

then

$$\begin{aligned}\mathbf{A}_1^{\dagger}\mathbf{A}\mathbf{A}_2^{\dagger} &= \mathbf{E}\mathbf{B}^{\dagger}\mathbf{B}\mathbf{B}^{\dagger} \\ &= \mathbf{E}\mathbf{B}^{\dagger} = \mathbf{A}_1^{\dagger}.\end{aligned} \tag{7–34}$$

Thus, $\mathbf{A}_1^{\dagger} = \mathbf{A}_2^{\dagger}$, and uniqueness has been established.

## 7.2 *APPLICATIONS OF THE PSEUDOINVERSE*

The system of equations in (7–1) will have a solution if and only if $\mathbf{B}\boldsymbol{y}$ lies in the column space of $\mathbf{A}$. This solution will be of the form [64]

$$\hat{\boldsymbol{b}} = \mathbf{A}^{\dagger}\mathbf{B}\boldsymbol{y} + \boldsymbol{z}, \tag{7–35}$$

where $\boldsymbol{z}$ is a vector orthogonal to the column space of $\mathbf{A}^T$, or equivalently

$$\mathbf{A}\boldsymbol{z} = \boldsymbol{0}. \tag{7–36}$$

Substitute (7–35) and (7–36) into (7–1) to verify the general solution

$$\begin{aligned}\mathbf{A}\hat{\boldsymbol{b}} &= \mathbf{B}\boldsymbol{y} \\ \mathbf{A}\mathbf{A}^{\dagger}\mathbf{B}\boldsymbol{y} + \mathbf{A}\boldsymbol{z} &= \mathbf{B}\boldsymbol{y} \\ \mathbf{I}_L\mathbf{B}\boldsymbol{y} &= \mathbf{B}\boldsymbol{y}.\end{aligned} \tag{7–37}$$

Suppose $\boldsymbol{u}$ is any solution of (7–35). Then, by application of the decomposition theorem for linear spaces, we can write the unique decomposition

$$\begin{aligned}\boldsymbol{u} &= \boldsymbol{v} + \boldsymbol{v}_p \\ &= \mathbf{I}_R\boldsymbol{u} + \boldsymbol{v}_p,\end{aligned} \tag{7–38}$$

where $\boldsymbol{v}$ is the projection of $\boldsymbol{u}$ on the column space of $\mathbf{A}^T$ and $\boldsymbol{v}_p$ is the projection on the orthogonal complement of that space. From these relations, it follows that

$$\begin{aligned}\mathbf{B}\boldsymbol{y} &= \mathbf{A}\boldsymbol{u} \\ \mathbf{A}^{\dagger}\mathbf{B}\boldsymbol{y} &= \mathbf{A}^{\dagger}\mathbf{A}\boldsymbol{u} = \mathbf{I}_R\boldsymbol{u} = \boldsymbol{v}.\end{aligned} \tag{7–39}$$

These arguments establish that (7–35) is the general solution of (7–1). Notice that if the rank of $\mathbf{A}$ is equal to the number of unknowns (elements of $\boldsymbol{b}$), then the zero vector is the only vector which is orthogonal to the column space of $\mathbf{A}^T$. This implies that in (7–35), $\boldsymbol{z} = \boldsymbol{0}$.

The important point is that, even when (7–1) does not have an exact solution, (7–35) is a *best* solution in the least squares sense [51]. The reason is simply that if $\mathbf{B}\boldsymbol{y}$ is not in the column space of $\mathbf{A}$, then (7–35) provides a vector $\hat{\boldsymbol{b}}$ such that $\mathbf{A}\hat{\boldsymbol{b}}$ is the projection of $\mathbf{B}\boldsymbol{y}$ on the column space of $\mathbf{A}$. In Chapter 3 we have shown that this projection yields a *best* least squares estimate. Consider the risk function corresponding to (5–33),

$$\text{R} = ||\boldsymbol{Y} - \mathbf{A}\boldsymbol{b}||^2. \tag{7–40}$$

For an arbitrary vector $\boldsymbol{Y}_0$, (7–40) can be written in the equivalent form

$$\begin{aligned} R &= ||\boldsymbol{Y} - \mathbf{A}\boldsymbol{b} - \boldsymbol{Y}_0||^2 + ||\boldsymbol{Y}_0||^2 \\ &\quad + \boldsymbol{Y}_0^T(\boldsymbol{Y} - \mathbf{A}\boldsymbol{b} - \boldsymbol{Y}_0) + (\boldsymbol{Y} - \mathbf{A}\boldsymbol{b} - \boldsymbol{Y}_0)^T\boldsymbol{Y}_0. \end{aligned} \tag{7–41}$$

By simple substitution, it can be verified that the last two terms in (7–41) vanish for the particular choice

$$\begin{aligned} &\boldsymbol{Y}_0 = (\mathbf{I} - \mathbf{A}\mathbf{A}^{+})\boldsymbol{Y}; \\ &\boldsymbol{Y}_0^T(\boldsymbol{Y} - \mathbf{A}\boldsymbol{b} - \boldsymbol{Y}_0) + (\boldsymbol{Y} - \mathbf{A}\boldsymbol{b} - \boldsymbol{Y}_0)^T\boldsymbol{Y}_0 \\ &\quad = \boldsymbol{Y}^T(\mathbf{I} - \mathbf{A}\mathbf{A}^{+})^T[\boldsymbol{Y} - \mathbf{A}\boldsymbol{b} - (\mathbf{I} - \mathbf{A}\mathbf{A}^{+})\boldsymbol{Y}] \\ &\quad\quad + [\boldsymbol{Y} - \mathbf{A}\boldsymbol{b} - (\mathbf{I} - \mathbf{A}\mathbf{A}^{+})\boldsymbol{Y}]^T(\mathbf{I} - \mathbf{A}\mathbf{A}^{+})\boldsymbol{Y} \\ &\quad = \boldsymbol{Y}^T(\mathbf{I} - \mathbf{A}\mathbf{A}^{+})\mathbf{A}(\mathbf{A}^{+}\boldsymbol{Y} - \boldsymbol{b}) + [\boldsymbol{Y}^T(\mathbf{I} - \mathbf{A}\mathbf{A}^{+})\mathbf{A}(\mathbf{A}^{+}\boldsymbol{Y} - \boldsymbol{b})]^T \\ &\quad = 0. \end{aligned} \tag{7–42}$$

Therefore, for this choice of $\boldsymbol{Y}_0$, the risk function attains its minimum when

$$\mathbf{A}\boldsymbol{b} = \boldsymbol{Y} - \boldsymbol{Y}_0 = \mathbf{A}\mathbf{A}^{+}\boldsymbol{Y}. \tag{7–43}$$

We must now show that (7–43) has the same form as (7–35), or that $\boldsymbol{Y}_0$ is orthogonal to the column space of $\mathbf{A}^T$. Note that $(\mathbf{I} - \mathbf{A}\mathbf{A}^{+})$ has this orthogonality property because

$$(\mathbf{I} - \mathbf{A}\mathbf{A}^{+})\mathbf{A} = \mathbf{A} - \mathbf{A} = \mathbf{0}. \tag{7–44}$$

Finally, combine (7–43) and (7–40) to show that the minimum risk is

$$\begin{aligned} R_{\min} &= ||\boldsymbol{Y}_0||^2 = ||(\mathbf{I} - \mathbf{A}\mathbf{A}^{+})\boldsymbol{Y}||^2 \\ &= \boldsymbol{Y}^T(\mathbf{I} - \mathbf{I}_L)\boldsymbol{Y}. \end{aligned} \tag{7–45}$$

As a second illustration of the application of the pseudoinverse of a matrix, we shall generalize the problem of Section 5.5 [49]. The observation data is assumed to have the form

$$\begin{aligned} &\text{Observation} = \text{signal} + \text{noise} \\ &\boldsymbol{y}^{[n\times 1]} = \mathbf{A}^{[n\times q]}\boldsymbol{b}^{[q\times 1]} + \boldsymbol{x}^{[n\times 1]}. \end{aligned} \tag{7–46}$$

We wish to find the matrix $\mathbf{B}$ and constant $\boldsymbol{b}_0$ which provide a *best* linear (not necessarily unbiased) estimate for the random variable $\hat{\boldsymbol{b}}$ having the form

$$\hat{\boldsymbol{b}}^{[q\times 1]} = \mathbf{B}^{[q\times n]}\boldsymbol{y}^{[n\times 1]} + \boldsymbol{b}_0, \tag{7–47}$$

where $\boldsymbol{b}_0$ is the estimate bias. *Best* is understood in the sense of minimizing the mean-squared risk,

$$\begin{aligned} R(\mathbf{B}, \boldsymbol{b}_0) &= \text{E}\{(\hat{\boldsymbol{b}} - \boldsymbol{b})^T\mathbf{M}(\hat{\boldsymbol{b}} - \boldsymbol{b})\} \\ &= \text{E}\{||\hat{\boldsymbol{b}} - \boldsymbol{b}||_M^2\}. \end{aligned} \tag{7–48}$$

The weighting matrix $\mathbf{M}^{[q\times q]}$ is arbitrary and is only restricted to being positive semidefinite. Define,

$$\begin{aligned}\bar{\boldsymbol{x}} &= \mathrm{E}\{\boldsymbol{x}\} = \boldsymbol{0}\\ \Lambda_x &= \mathrm{E}\{(\boldsymbol{x}-\bar{\boldsymbol{x}})(\boldsymbol{x}-\bar{\boldsymbol{x}})^T\}\\ \bar{\boldsymbol{b}} &= \mathrm{E}\{\boldsymbol{b}\}\\ \Lambda_b &= \mathrm{E}\{(\boldsymbol{b}-\bar{\boldsymbol{b}})(\boldsymbol{b}-\bar{\boldsymbol{b}})^T\}.\end{aligned} \tag{7–49}$$

The risk function can be transformed in the following fashion:

$$\begin{aligned}R(\mathbf{B}, \boldsymbol{b}_0) &= \mathrm{E}\{(\mathbf{B}\boldsymbol{y} + \boldsymbol{b}_0 - \boldsymbol{b})^T\mathbf{M}(\mathbf{B}\boldsymbol{y} + \boldsymbol{b}_0 - \boldsymbol{b})\}\\ &= \mathrm{E}\{(\mathbf{BA}\boldsymbol{b} + \mathbf{B}\boldsymbol{x} + \boldsymbol{b}_0 - \boldsymbol{b})^T\mathbf{M}(\mathbf{BA}\boldsymbol{b} + \mathbf{B}\boldsymbol{x} + \boldsymbol{b}_0 - \boldsymbol{b})\}.\end{aligned} \tag{7–50}$$

Expand (7–50), and consider the terms containing $\boldsymbol{b}_0$. It can be verified that these terms will vanish by selecting

$$\boldsymbol{b}_0 = (\mathbf{I} - \mathbf{BA})\bar{\boldsymbol{b}}. \tag{7–51}$$

When (7–51) and (7–49) are inserted into (7–50), the result can be placed in the form

$$\begin{aligned}R(\mathbf{B}, \boldsymbol{b}_0) &= \mathrm{tr}\,\mathrm{E}\{(\boldsymbol{b} - \mathbf{BA}\boldsymbol{b} - \mathbf{B}\boldsymbol{x} - \boldsymbol{b}_0)(\boldsymbol{b} - \mathbf{BA}\boldsymbol{b} - \mathbf{B}\boldsymbol{x} - \boldsymbol{b}_0)^T\mathbf{M}\}\\ &= \mathrm{tr}\,[(\Lambda_b - 2\mathbf{BA}\Lambda_b + \mathbf{BA}\Lambda_b\mathbf{A}^T\mathbf{B}^T + \mathbf{B}\Lambda_x\mathbf{B}^T)\mathbf{M}].\end{aligned} \tag{7–52}$$

Corresponding to (5–99), let

$$\begin{aligned}\mathbf{B} &= \Lambda_b\mathbf{A}^T(\mathbf{A}\Lambda_b\mathbf{A}^T + \Lambda_x)^\dagger + \mathbf{Z}\\ &= \Lambda_b\mathbf{A}^T\mathbf{Q}^\dagger + \mathbf{Z}.\end{aligned} \tag{7–53}$$

When (7–53) is combined with (7–52), the result can be written as

$$\begin{aligned}R(\mathbf{B}, \boldsymbol{b}_0) &= \mathrm{tr}\,[\Lambda_b\mathbf{M}] - 2\,\mathrm{tr}\,[\mathbf{Z}(\mathbf{I} - \mathbf{QQ}^\dagger)\mathbf{A}\Lambda_b\mathbf{M}]\\ &\quad - \mathrm{tr}\,[\Lambda_b\mathbf{A}^T\mathbf{Q}^\dagger\mathbf{A}\Lambda_b\mathbf{M}] + \mathrm{tr}\,[\mathbf{ZQZ}^T\mathbf{M}].\end{aligned} \tag{7–54}$$

We now wish to show that the second term in (7–54) vanishes and, therefore, the risk function is a minimum for the choice $\mathbf{Z} = \mathbf{0}$. At this point it is convenient to add the hypothesis that $\Lambda_b$ is positive define so that $\Lambda_b^{1/2}$ exists and can be used in the sequel. Note that

$$(\mathbf{I} - \mathbf{QQ}^\dagger)\mathbf{Q} = \mathbf{0} = (\mathbf{I} - \mathbf{QQ}^\dagger)(\mathbf{A}\Lambda_b\mathbf{A}^T + \Lambda_x) \tag{7–55}$$

or, because the noise and signal statistics are independent,

$$\begin{aligned}\mathbf{0} &= (\mathbf{I} - \mathbf{QQ}^\dagger)\mathbf{A}\Lambda_b\mathbf{A}^T\\ &= (\mathbf{I} - \mathbf{QQ}^\dagger)\mathbf{A}\Lambda_b^{1/2}(\Lambda_b^{1/2})^T\mathbf{A}^T.\end{aligned} \tag{7–56}$$

Since the matrix $\mathbf{A}\Lambda_b\mathbf{A}^T$ has the same range as $\mathbf{A}\Lambda_b^{1/2}$, it follows that

$$(\mathbf{I} - \mathbf{QQ}^\dagger)\mathbf{A}\Lambda_b^{1/2} = \mathbf{0}. \tag{7–57}$$

Thus, the second term in (7–54) is equal to zero, and $\mathbf{Z} = \mathbf{0}$ yields the minimum risk, which is

$$\begin{aligned}R_{\min}(\mathbf{B}, \boldsymbol{b}_0) &= \mathrm{tr}\,[(\mathbf{I} - \Lambda_b\mathbf{A}^T\mathbf{Q}^\dagger\mathbf{A})\Lambda_b\mathbf{M}]\\ &= \mathrm{tr}\,[(\mathbf{I} - \mathbf{BA})\Lambda_b\mathbf{M}].\end{aligned} \tag{7–58}$$

## 7.3 MATRIX INVERSE

Even when, at least in theory, the true inverse of a matrix exists, it may not be a simple matter actually to obtain good numerical results in practice. This one practical problem has at least one time or another arisen during the numerical applications of estimators. There is no universal *best* method of computing matrix inverses, and each computational center has evolved a series of algorithms which adequately handle the type of problems most frequently submitted to them. A complete discussion of the practical methods of matrix inversion is a major subject of numerical analysis, and only a brief summary is warranted here.

The analyst can blithely write the inverse of a matrix, after assuring his audience of the existence of the inverse, in the well-known form

$$\mathbf{A}^{-1} = \frac{\text{adjoint } \mathbf{A}}{\det \mathbf{A}}. \tag{7-59}$$

While this formulation is fine for theoretical work, it is hardly ever adequate for numerical work. For instance, if $\mathbf{A}$ is of large order, the number of steps required to compute $\mathbf{A}^{-1}$ from (7–59) soon gets out of hand. The reason is that, for a matrix of rank $n$, the evaluation of the det $\mathbf{A}$ requires $(n!)(n-1)$ individual multiplications. Adjoint $\mathbf{A}$ contains $n^2$ determinants of order $(n-1)$, or the evaluation requires $n^2(n-1)!(n-2)$ multiplications. Therefore, (7–59) requires a total of $(n!)(n^2-n-1)$ multiplications and $n^2$ divisions.

A second reason for not using (7–59) is that, when the elements in $\mathbf{A}$ are the result of physical measurements, these elements will all contain errors. In addition, the limitations on the word length, or numerical accuracy, of computational methods and computing machines will introduce an error for each multiplication and division caused by the significant-digit roundoff imposed by the computing process. Thus, numerical accuracy of the inversion process is a direct function of the number of multiplications and divisions employed in the inversion algorithm.

It is outside the scope of this book to discuss even a few representative numerical methods for inverting matrices. However, because of the dominant role that this process plays in the evaluation of estimators, some brief remarks are in order. The literature is very rich with algorithms for numerical matrix inversion, and the subject is treated in works on matrix theory, numerical analysis, and computational methods [15, 50, 55, 68, 71]. The following remarks are abstracted from a paper by Householder on a survey of some closed methods for inverting matrices [72, 73]. These techniques are not all-inclusive and represent only closed methods. One, of course, is not restricted to closed methods, and it is quite common to use approximation methods. Many computational laboratories have developed *pet* methods that are suitable for their own class of problems.

Householder's survey was intended to point out some relations among methods for inverting matrices or, equivalently, for solving linear algebraic equations. *Closed methods* are defined as those which yield the *exact* solution as a result of a *finite* number of arithmetic operations.

Almost all closed methods of matrix inversion are either methods of factorization or methods of modification. Suppose we wish to solve for $\boldsymbol{b}$, which is the solution of the set of linear equations

$$\mathbf{A}\boldsymbol{b} = \boldsymbol{y}. \tag{7–60}$$

The methods of factorization are based upon expressing $\mathbf{A}$ as the product of two matrices, each of which can be easily inverted. One tries to find matrices $\mathbf{P}$ and $\mathbf{Q}$ such that

$$\mathbf{PA} = \mathbf{Q}, \tag{7–61}$$

and $\mathbf{Q}$ is easily inverted so that the desired inverse is expressed as

$$\mathbf{A}^{-1} = \mathbf{Q}^{-1}\mathbf{P}. \tag{7–62}$$

The solutions to (7–60) would then be

$$\begin{aligned} \mathbf{PA}\boldsymbol{b} &= \mathbf{P}\boldsymbol{y} \\ \mathbf{Q}\boldsymbol{b} &= \mathbf{P}\boldsymbol{y} \\ \boldsymbol{b} &= \mathbf{Q}^{-1}\mathbf{P}\boldsymbol{y}. \end{aligned} \tag{7–63}$$

In order to carry out the method of factorization in a general case, it is desirable that the classes of matrices from which $\mathbf{P}$ and $\mathbf{Q}$ can be selected be sufficiently large to provide adequate choices in particular situations. Triangular matrices and matrices with orthogonal rows or orthogonal columns are the most frequently used classes for $\mathbf{P}$ and $\mathbf{Q}$. Frequently one chooses $\mathbf{P}$ as a lower triangle and $\mathbf{Q}$ as an upper triangle. It is also convenient to choose $\mathbf{P}$ as a upper triangle and $\mathbf{Q}$ as a lower triangle or to let $\mathbf{P}$ be strictly orthogonal and $\mathbf{Q}$ be an upper triangle.

An interesting observation is that a matrix with orthogonal rows is immediately invertible. Let $\mathbf{Q}$ be such a matrix, then

$$\mathbf{D}^2 = \mathbf{Q}\mathbf{Q}^T \tag{7–64}$$

yields a diagonal matrix $\mathbf{D}$. The desired inverse is

$$\mathbf{Q}^{-1} = \mathbf{Q}^T\mathbf{D}^{-2}. \tag{7–65}$$

Since the right side of (7–65) is defined in terms of a number of arithmetic operations, it follows that a matrix with orthogonal rows is readily invertible.

(i) Elimination Methods: The most elementary method of solving a set of simultaneous linear equations is to eliminate successively one unknown at a time by substitution of each unknown from a given algebraic expression. We shall now show how this type of elimination solution can be efficiently handled by matrix factorizations. Let **A** be partitioned in any arbitrary fashion

$$\mathbf{A}^{[n\times n]} = \begin{bmatrix} \mathbf{A}_{11}^{[p\times p]} & \mathbf{A}_{12}^{[p\times q]} \\ \mathbf{A}_{21}^{[q\times p]} & \mathbf{A}_{22}^{[q\times q]} \end{bmatrix} \tag{7–66}$$

with the restriction that both $\mathbf{A}_{11}$ and $\mathbf{A}_{22}$ be square, and $p + q = n$. Suppose **P** is a lower triangle and **Q** is an upper triangle, then (7–61) can be written in terms of pseudotriangles as

$$\mathbf{P}^{[n\times n]}\mathbf{A}^{[n\times n]} = \mathbf{Q}^{[n\times n]}$$

$$\begin{bmatrix} \mathbf{P}_{11}^{[p\times p]} & \mathbf{0}^{[p\times q]} \\ \mathbf{P}_{21}^{[q\times p]} & \mathbf{P}_{22}^{[q\times q]} \end{bmatrix} \begin{bmatrix} \mathbf{A}_{11}^{[p\times p]} & \mathbf{A}_{12}^{[p\times q]} \\ \mathbf{A}_{21}^{[q\times p]} & \mathbf{A}_{22}^{[q\times q]} \end{bmatrix} = \begin{bmatrix} \mathbf{Q}_{11}^{[p\times p]} & \mathbf{Q}_{12}^{[p\times q]} \\ \mathbf{0}^{[q\times p]} & \mathbf{Q}_{22}^{[q\times q]} \end{bmatrix}. \tag{7–67}$$

This factorization is worthwhile because now

$$\begin{aligned} \mathbf{Q}^{-1\,[n\times n]} &= \begin{bmatrix} \mathbf{Q}_{11}^{-1[p\times p]} & \mathbf{Q}_{12}^{\prime[p\times q]} \\ \mathbf{0}^{[q\times p]} & \mathbf{Q}_{22}^{-1[q\times q]} \end{bmatrix} \\ &= \begin{bmatrix} \mathbf{Q}_{11}^{-1[p\times p]} & (-\mathbf{Q}_{11}^{-1}\mathbf{Q}_{12}\mathbf{Q}_{22}^{-1})^{[p\times q]} \\ \mathbf{0}^{[q\times p]} & \mathbf{Q}_{22}^{-1[q\times q]} \end{bmatrix}, \end{aligned} \tag{7–68}$$

and the inverse only requires the inverse of two matrices $\mathbf{Q}_{11}$ and $\mathbf{Q}_{22}$, which have the orders of only $p$ and $q$, rather than **A**, which is of order $n = p + q$.

Equation (7–67) is satisfied if

$$\begin{aligned} &\mathbf{P}_{11}\mathbf{A}_{11} = \mathbf{Q}_{11} && \mathbf{P}_{11}\mathbf{A}_{12} = \mathbf{Q}_{12} \\ &\mathbf{P}_{21}\mathbf{A}_{11} + \mathbf{P}_{22}\mathbf{A}_{21} = \mathbf{0} && \mathbf{P}_{21}\mathbf{A}_{12} + \mathbf{P}_{22}\mathbf{A}_{22} = \mathbf{Q}_{22}. \end{aligned} \tag{7–69}$$

These are a set of $n^2$ linear homogeneous equations in $n^2 + p^2 + q^2$ unknowns. Thus $p^2 + q^2$ arbitrary relations can be imposed, provided that the appropriate conditions of independence and consistency are satisfied. A common choice is

$$\begin{aligned} \mathbf{P}_{11}^{[p\times p]} &= \mathbf{I}_{p}^{[p\times p]} \\ \mathbf{P}_{22}^{[q\times q]} &= \mathbf{I}_{q}^{[q\times q]}. \end{aligned} \tag{7–70}$$

Combine (7–70) with (7–67) to obtain

$$\begin{bmatrix} \mathbf{I}_p & \mathbf{0}_{pq} \\ \mathbf{P}' & \mathbf{I}_q \end{bmatrix} \begin{bmatrix} \mathbf{A}_{11} & \mathbf{A}_{12} \\ \mathbf{A}_{21} & \mathbf{A}_{22} \end{bmatrix} = \begin{bmatrix} \mathbf{A}_{11} & \mathbf{A}_{12} \\ \mathbf{0}_{qp} & \mathbf{A}' \end{bmatrix}, \tag{7–71}$$

where

$$\begin{aligned} \mathbf{P}' &= -\mathbf{A}_{21}\mathbf{A}_{11}^{-1} \\ \mathbf{A}' &= \mathbf{P}'\mathbf{A}_{12} + \mathbf{A}_{22}. \end{aligned} \tag{7–72}$$

Thus, if **A** can be partitioned so that any submatrix of order $p$ is readily invertible, then (7–72) enables us to replace the original problem with one of inverting a matrix of order $n - p$. If this matrix is not $\mathbf{A}_{11}$, it can be placed in this position by using appropriate permutation matrices.

The Gaussian elimination method starts by selecting $p = 1$. Then $\mathbf{A}_{11}$ consists of a single element $a_{11}$ and $\mathbf{A}_{11}^{-1} = 1/a_{11}$. From (7–72) it follows that both $\mathbf{P}'$ and $\mathbf{A}_{21}$ are column matrices of order $[(n - 1) \times 1]$,

$$\mathbf{P}' = -\frac{1}{a_{11}} \mathbf{A}_{21}^{[(n-1)\times 1]}, \tag{7–73}$$

and $\mathbf{A}_{12}$ is of order $[1 \times (n - 1)]$. Hence, $\mathbf{A}'$ is of order $[(n - 1) \times (n - 1)]$ because

$$\mathbf{A}' = \mathbf{P}'^{[(n-1)\times 1]} \mathbf{A}_{12}^{[1\times(n-1)]} \mathbf{A}_{22}^{[(n-1)\times(n-1)]}. \tag{7–74}$$

Hence, the rank has been reduced by one unit. A similar reduction of $\mathbf{A}'$ leads to a matrix $\mathbf{A}''$ of rank $(n - 2)$, and so on, until a single constant is reached.

Let $\mathbf{L}_i$ represent a unit lower-triangle matrix whose only non-null elements off the diagonal are in the $i$th column below the diagonal. Then (7–71) can be written as

$$\mathbf{L}_1 \mathbf{A} = \begin{bmatrix} \mathbf{A}_{11} & \mathbf{A}_{12} \\ \mathbf{0} & \mathbf{A}' \end{bmatrix}. \tag{7–75}$$

The final result of iterating the elimination process, ignoring possibly interspersed permutations, has the form

$$\begin{aligned} \mathbf{L}_{n-1}\mathbf{L}_{n-2} \ldots \mathbf{L}_2\mathbf{L}_1\mathbf{A} &= \mathbf{W} \\ \mathbf{L}\mathbf{A} &= \mathbf{W}, \end{aligned} \tag{7–76}$$

where $\mathbf{W}$ is an upper-triangle matrix and $\mathbf{L}$ is a unit lower-triangle. If $\mathbf{D}$ is the diagonal of $\mathbf{W}$,

$$\begin{aligned} \mathbf{W} &= \begin{bmatrix} w_{11} & w_{12} & w_{13} & \cdots & w_{1n} \\ 0 & w_{22} & w_{23} & \cdots & w_{2n} \\ 0 & 0 & w_{33} & \cdots & w_{3n} \\ \cdots & \cdots & \cdots & \cdots & \cdots \\ 0 & 0 & 0 & \cdots & w_{nn} \end{bmatrix}, \\ \mathbf{D} &= \begin{bmatrix} w_{11} & 0 & \cdots & 0 \\ 0 & w_{22} & & \vdots \\ \vdots & & \ddots & \vdots \\ 0 & 0 & \cdots & w_{nn} \end{bmatrix}, \end{aligned} \tag{7–77}$$

then

$$\mathbf{D}^{-1}\mathbf{W} = \begin{bmatrix} w_{11}^{-1} & 0 & \cdots & 0 \\ 0 & w_{22}^{-1} & & \cdot \\ \cdot & & \cdot & \cdot \\ \cdot & & \cdot & \cdot \\ \cdot & & \cdot & \cdot \\ 0 & 0 & \cdots & w_{nn}^{-1} \end{bmatrix} \begin{bmatrix} w_{11} & w_{12} & \cdots & w_{1n} \\ 0 & w_{22} & \cdots & w_{2n} \\ \cdot & & \cdot & \cdot \\ \cdot & & \cdot & \cdot \\ \cdot & & \cdot & \cdot \\ 0 & 0 & \cdots & w_{nn} \end{bmatrix} \tag{7-78}$$

$$= \begin{bmatrix} 1 & w_{11}^{-1}w_{12} & w_{11}^{-1}w_{13} & \cdots & w_{11}^{-1}w_{1n} \\ 0 & 1 & w_{22}^{-1}w_{23} & \cdots & w_{22}^{-1}w_{2n} \\ 0 & 0 & 1 & \cdots & w_{33}^{-1}w_{2n} \\ \cdots & \cdots & \cdots & \cdots & \cdots \\ 0 & 0 & 0 & \cdots & 1 \end{bmatrix}$$

$$= \mathbf{U},$$

a unit upper-triangle matrix.

Whence

$$\mathbf{LA} = \mathbf{W} = \mathbf{DU}, \tag{7-79}$$

or

$$\mathbf{A}^{-1} = \mathbf{U}^{-1}\mathbf{D}^{-1}\mathbf{L}. \tag{7-80}$$

The Gauss method is called *back elimination* because one first forms the upper triangle **W** and then inverts by back elimination as indicated by (7–80).

Frequently, in estimation problems, the inverse of a covariance matrix must be evaluated. In these situations it is possible to simplify the calculations by taking advantage of the fact that the covariance matrix is symmetric.

Notice that, if **A** is symmetric, (7–80) can be written in the equivalent forms

$$\begin{aligned} \mathbf{A}^{-1} &= \mathbf{U}^{-1}\mathbf{D}^{-1}\mathbf{L} \\ &= \mathbf{L}^{T}\mathbf{D}^{-1}(\mathbf{U}^{T})^{-1}. \end{aligned} \tag{7-81}$$

It follows that $\mathbf{L}^T = \mathbf{U}^{-1}$ and (7–62) can be written as

$$\begin{aligned} \mathbf{A}^{-1} &= \mathbf{L}^{T}\mathbf{D}^{-1}\mathbf{L} \\ &= \mathbf{S}^{T}\mathbf{S}, \end{aligned} \tag{7-82}$$

where

$$\mathbf{S} = \mathbf{D}^{-1/2}\mathbf{L}. \tag{7-83}$$

The positive semidefinitiveness of **A** (property of a covariance matrix) assures us that the elements $\mathbf{D}^{1/2}$ are all real or pure imaginaries. Equation (7–82) defines the *square-root* method for inverting a symmetric matrix.

(ii) Orthogonalization Methods: As an example of an orthogonalization method of matrix inversion, suppose we try to factor **A** into the factors

$$\mathbf{A} = \mathbf{B}\mathbf{C}, \tag{7–84}$$

where **B** has orthogonal columns and **C** is a unit upper-triangle matrix. That is,

$$\mathbf{C} = \begin{bmatrix} \mathbf{I} & \mathbf{C}_{12} \\ \mathbf{0} & \mathbf{I} \end{bmatrix} \tag{7–85}$$

and

$$\mathbf{B}^T\mathbf{B} = \mathbf{D}^2, \tag{7–86}$$

where $\mathbf{D}^2$ is a diagonal matrix. If $a_i$ is the $i$th column of **A** and $b_i$ is the corresponding column of **B**, the first choice is to let $b_1 = a_1$. $b_2$ is obtained by adding a multiple of $b_1$ to $a_2$. An induction equation can be formulated for this process. Let **E** be the matrix consisting of the first $i$ columns of **A**, and let **F** be the matrix consisting of the first $i$ columns of **B**. Define

$$\mathbf{E} = \mathbf{F}\mathbf{G}. \tag{7–87}$$

By definition, **G** will be an upper triangle of $i$th order, and

$$\mathbf{F}^T\mathbf{F} = \mathbf{H}^2, \tag{7–88}$$

where $\mathbf{H}^2$ is a diagonal matrix. The problem is to determine the elements of $\mathbf{G}_{12}$ at each stage. That is, for an element of **E**, $e = a_{j+1}$, and an element of **F**, $f = b_{i+1}$, we wish to find the vector $\boldsymbol{g} = \mathbf{G}_{12}$ which has $i$ elements and satisfies the particular form of (7–87):

$$[\mathbf{E} \quad e] = [\mathbf{F} \quad f]\begin{bmatrix} \mathbf{G} & \boldsymbol{g} \\ \mathbf{0} & 1 \end{bmatrix} \tag{7–89}$$

such that $\boldsymbol{f}$ is orthogonal to every column of **F**,

$$\mathbf{F}^T\boldsymbol{f} = \mathbf{0}. \tag{7–90}$$

$\boldsymbol{g}$ is uniquely defined, because from the definitions

$$\begin{aligned} \boldsymbol{e} &= \mathbf{F}\boldsymbol{g} + \boldsymbol{f} \\ \mathbf{F}^T\boldsymbol{e} &= \mathbf{F}^T\mathbf{F}\boldsymbol{g} + \mathbf{F}^T\boldsymbol{f} \\ &= \mathbf{F}^T\mathbf{F}\boldsymbol{g} \\ &= \mathbf{H}^2\boldsymbol{g} \end{aligned} \tag{7–91}$$

or

$$\boldsymbol{g} = \mathbf{H}^{-2}\mathbf{F}^T\boldsymbol{e}. \tag{7–92}$$

The required inverse is

$$\mathbf{A}^{-1} = \mathbf{C}^{-1}\mathbf{B}^{-1}; \tag{7–93}$$

but, since we have constructed $\mathbf{B}$ to have orthogonal columns, we can insert (7–86) into (7–93) to obtain

$$\mathbf{A}^{-1} = \mathbf{C}^{-1}\mathbf{D}^{-2}\mathbf{B}^{T}. \tag{7–94}$$

Each of the inverses in the expression can be readily obtained.

The Schmidt orthogonalization process (Chapter 3) is a special case of the preceding method in which $\mathbf{PA} = \mathbf{Q}$ and $\mathbf{P}$ is chosen as a lower triangle while $\mathbf{Q}$ is chosen as a matrix with orthogonal rows.

## 7.4 *ITERATIVE SOLUTIONS*

A common technique in the solution of estimators as well as in many areas of applied mathematics is to use an iterative process based upon some assumed initial estimate of the solution. This type of solution process was proposed in Chapter 6 where we considered the problem of finding the solution for a nonlinear set of normal equations. The iteration was based upon linearizing the residuals by means of a Taylor series expansion about an initial set of assumed values for the parameters to be estimated. It is not at all uncommon to find that the least squares estimation solution obtained by means of such linearization yields new values which may actually diverge from the original estimates. In fact, the process might never converge to the true values of the parameters. The divergence of the iteration process in such situations may be the result of neglecting the second- and higher-order terms in the Taylor series expansion, an act which may invalidate the process and can actually yield a larger value of the risk function than that corresponding to the initial estimate.

The problem of nonconvergence occurring in linearization methods using iterative solutions, which depend upon an assumption of local linearity about each iterated set of values of the parameters, can often be circumvented by employing the solution technique known as the *method of steepest descent*, or *gradient method.*

Before carrying out a lengthy iterative solution, it is desirable to have some confidence that the process will converge and will converge in some acceptable sense to the true solution. An example of a convergence proof of interest in estimation theory was given by Kiefer and Wolfowitz in conjunction with their discussion of the stochastic estimation of the maximum of a regression function [84, 127].

Consider the task of finding the estimated value $\hat{\boldsymbol{b}}$ of $\boldsymbol{b}$ that minimizes the risk function

$$R(\boldsymbol{b}) = \mathrm{E}\{l[\mathbf{W} - \mathbf{w}(\boldsymbol{b})]\}. \tag{7–95}$$

Define

$$Y(\boldsymbol{b}) = l[\mathbf{W} - \mathbf{w}(\boldsymbol{b})], \tag{7–96}$$

and restrict ourselves so that

$$\mathrm{E}\{[\mathbf{Y}(\boldsymbol{b}) - \mathbf{R}(\boldsymbol{b})]^2\} \leq S < \infty \tag{7–97}$$

and the risk function $R(\boldsymbol{b})$ is strictly increasing for $\boldsymbol{b} < \hat{\boldsymbol{b}}$ and is strictly decreasing for $\boldsymbol{b} > \hat{\boldsymbol{b}}$.

Let $\{a_n\}$ and $\{c_n\}$ be infinite sequences of positive numbers such that

$$\begin{aligned} &\lim_{n\to\infty} c_n = 0 \\ &\sum_n a_n = \infty \\ &\sum_n a_n c_n < \infty \\ &\sum_n a_n^2 c_n^{-2} < \infty. \end{aligned} \tag{7–98}$$

For example, $a_n = n^{-1}$, $c_n = n^{-1/3}$ will satisfy (7–98).

The recursive solution is now formulated as

$$\boldsymbol{b}_{j+1} = \boldsymbol{b}_j + \frac{a_j}{c_j}[\mathbf{Y}_{2j} - \mathbf{Y}_{2j-1}] \tag{7–99}$$

$$\begin{aligned} \mathbf{Y}_{2j} &= \mathbf{Y}(\boldsymbol{b}_j + c_j) \\ \mathbf{Y}_{2j-1} &= \mathbf{Y}(\boldsymbol{b}_j - c_j). \end{aligned} \tag{7–100}$$

If the following regularity conditions are satisfied by the risk function, Kiefer and Wolfowitz proved that $\boldsymbol{b}_j$ converges stochastically to $\hat{\boldsymbol{b}}$ as $j \to \infty$, or

$$\lim_{j\to\infty} P_r\{|\boldsymbol{b}_j - \hat{\boldsymbol{b}}| \geq \epsilon\} = 0; \qquad \text{for every } \epsilon > 0. \tag{7–101}$$

(i) There exist positive $\boldsymbol{\beta}$ and $\mathbf{B}$ such that

$$|\boldsymbol{b}' - \hat{\boldsymbol{b}}| + |\boldsymbol{b}'' - \hat{\boldsymbol{b}}| < \boldsymbol{\beta}$$

implies

$$|\mathbf{R}(\boldsymbol{b}') - \mathbf{R}(\boldsymbol{b}'')| < \mathbf{B}|\boldsymbol{b}' - \boldsymbol{b}''|.$$

(ii) There exist positive $\boldsymbol{\rho}$ and $\mathbf{M}$ such that

$$|\boldsymbol{b}' - \boldsymbol{b}''| < \boldsymbol{\rho}$$

implies

$$|\mathbf{R}(\boldsymbol{b}') - \mathbf{R}(\boldsymbol{b}'')| < \mathbf{M}.$$

(iii) For every $\boldsymbol{\delta} > \boldsymbol{0}$, there exists a positive $\boldsymbol{\pi}(\boldsymbol{\delta})$ such that

$$|\boldsymbol{b} - \hat{\boldsymbol{b}}| > \boldsymbol{\delta}$$

implies

$$\inf_{\frac{1}{2}\delta > \epsilon > 0} \frac{|\mathbf{R}(\boldsymbol{b} + \epsilon) - \mathbf{R}(\boldsymbol{b} - \epsilon)|}{\epsilon} > \boldsymbol{\pi}(\boldsymbol{\delta}).$$

Instead of placing regularity conditions on the risk function, it may be intuitively more appealing to place the restrictions on the loss function. A development of this nature has been given by Sakrison [127].

The theoretical and practical problems concerning recursive or iterative solutions are far from being completely solved. While it is comforting to know that a given solution formulation will converge, certain techniques can be frequently unattractive because of agonizingly slow convergence after the first few iterations. The slow rate of convergence of steepest-descent solutions, for instance, has motivated several modifications of the basic method in attempts to speed the convergence of the solution [4; 32; p. 205, 93; 94; 98]. The theoretical problem is to determine sequences $c_n$ and $a_n$ that would be optimal in some reasonable sense. An important associated problem, especially when automatic computing machines are used, is to determine a stopping rule, i.e., a rule by which the computer decides when the results are sufficiently close to $\hat{\boldsymbol{b}}$.

The most frequently used iterative solution technique is that of the method of steepest descent, or gradient method. Although it is impractical to present all the various modifications that have been used because of different numerical computing advantages, the basic method will be developed. The theory not only is of practical importance, but as we shall see, is intimately related to the important result of Chapter 3; i.e., the optimal estimate is the orthogonal projection on a linear space of random vectors.

Let us define the total matrix of observations $\boldsymbol{W}_j^{[p\times 1]}$ as

$$\boldsymbol{W}^{[pn\times 1]} = \begin{bmatrix} \boldsymbol{W}_1^{[p\times 1]} \\ \cdots\cdots \\ \boldsymbol{W}_n^{[p\times 1]} \end{bmatrix}. \tag{7–102}$$

Similarly, if the predicted values of the observations depend upon a set of parameters $\boldsymbol{b}^{[q\times 1]}$, the total prediction matrix corresponding to $\boldsymbol{W}$ is defined as

$$\boldsymbol{w}^{[pn\times 1]}(\boldsymbol{b}) = \begin{bmatrix} \boldsymbol{w}_1^{[p\times 1]}(\boldsymbol{b}) \\ \cdots\cdots\cdots \\ \boldsymbol{w}_n^{[p\times 1]}(\boldsymbol{b}) \end{bmatrix}. \tag{7–103}$$

The risk function is chosen as the weighted squares,

$$R(\boldsymbol{b}) = \| \boldsymbol{W} - \boldsymbol{w}(\boldsymbol{b}) \|_{\Phi}^2. \tag{7–104}$$

The minimization of $R$ can be made more tractable by linearizing the total prediction matrix by means of a Taylor series expansion. It is recognized that a certain element of danger lies in this assumption, and one may find the remaining steps in the process do not converge. Bearing this in mind, expand $\boldsymbol{w}(\boldsymbol{b})$ about an estimate $\boldsymbol{w}(\hat{\boldsymbol{b}}_0)$, and retain only the linear terms:

$$\begin{aligned} \boldsymbol{w}(\boldsymbol{b}) &= \boldsymbol{w}(\hat{\boldsymbol{b}}_0) + \mathbf{T}(\hat{\boldsymbol{b}}_0) \cdot [\boldsymbol{b} - \hat{\boldsymbol{b}}_0] \\ \mathbf{T}^T &= \nabla_b \boldsymbol{w}^T(\hat{\boldsymbol{b}}_0). \end{aligned} \tag{7–105}$$

Substitute (7–105) into (7–104) to find the linearized risk function

$$R_L(\boldsymbol{b}) = \| \boldsymbol{W} - \boldsymbol{w}(\hat{\boldsymbol{b}}_0) - \mathbf{T}(\hat{\boldsymbol{b}}_0) \cdot [\boldsymbol{b} - \hat{\boldsymbol{b}}_0]\|_\Phi^2. \tag{7–106}$$

The value of $\boldsymbol{b}$ that minimizes $R_L$ can be written down from (5–47) by noting the analogy between (7–106) and (5–45). Thus the solution for the minimizing estimate is

$$\begin{aligned} \mathbf{N} \cdot [\hat{\boldsymbol{b}} - \hat{\boldsymbol{b}}_0] &= \mathbf{T}^T \Phi \boldsymbol{\alpha} \\ [\mathbf{T}^T \Phi \mathbf{T}] \cdot [\hat{\boldsymbol{b}} - \hat{\boldsymbol{b}}_0] &= \mathbf{T}^T \Phi \cdot [\boldsymbol{W} - \boldsymbol{w}(\hat{\boldsymbol{b}}_0)]. \end{aligned} \tag{7–107}$$

Equation (7–107) cannot be quickly solved for $\hat{\boldsymbol{b}}$ without first observing that, if $pn < q$, then $\mathbf{N}$ will be a singular matrix. This condition would imply that an estimate is being attempted with less than a minimal data set in which the number of observation components is equal to the number of components in the parameter vector $\boldsymbol{b}$. The case in which $pn < q$ is treated in Chapter 8. For future consistency, we shall use the pseudoinverse of $\mathbf{N}$ and solve (7–107) in the form

$$\hat{\boldsymbol{b}} = \hat{\boldsymbol{b}}_0 + \mathbf{N}^\dagger \mathbf{T}^T \Phi \cdot \boldsymbol{\alpha}. \tag{7–108}$$

Of course, starting with $\hat{\boldsymbol{b}}$ in place of $\hat{\boldsymbol{b}}_0$, we could repeat the same estimation process. One is thereby led to the iterative solution

$$\begin{aligned} \hat{\boldsymbol{b}}_{j+1} &= \hat{\boldsymbol{b}}_j + [\mathbf{T}_j^T(\hat{\boldsymbol{b}}_j) \Phi \mathbf{T}_j(\hat{\boldsymbol{b}}_j)]^\dagger \mathbf{T}_j^T(\hat{\boldsymbol{b}}_j) \Phi \cdot \{\boldsymbol{W} - \boldsymbol{w}(\hat{\boldsymbol{b}}_j)\} \\ &= \hat{\boldsymbol{b}}_j + \mathbf{N}_j^\dagger \mathbf{T}_j^T \Phi \boldsymbol{\alpha}_j. \end{aligned} \tag{7–109}$$

We shall now demonstrate that this basic iterative solution is nothing more than the method of steepest descent [15, 71].

Several of the most commonly employed iterative solution methods are based upon the following geometric concept: Start with any $\boldsymbol{b}$ and a sequence of vectors $\{\boldsymbol{\beta}_j\}$. Define a sequence $\{\boldsymbol{b}_j\}$ such that

$$\begin{aligned} \boldsymbol{b}_0 &= \boldsymbol{b} \\ \boldsymbol{b}_{j+1} &= \boldsymbol{b}_j + \lambda_j \boldsymbol{\beta}_j, \end{aligned} \tag{7–110}$$

where $\lambda_j$ is chosen so that $\boldsymbol{b}_j$ is orthogonal to $\lambda_j \boldsymbol{\beta}_j$. The idea is that, if the vectors $\boldsymbol{\beta}_j$ span some $n$-dimensional space, in the limit the vectors $\boldsymbol{b}_j$ will approach a vector that is orthogonal to this space. This, as we have already seen, will yield the optimal estimate for a parameter when the risk is a mean-quadratic-loss function.

Even though (7–108) and (7–109) are similar, there is a distinct difference in the interpretation and use of these formulations. In (7–108), we seek a value $\hat{\boldsymbol{b}}$ which will yield immediately a minimum value of the risk. On the other hand, in (7–109), we start with some intermediate estimate in the direction of the vector $\boldsymbol{\alpha}_j$, and we seek the lowest level of the surface of $R_L$ which can be met by a scale-factor mutliple of $\boldsymbol{\alpha}_j$.

To conform with (7–109), write (7–110) as

$$\hat{\boldsymbol{b}}_{j+1}^{[q\times 1]} = \hat{\boldsymbol{b}}_j^{[q\times 1]} + \lambda_j \mathbf{G}_j^{[q\times pn]} \boldsymbol{\alpha}_j^{[pn\times 1]}, \tag{7–111}$$

where $\mathbf{G}_j$ is a nonzero, arbitrary matrix introduced to make $\boldsymbol{\alpha}_j$ compatible with the dimension of $\boldsymbol{b}$. The risk function $R_L(\boldsymbol{b}_{j+1})$ is defined from (7–106) by replacing $\hat{\boldsymbol{b}}_0$ by $\hat{\boldsymbol{b}}_j$. In this fashion, $R_L(\hat{\boldsymbol{b}}_{j+1})$ is expressed as a function of $\lambda_j$ by means of (7–111). The value of $\lambda_j$ that minimizes the risk can be found by differentiating the function and finding the condition for which the derivative vanishes. Thus, using the analogy with (5–45) and (5–47),

$$\begin{aligned} 0 &= \frac{\partial}{\partial \lambda_j} R(\hat{\boldsymbol{b}}_{j+1}) = \frac{\partial \hat{\boldsymbol{b}}_{j+1}^T}{\partial \lambda_j} \cdot \nabla_b R(\hat{\boldsymbol{b}}_{j+1}) \\ &= \boldsymbol{\alpha}_j^T \mathbf{G}^T [-\mathbf{T}_j^T \boldsymbol{\Phi} \boldsymbol{\alpha}_j + \mathbf{N}_j \cdot (\hat{\boldsymbol{b}}_{j+1} - \hat{\boldsymbol{b}}_j)] \\ &= \boldsymbol{\alpha}_j^T \mathbf{G}^T [-\mathbf{T}_j^T \boldsymbol{\Phi} \boldsymbol{\alpha}_j + \mathbf{N}_j \lambda_j \mathbf{G}_j \boldsymbol{\alpha}_j], \end{aligned} \tag{7–112}$$

or

$$\lambda_j \mathbf{G}_j = \mathbf{N}^{+} \mathbf{T}_j^T \boldsymbol{\Phi} = (\mathbf{T}_j^T \boldsymbol{\Phi} \mathbf{T}_j)^{+} \mathbf{T}_j^T \boldsymbol{\Phi}. \tag{7–113}$$

Notice that, if one compares (7–113) and (7–111) with (7–109), it is evident that (7–109) has the same form as that resulting from a steepest-descent, or gradient, solution operating directly on the risk function.

The steepest-descent method starts with some estimate $\hat{\boldsymbol{b}}_0$ and then determines the direction in which the surface $R(\hat{\boldsymbol{b}})$ diminishes most rapidly. The solution continues in this new direction until we find that we are now following a contour of the surface. At this state, we stop and compute a new direction of maximum descent and continue the search for the minimum. Since the direction of steepest descent is the gradient, it is always normal to the contours and, therefore, the directions $\hat{\boldsymbol{b}}_j$ and the change in $\hat{\boldsymbol{b}}_j$ will be orthogonal.

Various modifications of the steepest-descent method have been formulated for nonlinear minimization problems [32]. There exist many unsolved questions in the application of steepest-descent methods, and no universally *good* solution is available. As in most of the numerical problems connected with practical solutions of estimators, the choice of method will be largely influenced by the particular idiosyncrasies of the problem at hand.

## 7.5
## *ILL-CONDITIONED EQUATIONS*

The solution of a set of linear equations is frequently complicated by the fact that the equations may be *ill-conditioned* [50, 68]. For example, the solution of the set

$$300x + 400y = 700$$
$$100x + 133y = 233 \tag{7-114}$$

is $x = 1$, $y = 1$.

Observe that, if the coefficients are slightly altered to

$$300x + 400y = 700$$
$$100x + 132y = 234, \tag{7-115}$$

the solution is now $x = 3$, $y = -1/2$.

Ill-conditioned equations are extremely sensitive to small changes or small errors in the coefficients. Obviously, ill-conditioned equations are an undesirable situation and should be avoided whenever possible by reformulating the problem.

Precise definitions have been proposed for a measure of ill-conditioned equations. These definitions are of little help in numerical work because the determination of the measure of ill-conditioning may be about as long a process as the solution of the set of equations themselves. There is seldom any practical purpose in computing a measure of ill-conditioning as an advance indication of potential difficulty. In many instances, the discovery of ill-conditioning is indicated when small errors in certain coefficients yield large effects on the solutions. A characteristic feature of ill-conditioned equations is that a set of values for the unknowns, which differs considerably from the solution of the equations, may nevertheless yield small residuals for all the equations in a least squares estimator [68].

Ill-conditioned sets of equations are all too often the source of trouble which leads to nonconvergence of iterative solutions of estimation formulations. Instead of each successive estimate yielding a small change, the phenomena illustrated in (7–114) and (7–115) can lead to rather large changes because of small errors in the coefficients. Such large errors can cause the solution to diverge for at least two reasons. First, any linearizing expansions may be violated in the sense that the discarded remainder terms may not be truly negligible. Second, the convergence may fail because the terms do not conform with the restrictions of some convergence criterion such as the Kiefer-Wolfowitz criteria.

Several methods have been proposed for reducing the ill-conditioning of the normal equations and thereby improving the possibility of convergence for an iterated solution [112]. Another approach is to limit arbitrarily the correction that can be applied at each stage [28, 105]. Thus, if the ill-conditioning yields a *large* correction, one arbitrarily assumes the value to be too large and, instead, inserts a predetermined value. A formulation due to Morrison is used to illustrate a limiting technique.

Consider the risk function for a linear estimator corresponding to (7–106),

$$R = \|\mathbf{T}\boldsymbol{q} - \boldsymbol{W}\|^2_{\Phi}$$
$$\boldsymbol{q} = \hat{\boldsymbol{b}}_0 - \boldsymbol{b}. \tag{7-116}$$

We shall ask for a value of $\hat{\boldsymbol{b}}$ that minimizes the risk under the constraint that the various values of $\hat{\boldsymbol{b}}_j$ in the iterated solution do not exceed some certain bound. The normal equations for the estimate that minimizes (7–116) correspond to, (6–22),

$$\mathbf{T}^T\mathbf{\Phi}\mathbf{T}\boldsymbol{q} = \mathbf{T}^T\mathbf{\Phi}\boldsymbol{W}. \tag{7–117}$$

Define

$$\begin{aligned} \mathbf{N} &= \mathbf{T}^T\mathbf{\Phi}\mathbf{T} \\ \boldsymbol{f} &= \mathbf{T}^T\mathbf{\Phi}\boldsymbol{W} \\ \mathbf{G} &= \mathbf{D}^{-1}\mathbf{N}\mathbf{D}^{-1}, \end{aligned} \tag{7–118}$$

where $\mathbf{D}$ is a diagonal matrix to be defined later. Substitute (7–118) into (7–117) to obtain

$$\mathbf{D}(\mathbf{D}^{-1}\mathbf{N}\mathbf{D}^{-1})\mathbf{D}\boldsymbol{q} = \boldsymbol{f}, \tag{7–119}$$

or

$$\begin{aligned} \mathbf{G}\boldsymbol{y} &= \mathbf{D}^{-1}\boldsymbol{f} \\ \boldsymbol{y} &= \mathbf{D}\boldsymbol{q}. \end{aligned} \tag{7–120}$$

Let $\mathbf{\Phi}$ be symmetric and positive definite, then $\mathbf{N}$ will also be positive definite.

Notice that, by the manner in which we defined $\mathbf{G}^{[n\times n]}$, it is symmetric and positive definite. Therefore $\mathbf{G}$ will have a set of $n$ positive eigenvalues $\mu_j$ and corresponding eigenvectors $\boldsymbol{u}_j$ (Chapter 10). This observation permits us to write

$$\begin{aligned} \mathbf{G}\mathbf{U} &= \mathbf{U}\mathbf{M} \\ \mathbf{U}^T\mathbf{U} &= \mathbf{I}, \end{aligned} \tag{7–121}$$

where $\mathbf{U}$ is the matrix of eigenvectors and $\mathbf{M}$ is the diagonal matrix of eigenvalues,

$$\begin{aligned} \mathbf{U} &= [\boldsymbol{u}_1^{[n\times 1]} \dots \boldsymbol{u}_n^{[n\times 1]}], \\ \mathbf{M} &= \begin{bmatrix} \mu_1 & \cdots & 0 \\ & \mu_2 & \\ & & \ddots \\ 0 & \cdots & \mu_n \end{bmatrix}. \end{aligned} \tag{7–122}$$

Equation (7–121) can also be written as

$$\mathbf{G} = \mathbf{U}\mathbf{M}\mathbf{U}^T, \tag{7–123}$$

and (7–120) becomes

$$(\mathbf{U}\mathbf{M}\mathbf{U}^T)\boldsymbol{y} = \mathbf{D}^{-1}\boldsymbol{f} \tag{7–124}$$

or

$$\mathbf{M}\boldsymbol{z} = \mathbf{U}^T\mathbf{D}^{-1}\boldsymbol{f} = \boldsymbol{e} \tag{7–125}$$
$$\boldsymbol{z} = \mathbf{U}^T\boldsymbol{y}.$$

Morrison showed that, if one selects

$$z_j = \begin{cases} \dfrac{e_j}{\mu_j}; & \left|\dfrac{e_j}{\mu_j}\right| \leq 1 \\ \operatorname{sgn} e_j; & \left|\dfrac{e_j}{\mu_j}\right| > 1, \end{cases} \tag{7–126}$$

then

$$||\mathbf{T}\boldsymbol{q} - \boldsymbol{W}||^2_\Phi \leq ||\boldsymbol{W}||^2, \tag{7–127}$$

and the sum of the squares of the residuals is really reduced. From the previous definitions,

$$||\boldsymbol{z}||^2 = ||\mathbf{D}\boldsymbol{q}||^2 \leq n, \tag{7–128}$$

and, therefore,

$$|q_j| \leq d_j^{-1} n^{1/2}. \tag{7–129}$$

$d_j$ are the diagonal elements of $\mathbf{D}$.

The computing procedure can be summarized by the following steps:

(i) Select some $K_j$ such that, for $|q_j| \leq K_j$, a linearity expansion is valid. This selection is one of judicious guessing.

(ii) Let $d_j = n^{1/2} K_j^{-1}$.

(iii) Compute $\mathbf{N} = \mathbf{T}^T \mathbf{\Phi} \mathbf{T}$.

(iv) Compute $\mathbf{D}^{-1}\mathbf{N}\mathbf{D}^{-1}$ and $\mathbf{D}^{-1}\boldsymbol{f}$.

(v) Find the eigenvalues $\mu_j$ and the eigenvector matrix corresponding to $\mathbf{G}$.

(vi) Using the criteria of (7–126), evaluate the vectors

$$\boldsymbol{z} = \mathbf{M}^{-1}\mathbf{U}^T \cdot (\mathbf{D}^{-1}\boldsymbol{f})$$
$$\boldsymbol{y} = \mathbf{U}\boldsymbol{z}$$
$$\boldsymbol{q} = \mathbf{D}^{-1}\boldsymbol{y}, \qquad \text{desired result.}$$

The iterated least squares solution will converge if the bounds $K_j$ are chosen sufficiently small; unfortunately, the theory does not indicate the manner of making these choices.

Although this type of solution with a limiting procedure is about thirty times greater in computing time than a *straightforward* iteration solution, the fact that ill-conditioning is allowed for in the original formulation may in the end provide a quicker solution. The time lost in repeating calculations to discover the presence of numerical errors caused by ill-conditioned systems is often much longer than that lost by arbitrarily assuming that all equation sets may be ill-conditioned and proceeding accordingly.

## Problems

**7.1** Consider the set of equations [64],

$$\begin{aligned} 4x_1 - x_2 - 3x_3 + 2x_4 &= 7 \\ -2x_1 + 5x_2 - x_3 - 3x_4 &= 3 \\ 2x_1 + 13x_2 - 9x_3 - 5x_4 &= 20. \end{aligned}$$

Verify that the matrix $\mathbf{A}$ of the coefficients has rank 2 and the vector $\boldsymbol{y}^T = [7\ 3\ 20]$ is not in the column space of $\mathbf{A}$. Show that the pseudoinverse of $\mathbf{A}$ is

$$\mathbf{A}^{\dagger} = \frac{1}{6398}\begin{bmatrix} 608 & -362 & 130 \\ -197 & 212 & 242 \\ -431 & 204 & -250 \\ 324 & -235 & -57 \end{bmatrix}.$$

**7.2** The orthogonal complement of the column space of $\mathbf{A}^T$ of problem 7.1 is the column space of $\mathbf{I} - \mathbf{I}_R = \mathbf{I} - \mathbf{A}^{\dagger}\mathbf{A}$. Show that

$$\mathbf{I} - \mathbf{A}^{\dagger}\mathbf{A} = \frac{1}{914}\begin{bmatrix} 426 & 104 & 376 & -236 \\ 104 & 285 & 257 & 320 \\ 376 & 257 & 437 & 32 \\ -236 & 320 & 32 & 680 \end{bmatrix}.$$

Any two columns of the matrix can be taken as a basis for the space. Choose the first and fourth columns, and compute

$$\boldsymbol{x} = \mathbf{A}^{\dagger}\boldsymbol{y} + \boldsymbol{z} = \text{matrix of constants} + \text{matrix of constants} \times \boldsymbol{w},$$

where $\boldsymbol{w}$ is an arbitrary vector. Finally, compute $\mathbf{A}\boldsymbol{x}$ and $\boldsymbol{y} - \mathbf{A}\boldsymbol{x}$, and demonstrate that the minimum value of the squared residuals, attained only for these values of $\boldsymbol{x}$, is 9/14 [64].

**7.3** Find the pseudoinverse of the matrix

$$\mathbf{A} = \begin{bmatrix} 0 & 2 & 3 & 1 \\ 1 & 1 & 1 & 2 \\ 1 & 3 & 4 & 3 \\ 0 & 0 & 5 & 1 \end{bmatrix}.$$

**7.4** Carefully provide the detailed arguments which justify that in (7–54)

$$\operatorname{tr}[\mathbf{Z}(\mathbf{I} - \mathbf{Q}\mathbf{Q}^{\dagger})\mathbf{A}\boldsymbol{\Lambda}_b\mathbf{M}] = 0.$$

**7.5** Equation (7–67) can be used to solve a system of equations without the intermediate step of inverting a matrix. Let the given system $\mathbf{A}\boldsymbol{x} = \boldsymbol{y}$ be partitioned as

$$\begin{bmatrix} \mathbf{A}_{11} & \mathbf{A}_{12} \\ \mathbf{A}_{22} & \mathbf{A}_{22} \end{bmatrix}\begin{bmatrix} \boldsymbol{x}_1 \\ \boldsymbol{x}_2 \end{bmatrix} = \begin{bmatrix} \boldsymbol{y}_1 \\ \boldsymbol{y}_2 \end{bmatrix}.$$

Use (7–67) to show that

$$\begin{aligned} \mathbf{Q}_{22}\boldsymbol{x}_2 &= \mathbf{P}_{21}\boldsymbol{y}_1 + \mathbf{P}_{22}\boldsymbol{y}_2 \\ \mathbf{Q}_{11}\boldsymbol{x}_1 + \mathbf{Q}_{12}\boldsymbol{x}_2 &= \mathbf{P}_{11}\boldsymbol{y}_2. \end{aligned}$$

The first of these equations yields $\boldsymbol{x}_2$, which can then be used in the second to find $\boldsymbol{x}_1$.

**7.6** Invert the following matrix by means of the square-root method described in Section 7.3:

$$\mathbf{A} = \begin{bmatrix} 9 & 3 & 0 & 0 \\ 3 & 7 & 0 & 0 \\ 0 & 0 & 1 & 1 \\ 0 & 0 & 1 & 6 \end{bmatrix}.$$

**7.7** The secant method for solving $f(b) = 0$ is a two-point iterative method that is a generalization of the Newton-Raphson method. The method is defined by the relation

$$\begin{aligned} b_i &= F(b_{i-1}, b_{i-2}) \\ &= \frac{b_{i-1}f(b_{i-2}) - b_{i-2}f(b_{i-1})}{f(b_{i-2}) - f(b_{i-1})}. \end{aligned}$$

Compare the secant method used as an iteration scheme with that of the Newton-Raphson by computing $E$ from

$$E - 0.1 \sin E = 30.$$

# Chapter 8

# RECURSIVE ESTIMATORS

It is not an uncommon experience for an experimentalist to discover that, after reducing the results observed during a sequence of measurements, the estimated values of the parameters appear to vary more than the *expected* amount from some assumed or a priori known values. Such doubts may be raised because the end results are not *sufficiently close* to predicted theoretical magnitudes or because the computed variance of the measured values is so large that the precision and possibly the accuracy of the final values are questionable. Faced with this situation, the almost intuitive decision on the part of the experimenter is to conduct a new sequence of observations, the hope being that by obtaining additional data a new set of parameter estimates may be *closer* to the *desired* values or, at least, the standard deviations of the measurements might be reduced and thereby lend further confidence in the estimates. Instead of simply repeating the original measurements, the experimenter may well choose to use a modified or entirely different observation technique to provide an independent check on the first set of measurements.

Whether or not a new experimental method is used for the repetition of the observations, the yields of the original and the new sequences of measurements cannot be expected to coincide because of the inescapable presence of experimental errors. If the analyst has no a priori justification for accepting the repeated, or second, data set than for accepting the original data, then he can adopt a philosophy which dictates a proper combination of the results of both sets of data. Provided that the second set of data is the result of the same measurement procedure, both data sets can be combined into a single augmented data input to the statistical estimator. In spite of the analytical simplicity of a simple augmentation of data, the fact that computations using the augmented data set are both time-consuming and tedious if hand computations are used is frequently sufficient motivation for at least first using only the second set of data by itself. Furthermore, if a different experimental technique, or even a modification of the instruments, was employed for the repeated observations, the analyst would have no simple method for amending the original data set and would, for all practical purposes, be forced to make an independent estimation calculation.

Let us assume that the choice has been made, for any valid reason, to independently reduce the data from the repeated observations. As we anticipated, the new processing yields values of the estimated parameters which differ from those obtained from the first attempt. A practical problem, as well as a theoretical problem, is to devise a procedure for combining the two estimates in an appropriate *best* fashion. Since there is no universally accepted term for estimation obtained by a combination of estimates, we call this procedure a *stepwise combination of estimates* [60].

Rather than deciding beforehand to repeat an experiment if the results appear to be unsatisfactory, an alternative algorithm is to conduct the experiment concurrently with the data reduction and parameter estimation. One starts such a sequential or recursive process by making an initial estimate of the system parameters from a minimal data set. The *system parameters* are simply the unknown constants which are to be estimated from a set of measured data. These parameters are sometimes called the *state vector*. A minimal data set is a collection of a sufficient number of measurements to form a consistent set of equations (number of equations is equal to the number of unknowns), which in turn yield a solution that uniquely determines initial values of the system parameters. The initial estimate can be furnished just as well, in many cases, by a *judicious guess* rather than by resorting to the formality of solving a system of equations using a minimal data set.

In either case, whether one starts with either a guess of initial values or with the solution of a minimal data set, a procedure is established for combining each new data point with the previous parameter estimate. The combining is accomplished by using an appropriate weighting of the data point in order to yield an improved estimate of the system parameters. This updating process is iterated in a stepwise fashion as each new data point is introduced. At any stage in this sequential procedure, it is possible to terminate both the measurements and computations and have immediate access to the *best* estimate of the system parameters based upon all accumulated data to the instant of termination. Another advantage of sequential estimators is that at each step the calculations are fixed in size and format. New data points are merely inserted into a standard format for the estimator. Moreover, the sequential feature eliminates the necessity for storing or remembering previous data points. In many applications data can be immediately discarded at the conclusion of each estimation computational cycle. In this fashion a significant economy can be obtained in the required data-storage capacity. Such economy is particularly attractive in critical computing systems such as those performing data-processing functions in space vehicles.

Sequential estimators are not a new concept and have been the subject of numerous papers [26, 41, 52, 57, 58, 77, 84, 95, 141, 144, 158]. Sequential estimators have also been designated by the terms *stepwise*, *stagewise*, *recursive*, and *progressive*. No attempt has been made to establish priority or originality for the general concept of sequential estimators in the form discussed in this chapter.

## 8.1
## *STEPWISE COMBINATION OF ESTIMATES*

Suppose, that as a result of an experiment, a first set of measured data points has been reduced to yield an estimate $\hat{\boldsymbol{b}}$ for the system parameters $\boldsymbol{b}$. Let

$$\boldsymbol{q}_1 = \hat{\boldsymbol{b}}_1 - \boldsymbol{b} \tag{8–1}$$

be the estimate error. Either by postulating that $\mathrm{E}\{\boldsymbol{q}_1\} = \boldsymbol{0}$ or by introducing new variables which have zero mean, but retaining the same symbol, define the covariance matrix of the estimate error as

$$\boldsymbol{\Psi}_1 = \mathrm{E}\{\boldsymbol{q}_1\boldsymbol{q}_1^T\}. \tag{8–2}$$

Assuming that the decision has been made to repeat the measurements, a second data set may lead to an estimate $\hat{\boldsymbol{b}}_2$ with $\boldsymbol{q}_2$ and $\boldsymbol{\Psi}_2$ defined analogous to $\boldsymbol{q}_1$ and $\boldsymbol{\Psi}_1$. The problem is to combine the two independent estimates $\hat{\boldsymbol{b}}_1$ and $\hat{\boldsymbol{b}}_2$ to obtain a *best* estimate $\hat{\boldsymbol{b}}$ which is a weighted combination of the two estimates.

The risk function for the combined problem is chosen as [26, 12a]

$$R(\boldsymbol{b}) = (\hat{\boldsymbol{b}}_1 - \boldsymbol{b})^T\boldsymbol{\Psi}_1^{-1}(\hat{\boldsymbol{b}}_1 - \boldsymbol{b}) + (\hat{\boldsymbol{b}}_2 - \boldsymbol{b})^T\boldsymbol{\Psi}_2^{-1}(\hat{\boldsymbol{b}}_2 - \boldsymbol{b}). \tag{8–3}$$

There are several ways of justifying this particular form of the risk function. Of course, the risk function could be accepted on faith because of its *almost intuitive* form. In Chapter 9 it will be demonstrated that, if $\hat{\boldsymbol{b}}_1$ is stochastically independent of $\hat{\boldsymbol{b}}_2$ and if $\boldsymbol{q}_1$ and $\boldsymbol{q}_2$ are normal vectors, then (8–3) is equivalent to the maximum likelihood estimator. Even if the $\boldsymbol{q}_i$ are not normally distributed, the chosen risk function can be interpreted as a wide sense risk function because it is only a function of the first two moments of the random variable.

Differentiate the risk with respect to the parameter vector, and equate the result to zero to determine the minimizing condition. Thus, one finds

$$\nabla_b^{[j\times 1]} R(\hat{\boldsymbol{b}}^{[j\times 1]}) = \boldsymbol{0} = \boldsymbol{\Psi}_1^{-1}\cdot(\hat{\boldsymbol{b}}_1 - \hat{\boldsymbol{b}}) + \boldsymbol{\Psi}_2^{-1}\cdot(\hat{\boldsymbol{b}}_2 - \hat{\boldsymbol{b}}), \tag{8–4}$$

or

$$\hat{\boldsymbol{b}} = (\boldsymbol{\Psi}_1^{-1} + \boldsymbol{\Psi}_2^{-1})^{-1} \cdot (\boldsymbol{\Psi}_1^{-1}\hat{\boldsymbol{b}}_1 + \boldsymbol{\Psi}_2^{-1}\hat{\boldsymbol{b}}_2). \tag{8–5}$$

Using (8–1), (8–2), and (8–5), the covariance matrix of the combined estimate is

$$\begin{aligned} \boldsymbol{\Psi} &= \mathrm{E}\{(\hat{\boldsymbol{b}} - \boldsymbol{b})(\hat{\boldsymbol{b}} - \boldsymbol{b})^T\} \\ &= \mathrm{E}\{(\boldsymbol{\Psi}_1^{-1} + \boldsymbol{\Psi}_2^{-1})^{-1}[\boldsymbol{\Psi}_1^{-1}(\hat{\boldsymbol{b}}_1 - \boldsymbol{b}) + \boldsymbol{\Psi}_2^{-1}(\hat{\boldsymbol{b}}_2 - \boldsymbol{b})][\boldsymbol{\Psi}_1^{-1}(\hat{\boldsymbol{b}}_1 - \boldsymbol{b}) \\ &\quad + \boldsymbol{\Psi}_2^{-1}(\hat{\boldsymbol{b}}_2 - \boldsymbol{b})]^T(\boldsymbol{\Psi}_1^{-1} + \boldsymbol{\Psi}_2^{-1})^{-1}\} \\ &= (\boldsymbol{\Psi}_1^{-1} + \boldsymbol{\Psi}_2^{-1})^{-1}(\boldsymbol{\Psi}_1^{-1} + \boldsymbol{\Psi}_2^{-1})(\boldsymbol{\Psi}_1^{-1} + \boldsymbol{\Psi}_2^{-1})^{-1} \\ &= (\boldsymbol{\Psi}_1^{-1} + \boldsymbol{\Psi}_2^{-1})^{-1}. \end{aligned} \tag{8–6}$$

Equations (8–5) and (8–6) require three matrix inversions, a process which is time-consuming, can be inaccurate, and can also be a possible source of considerable numerical difficulty. Claus and Blackman [26, 12a] have proposed a manner of recasting these equations into a form which requires only a single matrix inversion.

Using the identity

$$\boldsymbol{\Psi}_1^{-1}\hat{\boldsymbol{b}}_1 = (\boldsymbol{\Psi}_1^{-1} + \boldsymbol{\Psi}_2^{-1})\hat{\boldsymbol{b}}_1 - \boldsymbol{\Psi}_2^{-1}\hat{\boldsymbol{b}}_1, \tag{8–7}$$

equation (8–5) can be written as

$$\hat{\boldsymbol{b}} = \hat{\boldsymbol{b}}_1 - (\boldsymbol{\Psi}_1^{-1} + \boldsymbol{\Psi}_2^{-1})^{-1}\boldsymbol{\Psi}_2^{-1} \cdot (\hat{\boldsymbol{b}}_1 - \hat{\boldsymbol{b}}_2). \tag{8–8}$$

Now note that

$$\begin{aligned} (\boldsymbol{\Psi}_1^{-1} + \boldsymbol{\Psi}_2^{-1})^{-1}\boldsymbol{\Psi}_2^{-1} &= [\boldsymbol{\Psi}_2(\boldsymbol{\Psi}_1^{-1} + \boldsymbol{\Psi}_2^{-1})]^{-1} \\ &= [\mathbf{I} + \boldsymbol{\Psi}_2\boldsymbol{\Psi}_1^{-1}]^{-1} \\ &= [(\boldsymbol{\Psi}_1 + \boldsymbol{\Psi}_2)\boldsymbol{\Psi}_1^{-1}]^{-1} \\ &= \boldsymbol{\Psi}_1(\boldsymbol{\Psi}_1 + \boldsymbol{\Psi}_2)^{-1}. \end{aligned} \tag{8–9}$$

After combining (8–8) and (8–9),

$$\hat{\boldsymbol{b}} = \hat{\boldsymbol{b}}_1 - \boldsymbol{\Psi}_1(\boldsymbol{\Psi}_1 + \boldsymbol{\Psi}_2)^{-1} \cdot (\hat{\boldsymbol{b}}_1 - \hat{\boldsymbol{b}}_2). \tag{8–10}$$

A symmetrical argument enables us to write

$$\hat{\boldsymbol{b}} = \hat{\boldsymbol{b}}_2 + \boldsymbol{\Psi}_2(\boldsymbol{\Psi}_1 + \boldsymbol{\Psi}_2)^{-1} \cdot (\hat{\boldsymbol{b}}_1 - \hat{\boldsymbol{b}}_2). \tag{8–11}$$

Next we introduce two auxiliary matrices $\mathbf{K}_1$ and $\mathbf{K}_2$, which are arbitrary and only restricted such that

$$\mathbf{K}_1^{[j\times j]} + \mathbf{K}_2^{[j\times j]} = \mathbf{I}^{[j\times j]}. \tag{8–12}$$

Multiply (8–10) by $\mathbf{K}_1$, and multiply (8–11) by $\mathbf{K}_2$; add the results to find

$$\hat{\boldsymbol{b}} = \mathbf{K}_1\hat{\boldsymbol{b}}_1 + \mathbf{K}_2\hat{\boldsymbol{b}}_2 - (\mathbf{K}_1\boldsymbol{\Psi}_1 - \mathbf{K}_2\boldsymbol{\Psi}_2)(\boldsymbol{\Psi}_1 + \boldsymbol{\Psi}_2)^{-1}(\hat{\boldsymbol{b}}_1 - \hat{\boldsymbol{b}}_2). \tag{8–13}$$

Let $\mathbf{G}^{[j\times j]}$ be an arbitrary nonsingular matrix, and define two additional auxiliary matrices $\mathbf{P}^{[j\times j]}$ and $\mathbf{Q}^{[j\times j]}$ by means of the relations

$$\Psi_1 = \mathbf{P}\mathbf{G}^{-1}$$
$$\Psi_2 = \mathbf{Q}\mathbf{G}^{-1}. \tag{8–14}$$

It follows that

$$(\Psi_1 + \Psi_2)^{-1} = \mathbf{G}(\mathbf{P} + \mathbf{Q})^{-1},$$
$$\mathbf{K}_1\Psi_1 - \mathbf{K}_2\Psi_2 = (\mathbf{K}_1\mathbf{P} - \mathbf{K}_2\mathbf{Q})\mathbf{G}^{-1}. \tag{8–15}$$

Insert (8–15) and previous definitions into (8–13) and (8–6). After a little manipulation, we can write the results as

$$\hat{\boldsymbol{b}} = \mathbf{K}_1\hat{\boldsymbol{b}}_1 + \mathbf{K}_2\hat{\boldsymbol{b}}_2 - (\mathbf{K}_1\mathbf{P} - \mathbf{K}_2\mathbf{Q})(\mathbf{P} + \mathbf{Q})^{-1}(\hat{\boldsymbol{b}}_1 - \hat{\boldsymbol{b}}_2), \tag{8–16}$$

$$\Psi = \tfrac{1}{2}[\mathbf{K}_1\Psi_1 + \mathbf{K}_2\Psi_2 - (\mathbf{K}_1\mathbf{P} - \mathbf{K}_2\mathbf{Q})(\mathbf{P} + \mathbf{Q})^{-1}(\Psi_1 - \Psi_2)]. \tag{8–17}$$

Equations (8–16) and (8–17) only require one matrix inversion. This is no real difficulty because $\mathbf{G}$ can be selected so that $(\mathbf{P} + \mathbf{Q})$ is well suited for inversion.

An even further simplification can be made for numerical efficiency by defining two additional auxiliary matrices by the relations

$$\mathbf{U} = \mathbf{S}\Psi_1\mathbf{S}$$
$$\mathbf{V} = \mathbf{S}\Psi_2\mathbf{S}, \tag{8–18}$$

where $\mathbf{S}$ is a diagonal matrix in which each diagonal term is the reciprocal of the square root of the corresponding diagonal terms of $\Psi_1$ and $\Psi_2$. That is, as a component relation,

$$S_{ii} = (\Psi_{1_{ii}} + \Psi_{2_{ii}})^{-1/2}. \tag{8–19}$$

The preceding definition leads to the fact that the matrix $(\mathbf{U} + \mathbf{V})$ has unit diagonal elements. By means of (8–18) and if $\mathbf{K}_1$ and $\mathbf{K}_2$ are restricted to being diagonal matrices, (8–16) and (8–17) become

$$\hat{\boldsymbol{b}} = \mathbf{K}_1\hat{\boldsymbol{b}}_1 + \mathbf{K}_2\hat{\boldsymbol{b}}_2 - \mathbf{A}\cdot(\hat{\boldsymbol{b}}_1 - \hat{\boldsymbol{b}}_2), \tag{8–20}$$

$$\Psi = \tfrac{1}{2}[\mathbf{K}_1\Psi_1 + \mathbf{K}_2\Psi_2 - \mathbf{A}\cdot(\Psi_1 - \Psi_2)], \tag{8–21}$$

where

$$\mathbf{A} = \mathbf{S}^{-1}[\mathbf{K}_1\mathbf{U}\mathbf{H} - \mathbf{K}_2\mathbf{V}\mathbf{H}][(\mathbf{U} + \mathbf{V})\mathbf{H}]^{-1}\mathbf{S}. \tag{8–22}$$

It is not necessary to construct the matrix $\mathbf{H}$ explicitly because it only represents a set of rules for combining rows and/or columns of $(\mathbf{U} + \mathbf{V})$ as well as $\mathbf{U}$ and $\mathbf{V}$ individually. The reason for introducing the formalism of the matrix $\mathbf{H}$ is that the sum $(\mathbf{U} + \mathbf{V})$ might be ill-conditioned for inversion.

The development of Blackman and Claus is a fine example of the cross-fertilization of estimation theory and numerical analysis. Although the theoretical problem was solved by the formulations (8–5) and (8–6), the practical computational problem requires further development in order that all predictable numerical difficulties can be prevented by the reformulation of the solution equations. Unfortunately, not all solutions to estimation problems have been carried through with the care exhibited in this instance and with a view to the numerical solutions.

## 8.2
## *SEQUENTIAL ESTIMATION*

A method of sequential estimation will be developed for a fairly general problem of reducing observed data to obtain estimates of system parameters which may not be system observables. Recently, there have been a score of publications which have independently formulated related versions of what we have defined as sequential estimators. The particular development chosen as representative of the general theory is directly motivated by the work of Swerling [41, Chapter 12; 144; 145].

Suppose that the parameters to be estimated are the $p$ components of the system parameter vector $\boldsymbol{b}^{[p\times 1]}$. $\boldsymbol{b}$ is also called the *system state vector*, or simply the state vector. An initial estimate $\hat{\boldsymbol{b}}_0$ for $\boldsymbol{b}$ can be obtained from the solution of a system of equations using a minimal data set for which the number of observables is equal to the number of components of $\boldsymbol{b}$, i.e., $p$. Because we do not restrict $\boldsymbol{b}$ to being a system observable, it is perfectly permissible to have each of the $p$ measurements correspond to different observables. Thus, for instance, if $\boldsymbol{b}$ consists of the six orbital parameters for an artificial earth satellite, the minimal data set can consist of two range measurements, two azimuth angles, and two elevation angles, each obtained at a measured instant of time. In fact, any combination of range and angles, taken six in each collection at known times, will serve equally well as a minimal data set.

We postulate the existence of a prediction function $\boldsymbol{w}(\boldsymbol{b})$ which has the property that, in the absence of numerical errors, it truly predicts an observation $\boldsymbol{W}$. The following theory can be readily generalized for the situation in which $\boldsymbol{w}(\boldsymbol{b})$ is only an approximation to the true mathematical model of the prediction function.

Let $\mathscr{W}_1$ denote an observation on a single observable at time $t = t_1$. Then, if $\boldsymbol{b}$ has $p$ components, the minimal data set is symbolized by the matrix

$$\boldsymbol{W}_0 = \begin{bmatrix} \mathscr{W}_1 \\ \cdots \\ \mathscr{W}_p \end{bmatrix}. \tag{8–23}$$

The initial estimate $\hat{\boldsymbol{b}}_0$ can be computed from the system of equations

$$\boldsymbol{w}_0(\hat{\boldsymbol{b}}_0) = \begin{bmatrix} w_{01}(\hat{\boldsymbol{b}}_0) \\ \cdots\cdots \\ w_{0p}(\hat{\boldsymbol{b}}_0) \end{bmatrix} = \boldsymbol{W}_0, \tag{8–24}$$

where each element of $\boldsymbol{w}_0$ represents a prediction of an observable at time $t = t_j; j = 1, \ldots, p$.

On occasion it is inconvenient to start the estimation procedure with the solution of a minimal data set. Instead, an initial estimate is simply assumed. This alternative will be discussed later.

Before the sequential estimator can be formulated, it is necessary to obtain the covariance matrix of the initial estimate error

$$\boldsymbol{q}_0 = \hat{\boldsymbol{b}}_0 - \boldsymbol{b}. \tag{8–25}$$

If more than a minimal data set is used to initiate the sequential estimator, the optimal estimator is chosen as that which minimizes the weighted-squared-risk function,

$$R(\boldsymbol{b}) = [\boldsymbol{W}_0 - \boldsymbol{w}_0(\boldsymbol{b})]^T \boldsymbol{\Psi}^{-1} [\boldsymbol{W}_0 - \boldsymbol{w}_0(\boldsymbol{b})], \tag{8–26}$$

where the measurement error, corresponding to the minimal data set, is

$$\begin{aligned} \text{Error} &= \text{observation} - \text{prediction} \\ \boldsymbol{a}_0 = \boldsymbol{W}_0 - \boldsymbol{w}_0(\boldsymbol{b}) &= \boldsymbol{w}_0(\hat{\boldsymbol{b}}_0) - \boldsymbol{w}_0(\boldsymbol{b}). \end{aligned} \tag{8–27}$$

The covariance matrix of the measurement error is

$$\boldsymbol{\Psi} = \mathrm{E}\{(\boldsymbol{a} - \mathrm{E}\{\boldsymbol{a}\})(\boldsymbol{a} - \mathrm{E}\{\boldsymbol{a}\})^T\} \tag{8–28}$$

and is assumed to be a known system constant which has been determined from previous measurements. It has been assumed that the inverse $\boldsymbol{\Psi}^{-1}$ exists. If the inverse does not exist, it can be formally replaced in the sequel by the pseudoinverse. In accordance with the usual arguments of no loss in generality, it is convenient to assume that $\mathrm{E}\{\boldsymbol{a}\} = \boldsymbol{0}$. Subscripts are not used in (8–28) because $\boldsymbol{\Psi}$ is, in this illustrative case, assumed to be a constant independent of any particular measurement.

Recalling the arguments and cautions described in Chapter 6, formally expand the prediction function $\boldsymbol{w}_0(\hat{\boldsymbol{b}}_0)$ for the minimal data set, based upon the initial estimate, about the value based upon the true parameter set $\boldsymbol{b}$. Retaining only the constant and linear term of the Taylor series expansion, the result is

$$\boldsymbol{w}_0(\hat{\boldsymbol{b}}_0) = \boldsymbol{w}_0(\boldsymbol{b}) + \mathscr{T}_0(\boldsymbol{b}) \cdot (\hat{\boldsymbol{b}}_0 - \boldsymbol{b}), \tag{8–29}$$

where

$$\mathscr{T}_0^{T[p\times p]}(\boldsymbol{b}) = \boldsymbol{\nabla}_b^{[p\times 1]}\, \boldsymbol{w}_0^{T[1\times p]}(\boldsymbol{b}). \tag{8–30}$$

By means of (8–25), we can write (8–29) as

$$\begin{aligned} \mathscr{T}_0(\boldsymbol{b}) \cdot \boldsymbol{q}_0 &= \boldsymbol{w}_0(\hat{\boldsymbol{b}}_0) - \boldsymbol{w}_0(\boldsymbol{b}) \\ &= \boldsymbol{a}_0. \end{aligned} \tag{8–31}$$

Multiply (8–31) by its transpose, and take the expected value of this product to obtain

$$\text{(8–32)} \qquad \mathrm{E}\{\mathscr{T}_0 \boldsymbol{q}_0 \boldsymbol{q}_0^T \mathscr{T}_0^T\} = \mathrm{E}\{\boldsymbol{a}_0 \boldsymbol{a}_0^T\} = \boldsymbol{\Psi}.$$

Let the covariance matrix of the parameter estimation error $\boldsymbol{q}_0$ be denoted by

$$\text{(8–33)} \qquad \boldsymbol{\Upsilon}_0 = \mathrm{E}\{\boldsymbol{q}_0 \boldsymbol{q}_0^T\}.$$

Then, if it is postulated that the inverses $\mathscr{T}_0^{-1}$ and $\boldsymbol{\Upsilon}_0^{-1}$ exist, (8–32) can be solved for

$$\text{(8–34)} \qquad \boldsymbol{\Upsilon}_0^{-1} = \mathscr{T}_0^T(\hat{\boldsymbol{b}}_0)\boldsymbol{\Psi}^{-1}\mathscr{T}_0(\hat{\boldsymbol{b}}_0).$$

It is convenient, for future consistency in notation, to define

$$\text{(8–35)} \qquad \mathscr{N}_0 = \mathscr{N}(\hat{\boldsymbol{b}}_0) = \boldsymbol{\Upsilon}_0^{-1}.$$

We have now completed the preliminary step of obtaining an initial estimate $\hat{\boldsymbol{b}}_0$ for the system parameters, as well as exhibiting a relationship between the covariance matrix of the initial parameter estimate error and the given, or assumed known, covariance matrix $\boldsymbol{\Psi}$ for the observational-system measurement errors. The desired relationship contains the matrix $\mathscr{T}_0$, consisting of the derivatives of the prediction function $\boldsymbol{w}$ with respect to each of the system parameters which are to be estimated. This matrix of partial derivatives is called the *sensitivity matrix*, a name derived from the observation that the component elements indicate the change in the prediction induced by changes in the parameter values.

At time $t = t_1$, following the initial estimation from the minimal data set, a new observation $\boldsymbol{W}_1$ is completed. Our task is to formulate an *optimal* procedure for combining the new observation with the original estimate in order to yield an *improved* estimate.

Although the individual observables in the observation set $\boldsymbol{W}_j$, $t = t_j$ are permitted to be statistically dependent, we shall restrict ourselves to the situation in which the elements in an observation $\boldsymbol{W}_i$ are stochastically independent of the corresponding elements in the observation $\boldsymbol{W}_j$. The independence hypothesis is not really essential to the theory of sequential estimation and can be removed at the expense of slightly more complicated formulations and procedures [13]. These complications are not warranted in many applications to physical problems using the sequential reduction of experimental observations for estimating system parameters.

Analogous to (8–3), the risk function for combining the new data with the previous estimate is selected to be

$$\text{(8–36)} \qquad \begin{aligned} R(\boldsymbol{b}\,|\,\boldsymbol{q}_0, \boldsymbol{a}_1) &= \boldsymbol{q}_0^T\boldsymbol{\Upsilon}_0^{-1}\boldsymbol{q}_0 + \boldsymbol{a}_1^T\boldsymbol{\Psi}^{-1}\boldsymbol{a}_1 \\ &= (\hat{\boldsymbol{b}}_0 - \boldsymbol{b})^T\boldsymbol{\Upsilon}_0^{-1}(\hat{\boldsymbol{b}}_0 - \boldsymbol{b}) \\ &\quad + [\boldsymbol{W}_1^{[s\times 1]} - \boldsymbol{w}_1(\boldsymbol{b})]^T\boldsymbol{\Psi}^{-1}[\boldsymbol{W}_1^{[s\times 1]} - \boldsymbol{w}_1(\boldsymbol{b})]. \end{aligned}$$

$\boldsymbol{w}_1(\boldsymbol{b})$ is the predicted value of the observation $\boldsymbol{W}_1$ at time $t = t_1$, based upon the value $\boldsymbol{b}$ of the system parameters. Our immediate task will be to determine an estimate $\hat{\boldsymbol{b}}_1$ of $\boldsymbol{b}$ which will minimize the given risk function. It is essential to note that in the general case, once an initial estimate has been obtained, the number of elements, $s$, in the observation set $\boldsymbol{W}_j^{[s\times 1]}$ *need not* be equal to the number of elements, $p$, in the system parameter set $\boldsymbol{b}^{[p\times 1]}$. Thus the theory is in no way restricted to the requirement of consistent, or minimal, data sets at each successive estimation stage. Moreover, if desired, the following formulations can readily be extended and generalized so that the nature of the observations or even the observation instrumentation can be varied at any desired step in the estimation process.

Operate on $R$ by the matrix differential operator $\nabla_b$, and solve for the value of $\hat{\boldsymbol{b}}_1$, which corresponds to a stationary point of the risk function. The result of these operations is

$$\Upsilon_0^{-1}\cdot(\hat{\boldsymbol{b}}_0-\hat{\boldsymbol{b}}_1)+[\nabla_b\,\boldsymbol{w}_1^T(\hat{\boldsymbol{b}}_1)]\Psi^{-1}[\boldsymbol{W}_1-\boldsymbol{w}_1(\hat{\boldsymbol{b}}_1)]=\boldsymbol{0}. \tag{8-37}$$

Expand $\boldsymbol{w}_1(\hat{\boldsymbol{b}}_1)$ about a neighborhood determined by the true value $\boldsymbol{b}$, and retain only the constant and linear term of the Taylor series expansion. When these terms are inserted into (8–37), we find

$$\begin{aligned}\Upsilon_0^{-1}\cdot(\hat{\boldsymbol{b}}_0-\hat{\boldsymbol{b}}_1)&=\mathbf{T}^T(\boldsymbol{b})\Psi^{-1}\mathbf{T}(\boldsymbol{b})\cdot(\hat{\boldsymbol{b}}_1-\boldsymbol{b})\\&\quad-\mathbf{T}^T(\boldsymbol{b})\Psi^{-1}[\boldsymbol{W}_1-\boldsymbol{w}_1(\boldsymbol{b})]\\&=\mathbf{N}\cdot(\hat{\boldsymbol{b}}_1-\boldsymbol{b})-\mathbf{T}^T(\boldsymbol{b})\Psi^{-1}\boldsymbol{a}_1,\end{aligned} \tag{8-38}$$

where, if small order terms are neglected,

$$\begin{aligned}\mathbf{T}^{T[p\times s]}(\boldsymbol{b})&=\nabla_b^{[p\times 1]}\,\boldsymbol{w}^{T[1\times s]}(\boldsymbol{b})\\\mathbf{N}&=\mathbf{T}^T(\boldsymbol{b})\Psi^{-1}\mathbf{T}(\boldsymbol{b})\\\mathbf{T}^T(\hat{\boldsymbol{b}}_1)&\approx\mathbf{T}^T(\boldsymbol{b}).\end{aligned} \tag{8-39}$$

If $\boldsymbol{w}_1(\boldsymbol{b})$ is expanded in a neighborhood of $\hat{\boldsymbol{b}}_0$, we obtain the following approximation for the observation error:

$$\begin{aligned}\boldsymbol{a}_1&=\boldsymbol{W}_1-\boldsymbol{w}_1(\boldsymbol{b})\\&=\boldsymbol{W}_1-\boldsymbol{w}_1(\hat{\boldsymbol{b}}_0)-\mathbf{T}(\hat{\boldsymbol{b}}_0)\cdot(\boldsymbol{b}-\hat{\boldsymbol{b}}_0)\\&\overset{d}{=}\boldsymbol{d}_1-\mathbf{T}(\hat{\boldsymbol{b}}_0)\cdot(\boldsymbol{b}-\hat{\boldsymbol{b}}_0).\end{aligned} \tag{8-40}$$

$\boldsymbol{d}_1$ is called the observation *residual*. Notice that the residual is defined as a function of the *estimated* value of the system parameters $\boldsymbol{b}$, whereas the observation, or measurement, error $\boldsymbol{a}_1$ is defined as a function of the *true* value of $\boldsymbol{b}$.

Therefore, to the adopted degree of approximation, the observation error is

$$\boldsymbol{a}_1=\boldsymbol{d}_1-\mathbf{T}(\hat{\boldsymbol{b}})\cdot(\boldsymbol{b}-\hat{\boldsymbol{b}}_0). \tag{8-41}$$

Combine (8–41) with (8–38) to find

$$\begin{aligned}\Upsilon_0^{-1}\cdot(\hat{\boldsymbol{b}}_0-\hat{\boldsymbol{b}}_1)&=\mathbf{N}\cdot(\hat{\boldsymbol{b}}_1-\boldsymbol{b})-\mathbf{T}^T(\boldsymbol{b})\Psi^{-1}\boldsymbol{d}_1\\&\quad+\mathbf{N}\cdot(\boldsymbol{b}-\hat{\boldsymbol{b}}_0),\end{aligned} \tag{8-42}$$

or

$$\hat{\boldsymbol{b}}_1 = \hat{\boldsymbol{b}}_0 + [\mathbf{N} + \boldsymbol{\Upsilon}_0^{-1}]^{-1}\mathbf{T}^T(\boldsymbol{b})\boldsymbol{\Psi}^{-1}\boldsymbol{d}_1 \tag{8–43}$$
$$\approx \hat{\boldsymbol{b}}_0 + [\mathbf{N}_0 + \boldsymbol{\Upsilon}_0^{-1}]^{-1}\mathbf{T}_0^T(\hat{\boldsymbol{b}}_0)\boldsymbol{\Psi}^{-1}\boldsymbol{d}_1,$$

where

$$\mathbf{N}_0 = \mathbf{T}_0^T(\hat{\boldsymbol{b}}_0)\boldsymbol{\Psi}^{-1}\mathbf{T}_0(\hat{\boldsymbol{b}}_0) \tag{8–44}$$
$$\stackrel{d}{=} \mathbf{T}_0^T\boldsymbol{\Psi}^{-1}\mathbf{T}_0.$$

The second form of (8–43) is a still further approximation resulting from the replacement of $\boldsymbol{b}$, which is unknown to the observer, by the best known estimate $\hat{\boldsymbol{b}}_0$ based upon all previously processed data.

It is tacitly assumed throughout this section that all square matrices are nonsingular and the indicated inverses exist. This restriction can be relaxed, as explained in Chapter 7, by introducing the pseudoinverse in an almost formal fashion.

Anticipating further developments, we introduce the *smoothing*, or *weighting* matrix. For the first stage in the sequential estimator, the weighting matrix is defined to be

$$\mathbf{M}_1(\hat{\boldsymbol{b}}_0) = [\mathbf{N}_0 + \boldsymbol{\Upsilon}_0^{-1}]^{-1}\mathbf{T}_0^T(\hat{\boldsymbol{b}}_0)\boldsymbol{\Psi}^{-1}. \tag{8–45}$$

Hence, at the end of the first stage we can write

$$\hat{\boldsymbol{b}}_1 = \hat{\boldsymbol{b}}_0 + \mathbf{M}_1(\hat{\boldsymbol{b}}_0) \cdot [\boldsymbol{W}_1 - \boldsymbol{w}_1(\hat{\boldsymbol{b}}_0)]. \tag{8–46}$$

Equation (8–46) is the estimation, or data smoothing relation, for the first stage. It indicates an *optimum* manner for modifying the initial estimate $\boldsymbol{b}_0$ by an appropriate weighting of the new set of observables, $\boldsymbol{W}_1$, with the known measurement-system errors $\boldsymbol{\Psi}$, the prediction function $\boldsymbol{w}$, and the sensitivity matrix $\mathbf{T}$.

The procedure used to formulate the estimator for the first stage is now iterated. The method will be briefly sketched for the second stage. At the end of the first stage, the *best* value of the parameter estimate error is

$$\boldsymbol{q}_1 = \hat{\boldsymbol{b}}_1 - \boldsymbol{b}, \tag{8–47}$$

having a covariance matrix

$$\boldsymbol{\Upsilon}_1 = \mathrm{E}\{\boldsymbol{q}_1\boldsymbol{q}_1^T\}. \tag{8–48}$$

Starting with (8–38), an approximate expression can be derived for the covariance matrix $\boldsymbol{\Upsilon}$. Consider the following sequence of manipulations:

$$\boldsymbol{\Upsilon}_0^{-1} \cdot (\hat{\boldsymbol{b}}_0 + \boldsymbol{b} - \boldsymbol{b} - \hat{\boldsymbol{b}}_1) = \mathbf{N}\boldsymbol{q}_1 - \mathbf{T}^T(\boldsymbol{b})\boldsymbol{\Psi}^{-1}\boldsymbol{a}_1$$
$$\boldsymbol{\Upsilon}_0^{-1} \cdot (\boldsymbol{q}_0 - \boldsymbol{q}_1) = \mathbf{N}\boldsymbol{q}_1 - \mathbf{T}^T(\boldsymbol{b})\boldsymbol{\Psi}^{-1}\boldsymbol{a}_1, \tag{8–49}$$
$$\boldsymbol{q}_1 = [\mathbf{N} + \boldsymbol{\Upsilon}_0^{-1}]^{-1} \cdot [\boldsymbol{\Upsilon}_0^{-1}\boldsymbol{q}_0 + \mathbf{T}^T(\boldsymbol{b})\boldsymbol{\Psi}^{-1}\boldsymbol{a}_1].$$

Let

$$\mathbf{Q}(\hat{\boldsymbol{b}}_0, \boldsymbol{b}) = [\mathbf{N} + \boldsymbol{\Upsilon}_0^{-1}]^{-1}. \tag{8–50}$$

Notice that according to their respective definitions, $\boldsymbol{\Psi}$, $\boldsymbol{\Upsilon}_0$, and $\mathbf{Q}$ are all symmetric matrices. Insert (8–49) and (8–50) into (8–48), and evaluate the expected value. The net result is

$$\begin{aligned}\Upsilon_1 &= \mathrm{E}\{\boldsymbol{q}_1\boldsymbol{q}_1^T\}\\ &= \mathbf{Q}\,\Upsilon_0^{-1}\,\mathbf{Q} + \mathbf{Q}\,\mathbf{T}^T(\boldsymbol{b})\boldsymbol{\Psi}^{-1}\mathbf{T}(\boldsymbol{b})\mathbf{Q}\\ &= \mathbf{Q}[\mathbf{N} + \Upsilon_0^{-1}]\mathbf{Q} = \mathbf{Q}\mathbf{Q}^{-1}\mathbf{Q}\\ &= \mathbf{Q}.\end{aligned} \tag{8–51}$$

At the start of the second estimation stage, the best known estimate of the parameters is $\hat{\boldsymbol{b}}_1$. Therefore, we define

$$\begin{aligned}\mathbf{N}_1(\hat{\boldsymbol{b}}_1) &= \mathbf{T}_1^T(\hat{\boldsymbol{b}}_1)\boldsymbol{\Psi}^{-1}\mathbf{T}_1(\hat{\boldsymbol{b}}_1)\\ \mathbf{N}_1 &\overset{d}{=} \mathbf{T}_1^T\boldsymbol{\Psi}^{-1}\mathbf{T}_1.\end{aligned} \tag{8–52}$$

Finally, the required approximation for the second-stage estimate error covariance matrix is found by substituting (8–52) and (8–50) into (8–51). Whence,

$$\Upsilon_1 \approx [\mathbf{N}_1(\hat{\boldsymbol{b}}_1) + \Upsilon_0^{-1}]^{-1} \overset{d}{=} \mathbf{Q}_2 = \mathbf{Q}_2(\hat{\boldsymbol{b}}_0, \boldsymbol{b}_1). \tag{8–53}$$

At the second estimation stage, a new observation $\boldsymbol{W}_2$ is available. The new measurement error is

$$\boldsymbol{a}_2 = \boldsymbol{W}_2 - \boldsymbol{w}_2(\boldsymbol{b}). \tag{8–54}$$

Analogous to (8–36), the risk function is

$$R(\boldsymbol{b}\,|\,\boldsymbol{q}_1, \boldsymbol{a}_2) = \boldsymbol{q}_1^T\Upsilon_1^{-1}\boldsymbol{q}_1 + \boldsymbol{a}_2^T\boldsymbol{\Psi}^{-1}\boldsymbol{a}_2. \tag{8–55}$$

Repeating the same steps used for the first estimation stage, we obtain the following relations, which correspond to (8–46):

$$\begin{aligned}\hat{\boldsymbol{b}}_2 &= \hat{\boldsymbol{b}}_1 + \mathbf{M}_2(\hat{\boldsymbol{b}}_1)\cdot[\boldsymbol{W}_2 - \boldsymbol{w}_2(\hat{\boldsymbol{b}}_1)],\\ \mathbf{M}_2(\hat{\boldsymbol{b}}_1) &= [\mathbf{N}_1 + \Upsilon_0^{-1}]^{-1}\mathbf{T}_1^T(\hat{\boldsymbol{b}}_1)\boldsymbol{\Psi}^{-1}.\end{aligned} \tag{8–56}$$

The process can be iterated at each step with the introduction of a new observation $\boldsymbol{W}_j$. By induction, the estimator at the $j$th step can be written. The fundamental sequential relation and associated definitions are

$$\hat{\boldsymbol{b}}_{i+1} = \hat{\boldsymbol{b}}_i + \mathbf{M}_{i+1}(\hat{\boldsymbol{b}}_i, \hat{\boldsymbol{b}}_{i-1}, \ldots, \hat{\boldsymbol{b}}_0)\cdot[\boldsymbol{W}_{i+1} - \boldsymbol{w}_{i+1}(\hat{\boldsymbol{b}}_i)], \tag{8–57}$$

$$\boldsymbol{d}_i = \boldsymbol{W}_i - \boldsymbol{w}_i(\hat{\boldsymbol{b}}_{i-1}), \tag{8–58}$$

$$\mathbf{N}_{i+1} = \mathbf{T}_{i+1}^T(\hat{\boldsymbol{b}}_{i+1})\boldsymbol{\Psi}^{-1}\mathbf{T}_{i+1}(\hat{\boldsymbol{b}}_{i+1}), \tag{8–59}$$

$$\mathbf{M}_{i+1}(\hat{\boldsymbol{b}}_i, \hat{\boldsymbol{b}}_{i-1}, \ldots, \boldsymbol{b}_0) = [\mathbf{N}_i + \Upsilon_{i-1}^{-1}]^{-1}\mathbf{T}_i^T(\hat{\boldsymbol{b}}_i)\boldsymbol{\Psi}^{-1}, \tag{8–60}$$

$$\boldsymbol{q}_i = \hat{\boldsymbol{b}}_i - \boldsymbol{b}, \tag{8–61}$$

$$\Upsilon_i = \mathrm{E}\{\boldsymbol{q}_i\boldsymbol{q}_i^T\} \approx \mathbf{Q}_{i+1} = [\mathbf{N}_i(\hat{\boldsymbol{b}}_i) + \Upsilon_{i-1}^{-1}]^{-1}. \tag{8–62}$$

These relations do not hold at the first stage for which $i = 0$. The initial stage requires the use of (8–46) with the corresponding definitions of the indicated terms; in particular $\Upsilon_0^{-1}$ is obtained from (8–35).

## 8.3
## *LINEAR SEQUENTIAL ESTIMATION*

If the prediction function can be written in the linear form

$$\boldsymbol{w}^{[s\times 1]}(\boldsymbol{b}^{[p\times 1]}) = \mathbf{A}^{[s\times p]}\boldsymbol{b} + \boldsymbol{B}, \tag{8–63}$$

where $\boldsymbol{B}$ is a constant matrix, then a development analogous to that of Section 8.2 can be written for a linear sequential estimator. A slightly generalized situation is one in which a nonlinear prediction function is replaced by a linear approximation. If $\boldsymbol{w}(\boldsymbol{b})$ is not actually a linear transformation of the form (8–63), expand the prediction function about some estimated *nominal* value $\hat{\boldsymbol{b}}_0$, as indicated in (7–105). We write

$$\boldsymbol{w}(\boldsymbol{b}) = \boldsymbol{B} + \mathrm{T}(\hat{\boldsymbol{b}}_0) \cdot \boldsymbol{b}, \tag{8–64}$$

where

$$\begin{aligned} \boldsymbol{B} &= \boldsymbol{w}(\hat{\boldsymbol{b}}_0) - \mathrm{T}(\hat{\boldsymbol{b}}_0) \cdot \hat{\boldsymbol{b}}_0 \\ \mathrm{T}^T(\hat{\boldsymbol{b}}_0) &= \boldsymbol{\nabla}_b\, \boldsymbol{w}^T(\hat{\boldsymbol{b}}_0). \end{aligned} \tag{8–65}$$

Notice that $\boldsymbol{B}$ depends upon the particular time applicable to the prediction function $\boldsymbol{w}$. $\hat{\boldsymbol{b}}_0$ can be obtained by some judicious guess, or it can be the solution found from a minimal data set.

Either (8–63) or (8–64) could be used as a starting point for formulating a linear sequential estimator. Equation (8–64) is chosen for illustrating the essential points in the method; the analogous formulations starting with (8–63) are easily written by use of an *almost obvious* change in symbols.

After the solution of a minimal data set (using the same definitions of symbols employed in Section 8.2), the observation error is

Observation error = prediction from estimated values − prediction from true values

$$\begin{aligned} \boldsymbol{a}_0 &= \boldsymbol{w}_0(\hat{\boldsymbol{b}}_0) - \boldsymbol{w}_0(\boldsymbol{b}) \\ &= \boldsymbol{B}_0 + \mathscr{T}_0(\hat{\boldsymbol{b}}_0) \cdot \hat{\boldsymbol{b}}_0 - \boldsymbol{B}_0 - \mathscr{T}_0(\hat{\boldsymbol{b}}_0) \cdot \boldsymbol{b} \\ &= \mathscr{T}_0(\hat{\boldsymbol{b}}_0) \cdot \boldsymbol{q}_0. \end{aligned} \tag{8–66}$$

The initial covariance matrix of the estimation error $\boldsymbol{q}_0$ is computed by multiplying (8–66) by its transpose and taking the expected value of the product. We find that

$$\begin{aligned} \mathscr{T}_0 \mathrm{E}\{\boldsymbol{q}_0 \boldsymbol{q}_0^T\} \mathscr{T}_0^T &= \Psi, \\ \mathscr{T}_0 \Upsilon_0 \mathscr{T}_0^T &= \Psi \end{aligned} \tag{8–67}$$

or, postulating the existence of the inverse matrices,

$$\Upsilon_0^{-1} = \mathscr{T}_0^T(\hat{\boldsymbol{b}}_0)\Psi^{-1}\mathscr{T}_0(\hat{\boldsymbol{b}}_0). \tag{8–68}$$

The result is exactly the same as that obtained for the initial matrix for the nonlinear estimate in which the normal equations are replaced by a linear approximation (8–34).

The remainder of the development closely parallels that of the previous section starting from (8–36). Our risk function for the first stage is now

$$(8\text{–}69)\qquad \begin{aligned} R(\boldsymbol{b}\,|\,\boldsymbol{q}_0, \boldsymbol{a}_1) &= \boldsymbol{q}_0^T \Upsilon_0^{-1} \boldsymbol{q}_0 \\ &\quad + [\boldsymbol{W}_1 - \boldsymbol{B}_1 - \mathbf{T}_1(\hat{\boldsymbol{b}}_0) \cdot \boldsymbol{b}]^T \boldsymbol{\Psi}^{-1} [\boldsymbol{W}_1 - \boldsymbol{B}_1 - \mathbf{T}_1(\hat{\boldsymbol{b}}_0) \cdot \boldsymbol{b}]. \end{aligned}$$

Corresponding to (8–43), we obtain by an exactly parallel sequence of operations,

$$(8\text{–}70)\qquad \hat{\boldsymbol{b}}_1 = \hat{\boldsymbol{b}}_0 + [\mathbf{N}_0 + \Upsilon_0^{-1}]^{-1} \mathbf{T}_1^T(\hat{\boldsymbol{b}}_0) \boldsymbol{\Psi}^{-1} [\boldsymbol{W}_1 - \boldsymbol{B}_1 - \mathbf{T}_1(\hat{\boldsymbol{b}}_0) \hat{\boldsymbol{b}}_0],$$

where, as before,

$$(8\text{–}71)\qquad \begin{aligned} \mathbf{N}_0 &= \mathbf{T}_1^T(\hat{\boldsymbol{b}}_0) \boldsymbol{\Psi}^{-1} \mathbf{T}_1(\hat{\boldsymbol{b}}_0), \\ \boldsymbol{T}_1^T(\hat{\boldsymbol{b}}_0) &= \nabla_b \boldsymbol{w}_1^T(\boldsymbol{b}_0). \end{aligned}$$

Equation (8–70) can be written as

$$(8\text{–}72)\qquad \begin{aligned} \Upsilon_0^{-1} \cdot (\boldsymbol{q}_0 - \boldsymbol{q}_1) + \mathbf{T}_1^T \boldsymbol{\Psi}^{-1} \cdot [\boldsymbol{W}_1 - \boldsymbol{B}_1 - \mathbf{T}_1 \hat{\boldsymbol{b}}_1 + \mathbf{T}_1 \boldsymbol{b} - \mathbf{T}_1 \boldsymbol{b}] &= \boldsymbol{0}, \\ [\Upsilon_0^{-1} + \mathbf{N}_0] \boldsymbol{q}_1 = \Upsilon_0^{-1} \boldsymbol{q}_0 + \mathbf{T}_1^T \boldsymbol{\Psi}^{-1} \cdot [\boldsymbol{W}_1 - \boldsymbol{B}_1 - \mathbf{T}_1 \boldsymbol{b}]&, \\ \boldsymbol{q}_1 = [\mathbf{N}_0 + \Upsilon_0^{-1}]^{-1} [\Upsilon_0^{-1} \boldsymbol{q}_0 + \mathbf{T}_1^T \boldsymbol{\Psi}^{-1} \boldsymbol{a}_1]& \\ \overset{d}{=} \mathbf{Q}_1 \Upsilon_0^{-1} \boldsymbol{q}_0 + \mathbf{Q}_1 \mathbf{T}_1^T \boldsymbol{\Psi}^{-1} \boldsymbol{a}_1&. \end{aligned}$$

From (8–72), compute the covariance matrix of the estimate error at the end of the first stage to be

$$(8\text{–}73)\qquad \Upsilon_1 = \mathrm{E}\{\boldsymbol{q}_1 \boldsymbol{q}_1^T\} = \mathbf{Q}_2 = [\mathbf{N}_0 + \Upsilon_0^{-1}]^{-1}.$$

Leaving the details as an exercise (Problem **8.9**), the fundamental relations for the linear sequential estimator are

$$(8\text{–}74)\qquad \hat{\boldsymbol{b}}_{i+1} = \hat{\boldsymbol{b}}_i + \mathcal{M}_{i+1} \cdot [\boldsymbol{W}_{i+1} - \boldsymbol{B}_{i+1} - \mathbf{T}_{i+1}(\hat{\boldsymbol{b}}_i) \hat{\boldsymbol{b}}_i],$$

$$(8\text{–}75)\qquad \boldsymbol{d}_{i+1} = \boldsymbol{W}_{i+1} - \boldsymbol{B}_{i+1} - \mathbf{T}_{i+1}(\hat{\boldsymbol{b}}_i) \hat{\boldsymbol{b}}_i,$$

$$(8\text{–}76)\qquad \mathbf{Q}_{i+1} = [\mathbf{N}_i + \Upsilon_{i-1}^{-1}]^{-1},$$

$$(8\text{–}77)\qquad \mathcal{M}_{i+1} = \mathbf{Q}_{i+1} \mathbf{T}_{i+1}^T(\hat{\boldsymbol{b}}_i) \boldsymbol{\Psi}^{-1},$$

$$(8\text{–}78)\qquad \boldsymbol{q}_i = \hat{\boldsymbol{b}}_i - \boldsymbol{b},$$

$$(8\text{–}79)\qquad \Upsilon_i = \mathrm{E}\{\boldsymbol{q}_i \boldsymbol{q}_i^T\} \approx \mathbf{Q}_{i+1}.$$

These relations are valid at all estimation stages after the initial stage, which requires the special form for the initial covariance matrix given by (8–68).

Claus [12a] recast (8–74) into an interesting form which has attractive features for practical estimation problems. Using previous definitions, (8–74) can be written in the following equivalent form, if in (8–64) the prediction function is expanded in the neighborhood of $\hat{\boldsymbol{b}} = \hat{\boldsymbol{b}}_0$:

$$\hat{\boldsymbol{b}} = \hat{\boldsymbol{b}}_1 + \mathbf{Q}_1\{\mathbf{N}_0 \cdot (\hat{\boldsymbol{b}}_0 - \hat{\boldsymbol{b}}_1) + \mathbf{T}_1^T(\hat{\boldsymbol{b}}_0)\boldsymbol{\Psi}^{-1} \cdot [\boldsymbol{W}_1 - \boldsymbol{B}_1 - \mathbf{T}_1(\hat{\boldsymbol{b}}_0) \cdot \hat{\boldsymbol{b}}_0]\}. \tag{8–80}$$

Thus, at each iteration of the sequential estimator, one can substitute $\hat{\boldsymbol{b}}$ for $\hat{\boldsymbol{b}}_0$ in (8–80) and continue the iteration process for each new data point $\boldsymbol{W}_j$ until $|\hat{\boldsymbol{b}} - \boldsymbol{b}_0|$ is negligible. An analogous form can be written corresponding to (8–57).

## 8.4
## *RECURRENCE RELATIONS FOR SMOOTHING MATRIX*

The usual irksome numerical difficulties are often encountered in the practical applications of either (8–57) or (8–74) because of the necessity of computing two matrix inversions in the formulation of the smoothing matrix at each successive estimation step. It is possible, under favorable circumstances, to avoid these undesirable inversion calculations and obtain a recursion relation for the smoothing matrices [26, 69].

Consider the matrix $\mathbf{Q}_i$ defined in (8–62). Taking the inverse of (8–62) and applying the definition to the result yields

$$\mathbf{Q}_{i+1}^{-1} = \mathbf{Q}_i^{-1} + \mathbf{T}_i^T(\hat{\boldsymbol{b}}_i)\boldsymbol{\Psi}^{-1}\mathbf{T}_i(\hat{\boldsymbol{b}}_i). \tag{8–81}$$

Using the fact that $\boldsymbol{\Psi}$ is a symmetric positive-definite matrix, we can introduce the matrix $\mathbf{A}$ defined as

$$\mathbf{A}_i^T = \mathbf{T}_i^T\boldsymbol{\Psi}^{-1/2}. \tag{8–82}$$

Thus, (8–81) can be written in the canonical form

$$\mathbf{Q}_{i+1}^{-1} = \mathbf{Q}_i^{-1} + \mathbf{A}_i^T\mathbf{A}_i. \tag{8–83}$$

Multiply (8–83) on the left by $\mathbf{Q}_{i+1}$ and then on the right by $\mathbf{Q}_i$. We find that

$$\mathbf{Q}_i = \mathbf{Q}_{i+1} + \mathbf{Q}_{i+1}\mathbf{A}_i^T\mathbf{A}_i\mathbf{Q}_i. \tag{8–84}$$

Equation (8–84) can be solved to obtain

$$\mathbf{Q}_{i+1} = \mathbf{Q}_i - \mathbf{Q}_i\mathbf{A}_i^T[\mathbf{A}_i\mathbf{Q}_i\mathbf{A}_i^T + \mathbf{I}]^{-1}\mathbf{A}_i\mathbf{Q}_i \tag{8–85}$$

or

$$\mathbf{Q}_{i+1}\mathbf{A}_i^T = \mathbf{Q}_i\mathbf{A}_i^T[\mathbf{A}_i\mathbf{Q}_i\mathbf{A}_i^T + \mathbf{I}]^{-1}. \tag{8–86}$$

At this point, we have been able to eliminate one matrix inversion. The second inversion can also be eliminated if we restrict ourselves to introducing data one at a time. That is, instead of using $\boldsymbol{W}_j$ as a vector observation point, each component is considered separately. Thus, $\boldsymbol{W}_j$ is considered to be a single number $\mathscr{W}_j$ with the corresponding measurement covariance matrix $\boldsymbol{\Psi}^{[1\times 1]}$ being the variance associated with the particular component of the observable $\mathscr{W}_j$. Inspection of (8–85) and (8–86) for the single observable shows that the matrix in the bracket is now simply a scalar constant, which is readily inverted as a numerical reciprocal.

If the prediction function is not a function of time, or equivalently if the observations $\boldsymbol{W}$ are made on a system which does not change with time, then further interesting results are possible. In this case $\boldsymbol{w}$ is a constant, and if the sequential process is initiated with a sufficiently good estimate of the system parameters, then we can assume that $\boldsymbol{A}_i = \boldsymbol{A}_0$ is substantially a constant matrix. Starting with (8–76), we find the following forms analogous to (8–85) and (8–86):

$$\mathbf{Q}_{i+1} = \mathbf{Q}_i - \mathbf{Q}_i\mathbf{A}_0^T[\mathbf{A}_0\mathbf{Q}_i\mathbf{A}_0^T + \mathbf{I}]^{-1}\mathbf{A}_0\mathbf{Q}_i, \tag{8–87}$$

and

$$\mathbf{Q}_{i+1}\mathbf{A}_0^T = \mathbf{Q}_i\mathbf{A}_0^T[\mathbf{A}_0\mathbf{Q}_i\mathbf{A}_0^T + \mathbf{I}]^{-1}, \tag{8–88}$$

where

$$\mathbf{A}_0^T = \mathbf{T}_0^T(\hat{\boldsymbol{b}}_0)\boldsymbol{\Psi}^{-1/2}. \tag{8–89}$$

The important difference is that in these formulations $\mathbf{A}_0$ is a constant for each estimation stage instead of changing at each stage. Therefore, (8–88) is truly an approximate recursion relation for the matrix $\mathbf{Q}_j$. Furthermore, if the data is restricted to being a single component at each observation, then (8–87) can be solved for the recurrence formula

$$\mathbf{Q}_{i+1} = \mathbf{Q}_i[\mathbf{A}_0\mathbf{Q}_i\mathbf{A}_0^T + 1]^{-1}; \tag{8–90}$$

in this special case the square bracket is a scalar quantity, not a matrix.

A form corresponding to (8–90) can be obtained in the general case of observations having several components. Combine (8–77) and (8–88) to formulate a recurrence relation for the smoothing relation,

$$\begin{aligned} \mathbf{Q}_{i+1}\mathbf{T}_0^T\boldsymbol{\Psi}^{-1/2} &= \mathbf{Q}_i\mathbf{T}_0^T\boldsymbol{\Psi}^{-1/2}[\boldsymbol{\Psi}^{-1/2}\mathbf{T}_0\mathbf{Q}_i\mathbf{T}_0^T\boldsymbol{\Psi}^{-1/2} + \mathbf{I}]^{-1} \\ \mathcal{M}_{i+1} &= \mathbf{Q}_i\mathbf{T}_0^T\boldsymbol{\Psi}^{-1/2}[\mathbf{T}_0\mathcal{M}_i\boldsymbol{\Psi}^{1/2} + \boldsymbol{\Psi}^{1/2}]^{-1} \\ &= \mathbf{Q}_i\mathbf{T}_0^T\boldsymbol{\Psi}^{-1}[\mathbf{T}_0\mathcal{M}_i + \mathbf{I}]^{-1} \\ &= \mathcal{M}_i[\mathbf{T}_0\mathcal{M}_i + \mathbf{I}]^{-1}. \end{aligned} \tag{8–91}$$

It is frequently a simpler matter to compute $\mathbf{Q}_{i+1}$ from either (8–88) or (8–90) and then compute the smoothing matrix $\mathcal{M}_{i+1}$ as indicated in (8–77).

A similar recursion formula can be used for the nonlinear sequential estimator if $\mathbf{A}_j^T$ is arbitrarily set equal to a constant $\mathbf{T}^T(\hat{\boldsymbol{b}})\boldsymbol{\Psi}^{-1/2}$, where $\hat{\boldsymbol{b}}$ is some a priori estimate of the system parameter set. Fortunately, for many practical applications, the value of $\hat{\boldsymbol{b}}$ in this approximation is not critical, and good results are obtained for any *reasonable* choice of $\hat{\boldsymbol{b}}$. The reason for this latitude can be heuristically demonstrated by the convergence characteristic of the smoothing matrix, particularly when accompanied by an assumed set of initial values which are not obtained from a minimal data set.

The user of a sequential estimator would like some assurance that the process converges and in fact converges to the true values of the parameter set. At least the corrections that are added to the previous estimates should ideally become vanishingly small as the number of iteration steps increases. This diminishing condition does hold and can be seen by repeated applications of the recurrence relation (8–88) to itself [69]. Note that we can write

$$\begin{aligned} \mathbf{Q}_{i+1}\mathbf{A}_0^T &= \mathbf{Q}_i\mathbf{A}_0^T[\mathbf{A}_0\mathbf{Q}_i\mathbf{A}_0^T + \mathbf{I}]^{-1} \\ &= \mathbf{Q}_{i-1}\mathbf{A}_0^T[2\mathbf{A}_0\mathbf{Q}_{i-1}\mathbf{A}_0^T + \mathbf{I}]^{-1} \\ &= \mathbf{Q}_1\mathbf{A}_0^T[(i+1)\mathbf{A}_0\mathbf{Q}_1\mathbf{A}_0^T + \mathbf{I}]^{-1}. \end{aligned} \tag{8–92}$$

Hence, in the limit

$$\lim_{i\to\infty} \mathbf{Q}_{i+1}\mathbf{A}_0^T = \frac{1}{i+1}\mathbf{Q}_1\mathbf{A}_0^T(\mathbf{A}_0\mathbf{Q}_1\mathbf{A}_0^T)^{-1}. \tag{8–93}$$

When (8–93) is combined with (8–74) and (8–77), we find that after a large number of estimation steps, the asymptotic relation is

$$\begin{aligned} \hat{\boldsymbol{b}}_{i+1} &= \hat{\boldsymbol{b}}_i + \frac{1}{i+1}\mathbf{Q}_1\mathbf{A}_0^T(\mathbf{A}_0\mathbf{Q}_1\mathbf{A}_0^T)^{-1}\boldsymbol{\Psi}^{-1/2}(\boldsymbol{W}_{i+1} - \boldsymbol{B}_{i+1} - \mathbf{T}_{i+1}\hat{\boldsymbol{b}}_i) \\ &= \hat{\boldsymbol{b}}_i + \frac{1}{i+1}\mathscr{M}_1(\mathbf{T}_0\mathscr{M}_1)^{-1}(\boldsymbol{W}_{i+1} - \boldsymbol{B}_{i+1} - \mathbf{T}_{i+1}\hat{\boldsymbol{b}}_i). \end{aligned} \tag{8–94}$$

Therefore, the smoothing matrix diminishes as $1/i$, so that vanishingly small corrections are added as the number of iteration steps increases, or the sequential process converges, because $|\hat{\boldsymbol{b}}_{i+1} - \hat{\boldsymbol{b}}_i|$ can be made arbitrarily small as $i$ increases. Since the estimator after a large number of steps is a function of $\mathscr{M}_1$, the confidence that can be placed in the estimated parameters is directly dependent upon the confidence we have in the initial estimate of $\mathscr{M}_1$.

## 8.5
## *INITIAL ESTIMATES*

Instead of obtaining initial estimates of $\hat{\boldsymbol{b}}_0$ and $\boldsymbol{\Upsilon}_0$ from the solution of a minimal data set, it is frequently desirable merely to assume values for these matrices. There are many reasons for not resorting to the minimal data set. One reason is that in some instances a substantial savings in computations can be made if the minimal data set is avoided. It is not uncommon to discover that the minimal data set for a given type of observables leads to a set of nonlinear or transcendental equations whose solutions may be extremely cumbersome. Again, because of prior experience with the experimental conditions, a *fairly good guess* can be made of the system parameters (state variables) as well as the covariance matrix of the errors in this guess.

If initial estimates are made without employing the intermediate steps of solving a minimal data set, the appropriate procedure is to use (8–57), or (8–74), starting with the index $i = 1$. Using this index convention, the initial estimates are called $\boldsymbol{b}_1$ and $\mathbf{Q}_2$. A real problem is encountered in the choice of $\mathbf{Q}_2$. The *intuitive choice* is to form $\mathbf{Q}_2$ as a diagonal matrix with elements that are the covariances arbitrarily assigned to each component of the state vector. This procedure can lead to substantial difficulties. First of all, the assumed $\mathbf{Q}_2$ does not truly represent the initial error covariance matrix because of the arbitrary selection of elements and the deletion of off-diagonal terms. Thus, at each stage, there is no true justification for believing that each $\mathbf{Q}_i$ does in fact represent a covariance matrix of the estimate error. The best that can be said is that $\mathbf{Q}_i$ is a factor of a smoothing matrix $\mathscr{M}_i$. Another, and rather insidious difficulty is illustrated by the convergence of $\mathbf{Q}_i$ given in (8–93). A similar approximate convergence relation also exists for a nonlinear estimator. Equation (8–93) implies that, no matter what our initial estimate of $\mathbf{Q}_2$, $\mathbf{Q}_i$ will converge to any arbitrarily small value as $i$ increases. Thus, not only may $\mathbf{Q}_i$ not represent the parameter error covariance matrix, but (8–94) shows that it is permissible for the weighting matrix to decrease with increasing steps and, in fact, not have the successive estimates converge to the true values.

The fundamental fallacy is that, when one arbitrarily selects $\boldsymbol{b}_1$ and $\mathbf{Q}_2$, he is neglecting the fact that for a good estimator his selection must be consistent with the system measurement errors which are represented by the covariance matrix $\boldsymbol{\Psi}$. To illustrate the intimate relationships between $\hat{\boldsymbol{b}}_1$, $\mathbf{Q}_2$, and $\boldsymbol{\Psi}$, suppose we consider a sequential estimator for which we desire to achieve corrections of a given magnitude to the state vector at the first estimation step. Lapins has investigated this problem for the case in which the observations consist of only a single component.*

It is assumed that $\mathbf{Q}_2$ is a diagonal matrix. Write (8–57) in the simplified form

(8–95) $$\Delta\hat{\boldsymbol{b}}^{[p\times 1]} = \mathbf{Q}^{[p\times p]}\mathbf{T}_0^{T[p\times 1]}\Psi^{-1}\,\Delta W,$$

where

| | |
|---|---|
| $\Delta\hat{\boldsymbol{b}} = \hat{\boldsymbol{b}}_1 - \hat{\boldsymbol{b}}_0,$ | the desired correction to the initial estimated state vector; |
| $\Delta W = W - w(\hat{\boldsymbol{b}}_0),$ | a scalar because each observation is assumed to consist of a single quantity. |

Let

(8–96) $$\boldsymbol{D} = \frac{1}{\Psi^{-1}\,\Delta W}\,\Delta\hat{\boldsymbol{b}} = \mathbf{Q}\mathbf{T}_0^T.$$

*U.E. Lapins, private communication.

Then,

$$(\mathbf{N}_0 + \boldsymbol{\Upsilon}_0^{-1})\boldsymbol{D} = \mathbf{T}_0^T \tag{8–97}$$
$$\mathbf{T}_0^T \Psi^{-1} \mathbf{T}_0 \boldsymbol{D} + \boldsymbol{\Upsilon}_0^{-1} \boldsymbol{D} = \mathbf{T}_0^T,$$

or

$$\boldsymbol{D} = \boldsymbol{\Upsilon}_0 \mathbf{T}_0^T (1 - \Psi^{-1} \mathbf{T}_0 \boldsymbol{D}). \tag{8–98}$$

Because $\mathbf{T}_0\boldsymbol{D}$ is a scalar and $\boldsymbol{\Upsilon}_0$ is postulated to be a diagonal matrix, (8–98) permits us to write the component relation

$$\boldsymbol{\Upsilon}_{ii} = \frac{\Delta b_i}{\left(1 - \dfrac{\mathbf{T}_0\, \Delta \boldsymbol{b}}{\Delta W}\right) \Psi^{-1}\, \Delta W\, \mathrm{T}_i}, \tag{8–99}$$

where the subscripts denote elements of the matrices having the same symbols. Notice that, since for all the corresponding $i$th elements $(1 - \mathbf{T}\Delta \boldsymbol{b}/\Delta W)$ and $\Delta W$ will have the same signs, the sign of each $\Delta b_i$ must be the same or opposite to the sign of the corresponding $T_i$.

Suppose

$$Y = \left(1 - \frac{\mathbf{T}\, \Delta \boldsymbol{b}}{\Delta W}\right) < 0, \tag{8–100}$$

then

(i) if $\Delta W > 0 \Longrightarrow \Delta b_i \sim -T_i \Longrightarrow 1 - Y < 0 \Longrightarrow Y > 0,$

(ii) if $\Delta W < 0 \Longrightarrow \Delta b_i \sim T_i \Longrightarrow 1 - Y < 0 \Longrightarrow Y > 0.$

Hence, (8–100) leads to a contradiction unless $\boldsymbol{\Upsilon}_{ii} < 0$, which is not consistent with the postulate that the diagonal elements are variances and must be positive or zero.

Next, suppose

$$Y > 0, \tag{8–101}$$

then

(i) if $\Delta W > 0 \Longrightarrow \Delta b_i \sim T_i \Longrightarrow 1 - Y > 0,$

(ii) if $\Delta W < 0 \Longrightarrow \Delta b_i \sim -T_i \Longrightarrow 1 - Y > 0.$

It follows that (8–99) is satisfied only when

$$0 < 1 - Y < 1 \tag{8–102}$$

and

$$\Delta W > 0 \Longrightarrow \Delta b_i \sim T_i$$
$$\Delta W < 0 \Longrightarrow \Delta b_i \sim -T_i.$$

With these restrictions, the desired goal of a given correction can be obtained at the first estimation stage. Therefore, it is possible to construct a covariance matrix which will *drive* the estimation process in an a priori determined direction at the first step. The conclusion is that care must be exercised in arbitrarily assuming initial estimates or the sequential estimation may not necessarily lead to values that even tend to converge to the true state vector.

Lapins found that, by judiciously employing (8–99), it is possible to obtain very rapid convergence of a sequential estimator because the first step can easily be made to correct the initial state vector by an amount equivalent to 30 to 50 steps of the *normal* estimator, starting from an initial estimate not using a *matched* covariance matrix.

## 8.6 *EXTENSIONS TO SEQUENTIAL ESTIMATION*

There are several extensions, modifications, and alternative formulations to the sequential estimation described in the preceding sections. Although it is beyond the desired scope of this book to describe these related estimation theories, we shall list some of the modifications which appear to have practical applications for particular estimation problems.

(i) CORRELATED OBSERVATIONS: In Section 8.2, the set of measurements that constituted a single observation was permitted to be statistically dependent, but the individual observations were postulated to be stochastically independent. At the expense of some equation complexity, the observation independence hypothesis can be eliminated and a sequential estimator can be formulated for correlated data sets [13].

(ii) STATIONARITY: Implicit in almost every estimation technique is the tacit assumption that the measurement errors constitute a stationary stochastic process (or discrete series). That is, one hypothesizes that the moments of the multivariate statistical distribution function characterizing the measurement errors are time independent. Strictly speaking, all that is really needed for most applications of estimation theory is that only the first and second statistical moments be time independent. The simpler restriction of second-order stationarity yields the equivalent theory of wide sense estimation that encompasses the majority of the topics in this book.

Occasionally one encounters a physical situation in which the measurement errors, particularly between successive observations, are not and cannot be safely assumed to be stationary or even wide sense stationary. An example of this situation occurs in the tracking of space vehicles by radar systems [41, p. 297]. The noise in a radar system is relatively constant, while the received signals vary as the fourth power of the distance between the radar station and the space vehicle. This relationship for the received-signal power as a function of the separation distance, coupled with the rapid relative motion of the space vehicle with respect to the radar, yields a received signal-to-noise power ratio which changes between successive measurements separated by seconds of time. The range and angle measurement errors produced by the radar are functions of the signal-to-noise power ratio, and, in turn, the covariance matrix $\boldsymbol{\Psi}$ of the measurement errors will not have the same component values for each observation point on the vehicle's trajectory (see Chapter 10).

The sequential estimation process can readily be reformulated so that the measurement error covariance matrix $\boldsymbol{\Psi}$ is permitted to vary with each estimation step. All that one need do is to alter the given formulations by inserting the symbol $\boldsymbol{\Psi}_i$ to denote the proper value of the covariance matrix for the $i$th stage.

The preceding scheme can also be employed if, during the course of an experiment coupled with sequential observation, one has reason to suspect that the conditions of the experiment have changed and, therefore, that $\boldsymbol{\Psi}$ has been altered. These changes might be the result of an equipment malfunction, an improved instrument calibration, etc. The sequential estimator allows the computations to continue after such a change without having to repeat the entire set of measurements and calculations.

(iii) Parameters Are Discrete Functions of Time: It may happen that the system parameters, or state variables, are functions of time. Even in this case, the sequential estimators can be applied provided that the parameters vary slower with time than do the prediction functions [145]. An example of sequential estimation of time-varying parameters is given in Chapter 12.

(iv) Parameters Are Continuous Functions of Time: Chapter 12 is essentially an extension to Chapter 8 and is mainly concerned with state variables which are continuous functions of time. These two chapters are intimately related and are only presented separately to illustrate how the same estimator formulations can be constructed from different points of view.

## 8.7
## *RESIDUAL ANALYSIS: STEPWISE LEAST SQUARES*

Suppose that an experiment has been designed and conducted for the purpose of estimating a parameter set $\boldsymbol{b}^{[p\times1]}$. At the conclusion of the experiments and data reduction, it may be concluded or suspected that one of the assumed system constants is not truly a known constant and should have been included as an element of the estimated parameter set. The amended estimation problem for $\boldsymbol{b}^{[(p+1)\times1]}$ could be handled as a new problem and solved by a new calculation using the original data set. Another and sometimes more inviting approach is to use the result of the original estimation as a first step and then use a second-step estimation to discover the values of the additional elements of the parameter set. It is assumed that the additional elements of $\boldsymbol{b}^{[q\times1]}$; $q > p$ are independent of the original set of elements. Notice that this is not the same situation treated in the sections on sequential estimation. In the previous cases the new values at each estimation step were simply new estimated values of exactly the same parameter-set elements.

For convenience, as well as to furnish variety, the theory of amended estimates is illustrated for linear unweighted least squares estimates [52, 57, 58]. The following development is essentially that of Goldberger [58].

The observations for a linear estimator can be characterized by the relation

$$\begin{aligned}\text{Observations} &= \text{linear estimate of first set of parameters}\\ &\quad + \text{linear estimate of second set of parameters}\\ &\quad + \text{errors}\\ \boldsymbol{y}^{[n\times 1]} &= \mathbf{A}_1^{[n\times p]}\boldsymbol{b}_1^{[p\times 1]} + \mathbf{A}_2^{[n\times q]}\boldsymbol{b}_2^{[q\times 1]} + \boldsymbol{x}^{[n\times 1]}; \qquad n \geq q.\end{aligned} \tag{8–103}$$

The first calculation is to estimate $\boldsymbol{b}_1$ from the observations, ignoring the parameter set $\boldsymbol{b}_2$. The optimum linear estimate is given by (5–36),

$$\hat{\boldsymbol{b}}_1 = (\mathbf{A}_1^T\mathbf{A}_1)^{-1}\mathbf{A}_1^T\boldsymbol{y}. \tag{8–104}$$

Define the estimated residuals for this process as

$$\begin{aligned}\tilde{\boldsymbol{y}} &= \boldsymbol{y} - \mathbf{A}_1\hat{\boldsymbol{b}}_1\\ &= \boldsymbol{y} - \mathbf{A}_1(\mathbf{A}_1^T\mathbf{A}_1)^{-1}\mathbf{A}_1^T\boldsymbol{y}\\ &= [\mathbf{I} - \mathbf{A}_1(\mathbf{A}_1^T\mathbf{A}_1)^{-1}\mathbf{A}_1^T]\boldsymbol{y}.\end{aligned} \tag{8–105}$$

The second step in the joint estimation process is to obtain a least squares estimate for $\boldsymbol{b}_2$ under the assumption that the residuals from the first step constitute the observation set. Corresponding to (8–104), the estimate for $\boldsymbol{b}_2$, consistent with this assumption, is

$$\begin{aligned}\hat{\boldsymbol{b}}_2 &= (\mathbf{A}_2^T\mathbf{A}_2)^{-1}\mathbf{A}_2^T\tilde{\boldsymbol{y}}\\ &= (\mathbf{A}_2^T\mathbf{A}_2)^{-1}\mathbf{A}_2^T[\mathbf{I} - \mathbf{A}_1(\mathbf{A}_1^T\mathbf{A}_1)^{-1}\mathbf{A}_1^T]\boldsymbol{y}.\end{aligned} \tag{8–106}$$

We shall now show how the results of the described two-stage estimation differ from those obtained by a single least squares estimate for the relation given by (8–103). Starting with (8–103), the least squares estimate can be written in a partitioned form corresponding to (5–36). Write (8–103) in the form

$$\begin{aligned}\boldsymbol{y} &= [\mathbf{A}_1 \;\; \mathbf{A}_2]\begin{bmatrix}\boldsymbol{b}_1\\ \boldsymbol{b}_2\end{bmatrix} + \boldsymbol{x}\\ &\overset{d}{=} \mathbf{A}\boldsymbol{b} + \boldsymbol{x}.\end{aligned}$$

Then,

$$\begin{aligned}\boldsymbol{b} &= (\mathbf{A}^T\mathbf{A})^{-1}\mathbf{A}^T\boldsymbol{y}\\ \begin{bmatrix}\bar{\boldsymbol{b}}_1\\ \bar{\boldsymbol{b}}_2\end{bmatrix} &= \begin{bmatrix}\mathbf{A}_1^T\mathbf{A}_1 & \mathbf{A}_1^T\mathbf{A}_2\\ \mathbf{A}_2^T\mathbf{A}_1 & \mathbf{A}_2^T\mathbf{A}_2\end{bmatrix}^{-1}\begin{bmatrix}\mathbf{A}_1^T\boldsymbol{y}\\ \mathbf{A}_2^T\boldsymbol{y}\end{bmatrix},\end{aligned} \tag{8–107}$$

where $\bar{\boldsymbol{b}}_i$ denotes a least squares estimate resulting from a simultaneous estimate of all the system parameters.

Let **C**, **E**, and **F** be square matrices having inverses. One can verify the following identity by straightforward definition of an inverse; i.e., we solve $\mathbf{x}\mathbf{x}^{-1} = \mathbf{I}$ for $\mathbf{x}^{-1}$ by identifying components. The result is

$$\begin{bmatrix} \mathbf{C} & \mathbf{D} \\ \mathbf{D}^T & \mathbf{E} \end{bmatrix}^{-1} = \begin{bmatrix} \mathbf{C}^{-1}(\mathbf{I} + \mathbf{D}\mathbf{F}^{-1}\mathbf{D}^T\mathbf{C}^{-1}) & -\mathbf{C}^{-1}\mathbf{D}\mathbf{F}^{-1} \\ -\mathbf{F}^{-1}\mathbf{D}^T\mathbf{C}^{-1} & \mathbf{F}^{-1} \end{bmatrix}, \tag{8–108}$$
$$\mathbf{F} = \mathbf{E} - \mathbf{D}^T\mathbf{C}^{-1}\mathbf{D}.$$

Apply (8–108) to the first matrix on the right-hand side of (8–107) and multiply the two matrices on this side to find

$$\begin{bmatrix} \bar{\boldsymbol{b}}_1 \\ \bar{\boldsymbol{b}}_2 \end{bmatrix} = \tag{8–109}$$
$$\begin{bmatrix} (\mathbf{A}_1^T\,\mathbf{A}_1)^{-1}\mathbf{A}_1^T\,\boldsymbol{y} - (\mathbf{A}_1^T\,\mathbf{A}_1)^{-1}\mathbf{A}_1^T\,\mathbf{A}_2\,\mathbf{G}^{-1}\mathbf{A}_2^T[\mathbf{I} - \mathbf{A}_1(\mathbf{A}_1^T\,\mathbf{A}_1)^{-1}\mathbf{A}_1^T]\boldsymbol{y} \\ \mathbf{G}^{-1}\mathbf{A}_2^T[\mathbf{I} - \mathbf{A}_1(\mathbf{A}_1^T\,\mathbf{A}_1)^{-1}\mathbf{A}_1^T]\boldsymbol{y} \end{bmatrix},$$

where

$$\mathbf{G} = \mathbf{A}_2^T\mathbf{A}_2 - \mathbf{A}_2^T\mathbf{A}_1(\mathbf{A}_1^T\mathbf{A}_1)^{-1}\mathbf{A}_1^T\mathbf{A}_2. \tag{8–110}$$

Equation (8–106) can be written as

$$\hat{\boldsymbol{b}}_2 = (\mathbf{A}_2^T\mathbf{A}_2)^{-1}\mathbf{G}\mathbf{G}^{-1}\mathbf{A}_2^T[\mathbf{I} - \mathbf{A}_1(\mathbf{A}_1^T\mathbf{A}_1)^{-1}\mathbf{A}_1^T]\boldsymbol{y}. \tag{8–111}$$

Notice that, from the partitioning of (8–109),

$$\bar{\boldsymbol{b}}_2 = \mathbf{G}^{-1}\mathbf{A}_2^T[\mathbf{I} - \mathbf{A}_1(\mathbf{A}_1^T\mathbf{A}_1)^{-1}\mathbf{A}_1^T]\boldsymbol{y}. \tag{8–112}$$

Combine (8–111), (8–112), and (8–110) to obtain

$$\begin{aligned} \hat{\boldsymbol{b}}_2 &= (\mathbf{A}_2^T\mathbf{A}_2)^{-1}\mathbf{G}\bar{\boldsymbol{b}}_2 \\ &= [\mathbf{I} - (\mathbf{A}_2^T\mathbf{A}_2)^{-1}\mathbf{A}_2^T\mathbf{A}_1(\mathbf{A}_1^T\mathbf{A}_1)^{-1}\mathbf{A}_1^T\mathbf{A}_2]\bar{\boldsymbol{b}}_2. \end{aligned} \tag{8–113}$$

An important observation is that the stepwise estimator, based upon using the residuals, produces a biased estimate because, in general, $\mathrm{E}\{\hat{\boldsymbol{b}}_2\} \neq \mathrm{E}\{\bar{\boldsymbol{b}}_2\}$. For the special case in which $\mathbf{A}_2^T\mathbf{A}_1 = \mathbf{0}$, the estimate is unbiased. It is also unbiased if $\mathrm{E}\{\bar{\boldsymbol{b}}_2\} = \boldsymbol{0}$.

Finally, consider the estimate $\bar{\boldsymbol{b}}_1$ given in the partitioning of (8–109), and insert $\bar{\boldsymbol{b}}_2$ from (8–109) into the expression for $\bar{\boldsymbol{b}}_1$. The net yield is

$$\bar{\boldsymbol{b}}_1 = (\mathbf{A}_1^T\mathbf{A}_1)^{-1}\mathbf{A}_1^T\boldsymbol{y} - (\mathbf{A}_1^T\mathbf{A}_1)^{-1}\mathbf{A}_1^T\mathbf{A}_2\bar{\boldsymbol{b}}_2. \tag{8–114}$$

Insert (8–104) into (8–114), and solve for

$$\hat{\boldsymbol{b}}_1 = \bar{\boldsymbol{b}}_1 + (\mathbf{A}_1^T\mathbf{A}_1)^{-1}\mathbf{A}_1^T\mathbf{A}_2\bar{\boldsymbol{b}}_2. \tag{8–115}$$

Equation (8–115) provides the specification error aspect of the particular case of an amended stepwise least squares estimator. Goldberger noted that (8–115) indicates that the stepwise estimator gives $\mathbf{A}_1$ credit not only for its own influence upon $\boldsymbol{y}$, but also for the influence of $\mathbf{A}_2$ upon $\boldsymbol{y}$, to the extent that $\mathbf{A}_1$ and $\mathbf{A}_2$ are correlated.

## PROBLEMS

**8.1** Verify (8–85), (8–86), and (8–91).

**8.2** For the nonlinear sequential estimator, Section 8.2, show that

$$\lim_{j\to\infty} \mathbf{Q}_j = \mathbf{0}.$$

**8.3** Suppose that the observation $\boldsymbol{W}_j^{[p\times 1]}$ is of higher dimension than the parameter set $\boldsymbol{b}^{[q\times 1]}$; $p > q$. Derive the sequential estimator corresponding to (8–74) for this case. Include the initial estimate equations based upon a minimal data set. Is there any simplification in the initial estimate if more than a minimal data set is used?

**8.4** Derive the formula corresponding to (8–90) and (8–91) for the nonlinear sequential estimator of Section 8.2. What is the error introduced if $\mathbf{A}_i$ is replaced by a constant matrix so that the smoothing matrix $\mathbf{M}_i$ is obtained from $\mathbf{M}_{i-1}$ by a recursion relation?

**8.5** Let a vehicle move along a rectilinear path with a constant known acceleration. The generic equation of motion is

$$x(t) = x_0 + vt + \tfrac{1}{2}at^2.$$

At discrete constant intervals of time, $t = t_i$; $i = 1, 2, 3, \ldots$ the position and velocity of the vehicle are observed. Write out the sequential estimator using a recursion relation, if applicable. The measurement covariance matrix [12a] is

$$\boldsymbol{\Psi} = \begin{bmatrix} \sigma_x^2 & 0 \\ 0 & \sigma_v^2 \end{bmatrix}.$$

**8.6** Suppose that in problem 8.5 a set of observations have been made from which $x_0$ and $v_0$ have been estimated. It is now suspected that the acceleration $a$ is not a constant and should have been also estimated from the data. Derive the appropriate two-step estimator for this case, and determine the bias in the estimates.

**8.7** How should the estimator relations in (8–74) be modified if the parameters are functions of the time or of the smoothing step?

**8.8** Suppose that the prediction function $\boldsymbol{w}(\boldsymbol{b})$ is imperfectly known. That is,

$$\boldsymbol{w}(\boldsymbol{b}) = \text{assumed function} + \text{error}$$
$$= \boldsymbol{g}(\boldsymbol{b}) + \boldsymbol{\eta}.$$

Derive the estimator corresponding to (8–57), and determine what knowledge of $\boldsymbol{\eta}$ must be known so that an estimate can be made of the covariance matrix of the parameter-set estimate.

**8.9** Derive the relations given in (8–74).

# Chapter 9

# MOMENT AND MAXIMUM LIKELIHOOD ESTIMATORS

## 9.1
### *MOMENT ESTIMATORS*

In this section we shall be concerned with the technique of forming estimates of the distribution parameters of a sequence of random variables by means of information based on a set of sample values. The first extensive theory of this type is generally credited to Pearson [115, 116] and is called the *method of moments*. The method of moments has been almost completely neglected in recent years because of the current popularity and seemingly universal appeal of maximum likelihood estimation. However, the method of moments is still an expedient procedure and can frequently be employed in situations wherein other estimators bog down in mathematical manipulative difficulties.

The method of moments is extremely simple in concept and almost self-intuitive. Suppose, for example, that the probability density of a random variable $x$ is a function of $h$ parameters: $\theta_1, \ldots, \theta_h$. Given a set of sample values of $x$, the task is to estimate the best values of the parameters $\theta_i$. Based upon the $n$ sample values of $x$, we can compute the $j$th sample moments.

$$m_j(\theta_1, \ldots, \theta_h) = \frac{1}{n} \sum_{k=1}^{n} x_k^j. \tag{9–1}$$

We have ignored possible biases in formulating (9–1). This is a point that is expanded in Section 9.2.

Assuming that we know the probability density function $f(x; \theta_1, \ldots, \theta_h)$, the theoretical, or population, moments are

$$\mu_j(\theta_1, \ldots, \theta_h) = \int x^j f(x; \theta_1, \ldots, \theta_h)\, dx. \tag{9–2}$$

Therefore, by computing as many moments $m_j$ and $\mu_j$ as there are unknown parameters $\theta_i$, $j = h$, (9–1) and (9–2) can be used to solve for $\theta_1, \ldots, \theta_h$ from the measured values of the given population samples.

The particularly attractive feature of the method of moments is that there is seldom any difficulty in computing the moments defined in (9–1) and (9–2). Moreover, even if the estimation problem is complicated in the sense that, instead of $x$, some nonlinear function such as $V(x)$ is observed, it is still frequently *fairly easy* to compute the moments $\mathrm{E}\{V^j(x)\}$, [40]. A novice's rule of thumb in chess is: *When in doubt, push a pawn.* By the same token, a rule of thumb for dealing with nonlinear transformations of random variables might well be: *When in doubt, compute the sample moments.* Paraphrased, this advice is to resort to the method of moments when the nonlinearity of the relations between the observables and the system parameters are such that other methods of estimation appear to be hopeless because of manipulative problems.

## 9.2
## *SAMPLE MOMENTS*

Suppose that we select at *random* a set of samples from a given population. The population can be quite universal and might consist of a collection of objects, the results of operations or measurements, etc. Customary usage, dictated by convenience, is to let $x_1$ denote the random variable selected by the first drawing from the population, $x_2$ denote the second selection, etc. The *theory of statistical sampling* is concerned with the distribution of functions of the $n$ random variates which comprise the population sample. Sample theory is a major topic in statistics because of its dominant role in both the theoretical development and practical application of statistical methods. There exists an extensive literature on the subject of sampling, and only a few explicit results needed for our limited purposes will be developed. Further information on sampling theory can be found in almost every comprehensive book on introductory statistics [for example, 31, 103, 154].

We shall confine ourselves to the limited objective of estimating population parameters from sampling moments because of the immediate connection of this topic with the method of moments. In Section 9.8, sample moments will also be related to the maximum likelihood estimator.

The statistical sample moments $a_\nu$, of order $\nu$, corresponding to a sample $x_1, \ldots, x_n$ drawn from a single given population, are defined by the relation

$$a_\nu = \frac{1}{n} \sum_{i=1}^{n} x_i^\nu; \qquad i = 1, 2, \ldots . \tag{9-3}$$

Corresponding to $a_\nu$ are the central moments $m_\nu$ having the definition

$$m_\nu = \frac{1}{n} \sum_{i=1}^{n} (x_i - \bar{x})^\nu, \tag{9-4}$$

where

$$\bar{x} = a_1 = \frac{1}{n} \sum_{i=1}^{n} x_i. \tag{9-5}$$

Equation (9–5) defines the *sample mean*. By analogy with (9–5), we define the *sample variance* to be

$$s^2 = \frac{1}{n} \sum_{i=1}^{n} (x_i - \bar{x})^2. \tag{9-6}$$

The sample variance defined by (9–6) will be a biased estimator of the population variance. This bias soon will be exhibited, as well as the necessary correction to obtain an unbiased estimate.

It is perhaps important to remark that, unlike theoretical statistical moments, which are computed from a given probability density function and are, therefore, known functions of the distribution parameters, sample moments will themselves be random variables and are associated with probability distributions. In many of the sampling problems encountered in the application of statistical methods, we are usually interested in relatively simple statistics such as averages, sums of squares, ratios, and covariances. Explicit formulations can be found for the distribution functions of these sample statistics only for rather special types of parent population distributions. On the other hand, it is fortunate for our objectives that we can formulate relations for the means, variances, and some of the lower moments of these statistics for many general forms of the parent population distributions.

As a first example, consider the moments of the distribution of the sample moments $\bar{x}$, which were defined by (9–5). Define the first sample moment to be

$$\mu(\bar{x}) = \mathrm{E}\{\bar{x}\} = \frac{1}{n} \sum_{i=1}^{n} \mathrm{E}\{x_i\}. \tag{9-7}$$

Suppose that each of the $x_i$ are independent samples drawn from populations having the same distribution function. This being so, (9–7) becomes

$$\mu(\bar{x}) = \frac{1}{n} \sum_{i=1}^{n} \mathrm{E}\{x_i\} = \frac{1}{n} \cdot n\mu = \mu, \tag{9-8}$$

where $\mu = \mathrm{E}\{x_i\}$ is the true population moment. In other words, (9–8) asserts that the sample moment $\bar{x}$ is an *unbiased* estimate of the true population moment $\mu$.

Next we consider the variance of the estimate $\bar{x}$. By definition, this variance is

$$\sigma^2(\bar{x}) = \mathrm{E}\{[\bar{x} - \mu(\bar{x})]^2\}, \tag{9–9}$$

where

$$\bar{x} - \mu(\bar{x}) = \frac{1}{n}\sum_{i=1}^{n}(x_i - \mu). \tag{9–10}$$

Combine (9–9) and (9–10) to find

$$\begin{aligned} \sigma^2(\bar{x}) &= \mathrm{E}\left\{\left[\frac{1}{n}\sum_{i=1}^{n}(x_i - \mu)\right]^2\right\} \\ &= \frac{1}{n^2}\sum_{i=1}^{n}\mathrm{E}\{(x_i - \mu)^2\} + \frac{1}{n^2}\sum_{\substack{i \neq j \\ i=1}}^{n}\mathrm{E}\{(x_i - \mu)(x_j - \mu)\}. \end{aligned} \tag{9–11}$$

It follows, because the $x_1, \ldots, x_n$ were postulated to be independent samples from the same distributions, that

$$\begin{aligned} \mathrm{E}\{(x_i - \mu)^2\} &= \sigma^2; \qquad i = 1, \ldots, n \\ \mathrm{E}\{(x_i - \mu)(x_j - \mu)\} &= 0; \qquad i \neq j. \end{aligned} \tag{9–12}$$

Whence (9–11) collapses to

$$\sigma^2(\bar{x}) = \frac{\sigma^2}{n}, \tag{9–13}$$

where $\sigma^2$ is the parent population variance. Continuing in the same manner for the higher moments of the sample variate $\bar{x}$, one finds [31]

$$\begin{aligned} \mu_3(\bar{x}) &= \mathrm{E}\{[\bar{x} - \mu(\bar{x})]^3\} = \frac{\mu^3}{n^2} \\ \mu_4(\bar{x}) &= \mathrm{E}\{[\bar{x} - \mu(\bar{x})]^4\} = \frac{\mu^4}{n^3} + \frac{3(n-1)}{n^3}\mu_2^2 \\ &\cdots\cdots \\ \mu_{2k-1}(\bar{x}) &= \mathrm{E}\{[\bar{x} - \mu(x)]^{2k-1}\} = O\left(\frac{1}{n^k}\right) \\ \mu_{2k}(\bar{x}) &= \mathrm{E}\{[\bar{x} - \mu(\bar{x})]^{2k}\} = O\left(\frac{1}{n^k}\right). \end{aligned} \tag{9–14}$$

Exactly similar analyses can be made for the moments of the sample variance. For example, write (9–6) in the equivalent forms

$$\begin{aligned} s^2 &= \frac{1}{n}\sum_{i=1}^{n}(x_i - \bar{x})^2 \\ &= \frac{1}{n}\sum_{i=1}^{n}[(x_i - \mu) - (\bar{x} - \mu)]^2 \end{aligned}$$

$$= \frac{1}{n} \sum_{i=1}^{n} \left[ (x_i - \mu) - \frac{1}{n} \sum_{j=1}^{n} (x_j - \mu) \right]^2$$

(9–15)

$$= \frac{1}{n} \sum_{i=1}^{n} \left\{ (x_i - \mu)^2 - \frac{2(x_i - \mu)}{n} \sum_{j=1}^{n} (x_j - \mu) + \frac{1}{n^2} \sum_{j=1}^{n} \sum_{k=1}^{n} (x_j - \mu)(x_k - \mu) \right\}$$

$$= \frac{1}{n} \sum_{i=1}^{n} (x_i - \mu)^2 - \frac{2}{n^2} \sum_{i=1}^{n} (x_i - \mu) \sum_{j=1}^{n} (x_j - \mu) + \frac{1}{n^2} \sum_{j,k=1}^{n} (x_j - \mu)(x_k - \mu).$$

Therefore, if the expected value of (9–15) is performed, the desired result is

(9–16) $$\mathrm{E}\{s^2\} = \sigma^2 - \frac{\sigma^2}{n} = \frac{n-1}{n} \sigma^2.$$

The interesting and often overlooked fact is that (9–16) implies that (9–6) is a biased estimate of the population variance. If, instead of (9–6), we define the sample variance to be

(9–17) $$s'^2 = \frac{1}{n-1} \sum_{i=1}^{n} (x_i - \bar{x})^2,$$

then a repetition of the steps indicated by (9–15) and (9–16) will yield the relation

(9–18) $$\mathrm{E}\{s'^2\} = \sigma^2,$$

or $s'^2$ is an unbiased estimate of the population variance $\sigma^2$.

Analogous arguments can be employed to show that unbiased estimates for the central moments $m'_\nu$ corresponding to $m_\nu$, defined in (9–4), require the following correction factors [31]:

(9–19)
$$m'_2 = \frac{n}{n-1} m_2$$
$$m'_3 = \frac{n^2}{(n-1)(n-2)} m_3$$
$$m'_4 = \frac{n(n^2 - 2n + 3)}{(n-1)(n-2)(n-3)} m_4 - \frac{3n(2n-3)}{(n-1)(n-2)(n-3)} m_2^2.$$

Sampling theory has been formulated to include the distribution functions of the various sampling moments and moments of functions of the samples for particular classes of parent population distribution functions. An interesting result of these extended studies is that, if a set of samples $x_1, \ldots, x_n$ is drawn from a distribution having mean $\mu$ and variance $\sigma^2$, then $\bar{x}$ will be the minimum variance linear estimator for $\mu$. Further, under certain mild restrictions, it can be shown that the sample variance $s^2$ is the minimum variance quadratic estimator for the variance $\sigma^2$ of the parent population distribution [154].

## 9.3
## *MAXIMUM LIKELIHOOD ESTIMATOR*

Let $x_1, \ldots, x_n$ be a set of $n$ independent random samples drawn from a given population. The population is characterized by a probability density function $f_n(\boldsymbol{x}; \theta) = f_n(x_1, \ldots, x_n; \theta)$. $\theta$ is a parameter of the population distribution. The likelihood function $L$ is defined in this case by the relation

$$\begin{aligned} L(x_1, \ldots, x_n; \theta) &= f_n(x_1, \ldots, x_n; \theta) \\ &= f(x_1; \theta) f(x_2; \theta) \ldots f(x_n; \theta) \\ &= \prod_{i=1}^{n} f(x_i; \theta). \end{aligned} \tag{9–20}$$

If the population consists of discrete elements, the likelihood function corresponding to (9–20) is

$$L(x_1, \ldots, x_n; \theta) = \prod_{i=1}^{n} p_i(\theta), \tag{9–21}$$

where $p_i(\theta)$ is the probability associated with the $i$th sample.

In other words, when the sample values are given as well as the functional form of the population probability density function (or discrete probabilities if the population has discrete elements), the likelihood function can be regarded as a function of the distribution parameter $\theta$. A similar relation holds in which the density functions are replaced by the probability distribution functions. The method of maximum likelihood is one of selecting an estimate $\hat{\theta}$ for $\theta$ which will maximize the likelihood function $L$. Since $\ln L$ is a monotonic function and attains its maximum when $L$ is a maximum, (9–20) or (9–21) are usually solved for the estimate $\hat{\theta}$ by considering the simpler expression

$$\frac{\partial}{\partial \theta} \ln L = 0 = \frac{\partial}{\partial \theta} \sum_{i=1}^{n} \ln f(x_i; \theta), \tag{9–22}$$

rather than the usually more cumbersome form of

$$\frac{\partial}{\partial \theta} L = 0 = \frac{\partial}{\partial \theta} \prod_{i=1}^{n} f(x_i; \theta). \tag{9–23}$$

Any solution $\hat{\theta}$ for $\theta$ which satisfies (9–22) and is not identically a constant is called an MLE (*M*aximum *L*ikelihood *E*stimate) of $\theta$. Equation (9–22) is called the *likelihood equation*.

The principle of the likelihood function as well as the solution method using logarithmic derivatives were known and used by Gauss in his original development of the theory of least squares estimation [see Chapter 4]. Regardless of this early publication, the method was not formulated or used as a general estimation technique until a generalized and rigorized form was introduced by R. A. Fisher in 1912 [46]. Fisher did more than reintroduce the simple concept given almost in passing in Gauss's work. Fisher published a series of papers which extended these concepts to a comprehensive and unified system of mathematical statistics as well as to a philosophy of statistical inference which has had profound and wide development.

It is certainly interesting to conjecture on the reasons that Gauss may have had for basing his publication of the theory of least squares upon what we now call maximum likelihood estimation and then not adopting maximum likelihood estimators as the basic concept rather than choosing his derived principle of least squares. Berkson (1956) made some pertinent comments on this point, which, although they are certainly arguable, do at least illustrate the fact that not all contemporary theoretical statisticians have the same universal feelings concerning maximum likelihood estimation [10].

> F. Y. Edgeworth [45] in an article published in 1908 presented in translation excerpts from a letter of Gauss to Bessel, in which Gauss specifically repudiated the principle of maximum likelihood in favor of minimizing some function of the difference between estimate and observation, the square, the cube or perhaps some other power of the difference. Edgeworth scolded Gauss for considering the cube or any power other than the square, and advocated the square on the basis of considerations that he advanced himself as well as on the basis of Gauss's own developments in the theory of least squares. Fisher's revival of maximum likelihood in 1922 is thus seen to be historically a retrogression. Whether scientifically it was also a retrogression or an advance awaits future developments of statistical theory for an answer, for I do not think the question is settled by what is now known.

The theoretical problems inherent in maximum likelihood estimators are primarily those concerning the variance properties of the estimates, particularly for small sample sizes. For large sample size, the theory has been fairly well developed, and a host of theories exist for asymptotic characteristics of the estimates as well as for the variances of the estimates. In spite of some drawbacks, particularly those involving small sample size, the method of maximum likelihood is inviting as an almost universal, practical technique for formulating estimator equations. The method has been widely adopted and, as we shall see, complements the least squares estimators which it encompasses for a special situation.

The reason that maximum likelihood estimates lack reasonable small-sample-size properties and do have reasonable large-sample-size properties is that the estimator is based upon trying to find the mode of a distribution by attempting to select the true value of a parameter. Estimators, in general, are designed to approach the true value rather than hitting it exactly right. Thus, one would expect that other statistics such as the mean or median of the a posteriori distribution should be better choices. The fact that the mode, mean, and median values can vary significantly for small sample sizes leads to the undesirable characteristics of MLE for these cases. On the other hand, for large samples, the a posteriori distribution tends to become more or less independent of the a priori distribution, and the mode, mean, and median statistics approach each other. Thus, it is not surprising that MLE has satisfactory asymptotic characteristics for large samples.

## 9.4
## *MLE OF NORMAL VARIATES*

In concert with many statistical developments, the almost obvious first special case to consider would be the MLE for samples drawn from a parent population known to have a normal distribution. Let $\boldsymbol{W}$ represent the observations, and let $\boldsymbol{w}(\boldsymbol{b})$ represent the predicted observation based upon knowledge of the system parameters $\boldsymbol{b}^{[p\times 1]}$. By definition, the observation, or measurement, errors are

$$\boldsymbol{a}^{[n\times 1]} = \boldsymbol{W} - \boldsymbol{w}(\boldsymbol{b}). \tag{9–24}$$

Because the observation errors are postulated to be normally distributed, the likelihood function, which is considered to be a function of the parameter $\boldsymbol{b}$, is

$$L(\boldsymbol{b}) = (2\pi)^{-n/2}|\boldsymbol{\Psi}|^{-1/2}\exp\{-\tfrac{1}{2}[\boldsymbol{W} - \boldsymbol{w}(\boldsymbol{b})]^T\boldsymbol{\Psi}^{-1}[\boldsymbol{W} - \boldsymbol{w}(\boldsymbol{b})]\}. \tag{9–25}$$

The logarithm of this likelihood function is

$$\begin{aligned}\ln L(\boldsymbol{b}) = &-\tfrac{1}{2}[\boldsymbol{W} - \boldsymbol{w}(\boldsymbol{b})]^T\boldsymbol{\Psi}^{-1}[\boldsymbol{W} - \boldsymbol{w}(\boldsymbol{b})]\\ &-\frac{n}{2}\ln 2\pi - \frac{1}{2}\ln|\boldsymbol{\Psi}|.\end{aligned} \tag{9–26}$$

Notice that, because the last two terms are independent of the parameter $\boldsymbol{b}$, (9–26) is equivalent to the risk function

$$R(\boldsymbol{b}) = [\boldsymbol{W} - \boldsymbol{w}(\boldsymbol{b})]^T\boldsymbol{\Psi}^{-1}[\boldsymbol{W} - \boldsymbol{w}(\boldsymbol{b})] + \text{constant}. \tag{9–27}$$

Equation (9–27) can be identified (except for the constant, which will not affect the minimization) as the risk function corresponding to a minimum variance estimator. This form, of course, is one corresponding to a least squares estimator. Thus, we have established the *well-known* property that the MLE for normal variates is equivalent to a least squares estimate.

Further, in fact, we have shown that in this case the MLE is equivalent to a minimum variance estimate.

To illustrate some properties of the MLE for normal distributions, a simple example will be examined. Let $x_1, \ldots, x_n$ be a sample set drawn from a population having the probability density function

$$f(x_i; \mu, \sigma^2) = (2\pi\sigma^2)^{-1/2} \exp\left\{-\frac{1}{2\sigma^2}(x_i - \mu)^2\right\}. \tag{9–28}$$

Based upon the $n$ samples, we wish to estimate the distribution parameters $\mu$ and $\sigma^2$. The likelihood function, for this example, is

$$L(\mu, \sigma^2) = \prod_{i=1}^{n} (2\pi\sigma^2)^{-1/2} \exp\left\{-\frac{1}{2\sigma^2}(x_i - \mu)^2\right\}, \tag{9–29}$$

and its logarithm is

$$\begin{aligned} \ln L = &-\frac{1}{2\sigma^2}\sum_{i=1}^{n}(x_i - \mu)^2 \\ &-\frac{n}{2}\ln\sigma^2 - \frac{n}{2}\ln 2\pi. \end{aligned} \tag{9–30}$$

The MLE of $\mu$ and $\sigma^2$ are found by differentiating $\ln L$ with respect to these parameters and solving for the values which yield a stationary point. These minimizing equations are

$$\begin{aligned} \frac{\partial}{\partial\mu}\ln L &= 0 = \frac{1}{\sigma^2}\sum_{i=1}^{n}(x_i - \mu) \\ \frac{\partial}{\partial\sigma^2}\ln L &= 0 = \frac{1}{2\sigma^4}\sum_{i=1}^{n}(x_i - \mu)^2 - \frac{n}{2\sigma^2}. \end{aligned} \tag{9–31}$$

Solving (9–31), the MLE are found to be

$$\begin{aligned} \hat{\mu} &= \frac{1}{n}\sum_{i=1}^{n} x_i = \bar{x} \\ \hat{\sigma}^2 &= \frac{1}{n}\sum_{i=1}^{n}(x_i - \hat{\mu})^2. \end{aligned} \tag{9–32}$$

Notice that these are exactly the values of the parameters that would have been obtained by the method of moments. In particular, we observe that, while $\hat{\mu}$ is unbiased, the discussion in Section 9.2 indicates the MLE $\hat{\sigma}^2$ is biased. This is a simple illustration of the characteristic fact that MLE are, in general, biased estimators.

We are now in a position to rationalize an assumption invoked in Chapter 8. Suppose that $\boldsymbol{a}_1^{[m\times 1]}$ and $\boldsymbol{a}_2^{[n\times 1]}$ are normal random vectors, which represent samples drawn from two distinct normal distributions that are statistically independent collections of elements. Assume that the two normal distributions have zero mean value (an assumption of convenience), then the joint likelihood function, considered as a function of the system parameters $\boldsymbol{b}_1$ and $\boldsymbol{b}_2$, is

$$\begin{aligned} L(\boldsymbol{b}_1, \boldsymbol{b}_2) &= f(\boldsymbol{a}_1; \boldsymbol{b}_1) f(\boldsymbol{a}_2; \boldsymbol{b}_2) \\ &= (2\pi)^{-m/2} |\boldsymbol{\Psi}_1|^{-1/2} \exp\{-\tfrac{1}{2}\boldsymbol{a}_1^T(\boldsymbol{b}_1)\boldsymbol{\Psi}_1^{-1}\boldsymbol{a}_1(\boldsymbol{b}_1)\} \\ &\quad \times (2\pi)^{-n/2} |\boldsymbol{\Psi}_2|^{-1/2} \exp\{-\tfrac{1}{2}\boldsymbol{a}_2^T(\boldsymbol{b}_2)\boldsymbol{\Psi}_2^{-1}\boldsymbol{a}_2(\boldsymbol{b}_2)\}. \end{aligned} \tag{9-33}$$

The logarithm of this likelihood function is

$$\begin{aligned} \ln L(\boldsymbol{b}_1, \boldsymbol{b}_2) = &-\frac{1}{2}\boldsymbol{a}_1^T(\boldsymbol{b}_1)\boldsymbol{\Psi}_1^{-1}\boldsymbol{a}_1(\boldsymbol{b}_1) - \frac{1}{2}\boldsymbol{a}_2^T(\boldsymbol{b}_2)\boldsymbol{\Psi}_2^{-1}\boldsymbol{a}_2(\boldsymbol{b}_2) \\ &-\left(\frac{n+m}{2}\right)\ln 2\pi - \frac{1}{2}\ln|\boldsymbol{\Psi}_1||\boldsymbol{\Psi}_2|. \end{aligned} \tag{9-34}$$

The crucial point is in the observation that, since only the first two terms are functions of the system parameters, the conditions that minimize the logarithmic derivative of the likelihood function are exactly those which minimize the risk function

$$R(\boldsymbol{b}_1, \boldsymbol{b}_2) = \boldsymbol{a}_1^T(\boldsymbol{b}_1)\boldsymbol{\Psi}_1^{-1}\boldsymbol{a}_1(\boldsymbol{b}_1) + \boldsymbol{a}_2^T(\boldsymbol{b}_2)\boldsymbol{\Psi}_2^{-1}\boldsymbol{a}_2(\boldsymbol{b}_2). \tag{9-35}$$

Thus, in effect, the relationship between (9–34) and (9–35) is equivalent to a wide sense justification of the risk functions which were somewhat arbitrarily selected in Chapter 8.

## 9.5
## *SOME PROPERTIES OF MLE*

To illustrate some properties of MLE, let us consider the case of a single system parameter $\theta$ and a set of samples $x_1, \ldots, x_n$ drawn from a population having the joint probability density function $f_n(x_1, \ldots, x_n; \theta)$. Based upon these samples, we wish to find an *unbiased* estimate of the parameter $\theta$. That is, we specify that

$$\begin{aligned} &\mathrm{E}\{\hat{\theta} - \theta - b_n(\theta)\} = 0 \\ &\int \cdots \int [\hat{\theta} - \theta - b_n(\theta)] f_n(x_1, \ldots, x_n; \theta)\, dx_1 \ldots dx_n = 0, \end{aligned} \tag{9-36}$$

where $b_n(\theta)$ is the *bias* of the maximum likelihood estimate $\hat{\theta}(x_1, \ldots, x_n)$. Differentiate (9–36) with respect to $\theta$. One finds that

$$\begin{aligned} &-\int \cdots \int \left(1 + \frac{\partial b_n(\theta)}{\partial \theta}\right) f_n(x_1, \ldots, x_n; \theta)\, dx_1 \ldots dx_n \\ &+ \int \cdots \int [\hat{\theta} - \theta - b_n(\theta)] \left[\frac{\partial}{\partial \theta} \ln f_n(x_1, \ldots, x_n; \theta)\right] \\ &\qquad\qquad f_n(x_1, \ldots, x_n; \theta)\, dx_1 \ldots dx_n = 0, \end{aligned} \tag{9-37}$$

or

$$\int \cdots \int [\hat{\theta} - \theta - b_n(\theta)] \frac{\partial \ln f_n}{\partial \theta} f_n\, dx_1 \ldots dx_n$$

$$(9\text{–}38) \qquad = \int \cdots \int \left[1 + \frac{\partial b_n(\theta)}{\partial \theta}\right] f_n \, dx_1 \ldots dx_n$$
$$\stackrel{d}{=} 1 + b_n'(\theta).$$

Next, apply the Schwarz inequality to (9–38). The inequality yields

$$(9\text{–}39) \qquad \begin{aligned} [1 + b_n'(\theta)]^2 &= \left[\int \cdots \int [\hat{\theta} - \theta - b_n(\theta)] \frac{\partial \ln f_n}{\partial \theta} f_n \, dx_1 \ldots dx_n\right]^2 \\ &\leq \int \cdots \int [\hat{\theta} - \theta - b_n(\theta)]^2 f_n \, dx_1 \ldots dx_n \int \cdots \int \left(\frac{\partial \ln f_n}{\partial \theta}\right)^2 \\ &\qquad \times f_n \, dx_1 \ldots dx_n. \end{aligned}$$

By definition, the variance of the parameter estimate $\hat{\theta}$ is

$$(9\text{–}40) \qquad \sigma^2(\hat{\theta}) = \int \cdots \int [\hat{\theta} - \theta - b_n(\theta)]^2 f_n \, dx_1 \ldots dx_n.$$

Combine (9–39) and (9–40). The combination can be written as

$$(9\text{–}41) \qquad \sigma^2(\hat{\theta}) \geq \frac{[1 + b_n'(\theta)]^2}{\mathrm{E}\left\{\left(\frac{\partial \ln f_n}{\partial \theta}\right)^2\right\}}.$$

Moreover, equality in (9–39) or, in turn, (9–41) holds if and only if

$$(9\text{–}42) \qquad K \cdot [\hat{\theta} - \theta - b_n(\theta)] \equiv \frac{\partial}{\partial \theta} \ln f_n(x_1, \ldots, x_n; \theta)$$

with probability 1; $K$ may depend upon $\theta$, but may not depend upon $(x_1, \ldots, x_n)$. Equation (9–41) gives the lower bound of the variance of an MLE, with or without bias. If the equality holds in (9–41), then we have an *efficient* estimator (Section 2.6). Equation (9–41) is called the *Cramér-Rao Inequality*.

Compare (9–42) with (9–22). From this comparison it is concluded that, if an efficient estimate $\hat{\theta}$ exists, the likelihood equation will have the *unique solution* $\theta = \hat{\theta} - b_n(\theta)$.

The next MLE property to be demonstrated is that, if a *sufficient* estimate $\hat{\theta}$ exists for $\theta$, then any solution of the likelihood equation must be a function of $\hat{\theta}$, [31, 154]. The proof of this assertion closely follows the proof given by Wilks [154].

It is postulated that the samples $x_1, \ldots, x_n$ selected from a distribution have a joint probability density function $f_n(x_1, \ldots, x_n; \theta)$ depending upon a single parameter $\theta$. The proof is readily extended to $n$ parameters. Further, it is postulated that the joint density function is expressible as a product of the form

$$(9\text{–}43) \qquad f_n(x_1, \ldots, x_n; \theta) = g(\tilde{\theta}; \theta) h(x_1, \ldots, x_n | \tilde{\theta}),$$

where $g(\tilde{\theta}; \theta)$ is the probability density function of the parameter $\tilde{\theta}$, while $h(x | \tilde{\theta})$ is the probability density function of the conditional random variable $(x_1, \ldots, x_n | \tilde{\theta})$, which does not depend upon $\theta$.

We assert that, as defined, $\tilde{\theta}$ is a sufficient estimate of $\theta$. Suppose that $\theta_0$ is any other estimate which does not depend upon $\tilde{\theta}$. In this case the distribution of the conditional random variable $\Theta = (\theta_0 | \tilde{\theta})$ is completely determined from the given conditional density function $h(x_1, \ldots, x_n | \tilde{\theta})$. Conversely, given that $\tilde{\theta}$ is a sufficient estimate having the probability density function $g(\tilde{\theta}; \theta)$, it must be verified that the joint probability density function can be written in the form of (9–43).

Introduce a change of variables from $(x_1, \ldots, x_n)$ to $(\tilde{\theta}, y_2, \ldots, y_n)$. The new probability function is derived from the original function by the relation

$$m(\tilde{\theta}, y_2, \ldots, y_n; \theta) = \frac{1}{|J|} f_n(x_1, \ldots, x_n; \theta), \tag{9–44}$$

where $J$ is the Jacobian of the transformation of variables.

Define $k(y_2, \ldots, y_n | \tilde{\theta}; \theta)$ to be the probability density function of the conditional random variable $(y_2, \ldots, y_n | \tilde{\theta})$. It then follows from the definition of conditional density functions (2–21) that

$$k(y_2, \ldots, y_n | \tilde{\theta}; \theta) = \frac{m(\tilde{\theta}, y_2, \ldots, y_n; \theta)}{g(\tilde{\theta}; \theta)}, \tag{9–45}$$

where

$$g(\tilde{\theta}; \theta) = \int \cdots \int m(\tilde{\theta}, y_2, \ldots, y_n; \theta)\, dy_2 \ldots dy_n \neq 0. \tag{9–46}$$

If $k$ does not depend upon $\theta$, $\tilde{\theta}$ is a sufficient estimate of $\theta$. Replace $k$ by the symbol $k^*$, and we can write

$$m(\tilde{\theta}, y_2, \ldots, y_n; \theta) = g(\tilde{\theta}; \theta) k^*(y_2, \ldots, y_n | \tilde{\theta}). \tag{9–47}$$

Combine (9–44) and (9–47) to obtain

$$f_n(x_1, \ldots, x_n; \theta) = g(\tilde{\theta}; \theta) k^*(y_2, \ldots, y_n | \tilde{\theta}) |J|. \tag{9–48}$$

Equation (9–48) indicates that, while $k^* \cdot |J|$ depends upon the variates $(\tilde{\theta}, y_2, \ldots, y_n)$ and, in turn, upon $(x_1, \ldots, x_n)$, the product is independent of $\theta$. Hence, any statistic which depends upon $(x_1, \ldots, x_n)$ through $(y_2, \ldots, y_n)$ but does not depend upon $\theta$, would have a distribution which is independent of $\theta$.

The conclusion drawn from the preceding arguments is that (9–43) is a necessary and sufficient condition for $\tilde{\theta}$ to be a sufficient estimate of $\theta$. The sufficiency of the factorability criterion was demonstrated by Fisher in 1922 [47], while the necessity of the criterion was shown by Neyman in 1935 [154].

A characteristic of a sufficient estimator is that, given an unbiased estimate of a system parameter which is not functionally related to a sufficient estimator, then there exists an unbiased estimator, which is a function of a sufficient estimator and has a smaller variance than the given estimator [154, p. 357].

We can now prove our contention that, if a sufficient estimate $\hat{\theta}$ exists for $\theta$, then any solution of the likelihood equation must be a function of $\hat{\theta}$. According to the factorability criterion (9–43), if a sufficient estimate $\hat{\theta}$ exists, the likelihood function must be of the form

$$L(\theta) = g(\tilde{\theta}; \theta) h(x_1, \ldots, x_n | \tilde{\theta}). \tag{9–49}$$

The corresponding likelihood equation is

$$\frac{\partial}{\partial \theta} \ln L(\theta) = \frac{\partial}{\partial \theta} \ln g(\tilde{\theta}; \theta) = 0. \tag{9–50}$$

Because the function $g$ only depends upon the arguments $\tilde{\theta}$ and $\theta$, any solution $\hat{\theta}$ which satisfies (9–50) must be a function of $\tilde{\theta}$. Hence, our contention has been verified.

## 9.6
## *ASYMPTOTIC DISTRIBUTION OF MLE*

The distribution of the MLE as a function of the sample size is of special interest in many applications of the maximum likelihood method of estimation. Unfortunately, at the present stage of development of the theory, very little can be said concerning small sample sizes. This void is the heart of most criticisms of MLE. On the other hand, for large sample sizes it can be shown that the MLE are asymptotically normal. The proof that follows is based upon one given by Dugué [31, 44, 103, 154].

Let $x_1, \ldots, x_n$ be samples drawn from a population having a probability density function $f_n(x_1, \ldots, x_n; \theta)$. Further, the density function is postulated to satisfy the following conditions [31]:

(i)
$$\frac{\partial}{\partial \theta} \ln f_n, \quad \frac{\partial^2}{\partial \theta^2} \ln f_n, \quad \frac{\partial^3}{\partial \theta^3} \ln f_n$$

exist for each $\theta$ in some nondegenerate interval $\Theta$;

(ii) for each $\theta$ in $\Theta$

$$\left| \frac{\partial f_n}{\partial \theta} \right| < F_1(x)$$

$$\left| \frac{\partial^2 f_n}{\partial \theta^2} \right| < F_2(x)$$

$$\left| \frac{\partial^3 f_n}{\partial \theta^3} \right| < H(x),$$

$F_1$ and $F_2$ are integrable along the entire real axis and

$$\int_{-\infty}^{\infty} \cdots \int_{-\infty}^{\infty} H(x_1, \ldots, x_n) f_n(x_1, \ldots, x_n)\, dx_1 \ldots dx_n < M,$$

$M$ is independent of $\theta$;

(iii) $$\infty > \int_{-\infty}^{\infty} \cdots \int_{-\infty}^{\infty} \left(\frac{\partial \ln f_n}{\partial \theta}\right)^2 f_n\, dx_1 \ldots dx_n > 0.$$

The variate

(9–51) $$S(x_1, \ldots, x_n; \theta) = \frac{\partial}{\partial \theta} \ln f_n(x_1, \ldots, x_n; \theta)$$

is called the *score*. As a first step in establishing the normality of the asymptotic distribution of the MLE, we shall obtain the asymptotic distribution of the score.

The expected value of the score is by definition

(9–52) $$\begin{aligned} \mathrm{E}\{S_n\} &= \int \cdots \int \left[\frac{\partial}{\partial \theta} \ln f_n(x_1, \ldots, x_n; \theta)\right] f_n(x_1, \ldots, x_n; \theta)\, dx_1 \ldots dx_n \\ &\overset{d}{=} \int \left(\frac{\partial}{\partial \theta} \ln f_n\right) f_n\, d\boldsymbol{x} \\ &= \int \frac{\partial f_n}{\partial \theta}\, d\boldsymbol{x} = \frac{\partial}{\partial \theta} \int f_n\, d\boldsymbol{x} \\ &= 0, \end{aligned}$$

provided that the interchange of differentiation and integration is a valid operation. Assume that the interchange of operations is permissible, then the variance of the score is

(9–53) $$\begin{aligned} \sigma_S^2 &= \mathrm{E}\{(S - \mathrm{E}\{S\})^2\} \\ &= \mathrm{E}\{S^2\} \\ &= \int \left(\frac{\partial}{\partial \theta} \ln f_n\right)^2 f_n\, d\boldsymbol{x} \\ &= \int \frac{1}{f_n} \left(\frac{\partial f_n}{\partial \theta}\right)^2 d\boldsymbol{x}. \end{aligned}$$

From (9–52), we have

(9–54) $$\begin{aligned} &\frac{\partial}{\partial \theta} \int \left(\frac{\partial}{\partial \theta} \ln f_n\right) f_n\, d\boldsymbol{x} = 0 \\ &\int \left(\frac{\partial^2}{\partial \theta^2} \ln f_n\right) f_n\, d\boldsymbol{x} + \int \left(\frac{\partial}{\partial \theta} \ln f_n\right) \frac{\partial f_n}{\partial \theta}\, d\boldsymbol{x} = 0 \\ &\int \left(\frac{\partial^2}{\partial \theta^2} \ln f_n\right) f_n\, d\boldsymbol{x} + \int \frac{1}{f_n} \left(\frac{\partial f_n}{\partial \theta}\right)^2 d\boldsymbol{x} = 0. \end{aligned}$$

Substitute (9–54) into (9–53), which then becomes

(9–55) $$\begin{aligned} \sigma_S^2 &= -\int \left(\frac{\partial^2}{\partial \theta^2} \ln f_n\right) f_n\, d\boldsymbol{x} \\ &= -\,\mathrm{E}\left\{\frac{\partial^2}{\partial \theta^2} \ln f_n\right\}. \end{aligned}$$

Define

(9–56) $$B^2(\theta) = -\int\left[\frac{\partial^2}{\partial\theta^2}\ln f_n(\boldsymbol{x};\theta)\right]f_n(\boldsymbol{x};\theta)\,d\boldsymbol{x},$$

then (9–55) can be written as

(9–57) $$\sigma_S^2 = B^2(\theta).$$

If a set of $n$ independent samples $x_1, \ldots, x_n$ are drawn from a population, the corresponding *sample score* values would be

(9–58) $$S_i = \frac{\partial}{\partial\theta}\ln f(x_i;\theta); \qquad i = 1, \ldots, n.$$

Further, if the samples $x_i$ are statistically independent, then the central limit theorem applied to the samples $S_i$ states that the sample average

(9–59) $$\bar{S} = \frac{1}{n}\sum_{i=1}^{n} S_i$$

is asymptotically normally distributed for large $n$, with zero mean value and variance $\sigma_S^2/n$; $N(0;\sigma_S^2/n)$.

Combine (9–58) with (9–59) and (9–22):

(9–60) $$\begin{aligned}\bar{S} &= \frac{1}{n}\sum_{i=1}^{n}\frac{\partial}{\partial\theta}\ln f(x_i;\theta)\\ &= \frac{1}{n}\frac{\partial}{\partial\theta}\ln L(\theta).\end{aligned}$$

Therefore, we can conclude that $\partial \ln L/\partial\theta$ is also asymptotically normal for large $n$, with zero mean value and variance $n\sigma_S^2$; $N(0, n\,\sigma_S^2)$.

It now remains to use the preceding results to discover the asymptotic distribution of the MLE $\hat{\theta}$. Let $\hat{\theta}$ be a root of the likelihood equation. Expand $\partial L(\hat{\theta})/\partial\theta$ in a Taylor series about $\theta$. The series can be written as

(9–61) $$\frac{\partial L(\hat{\theta})}{\partial\theta} = \frac{\partial L(\theta)}{\partial\theta} + (\hat{\theta}-\theta)\frac{\partial^2 L(\theta)}{\partial\theta^2} + \frac{1}{2}(\hat{\theta}-\theta)^2\frac{\partial^3 L(\phi)}{\partial\theta^3} = 0,$$

where $\phi$ is an intermediate point in the interval $(\theta, \hat{\theta})$. Corresponding to (9–61), we can also write the series expansion for the likelihood equation (9–22). That is, since

(9–62) $$\frac{\partial \ln f}{\partial\theta} = \left(\frac{\partial \ln f}{\partial\theta}\right)_{\theta=\theta_0} + (\theta-\theta_0)\left(\frac{\partial^2 \ln f}{\partial\theta^2}\right)_{\theta=\theta_0} + \frac{1}{2}\beta(\theta-\theta_0)^2 H(x),$$

where $\theta_0$ is the true value of $\theta$ and $|\beta| < 1$, we can multiply (9–62) by $1/n$ and obtain

(9–63) $$\begin{aligned}&\frac{1}{n}\frac{\partial \ln L}{\partial\theta} = B_0 + (\theta-\theta_0)B_1 + \frac{1}{2}\beta(\theta-\theta_0)^2 B_2 = 0;\\ &B_0 = \frac{1}{n}\sum_{i=1}^{n}\left(\frac{\partial \ln f(x_i;\theta)}{\partial\theta}\right)_{\theta=\theta_0} \stackrel{d}{=} \frac{1}{n}\sum_{i=1}^{n}\left(\frac{\partial \ln f_i}{\partial\theta}\right)_{\theta=\theta_0}\\ &B_1 = \frac{1}{n}\sum_{i=1}^{n}\left(\frac{\partial^2 \ln f_i}{\partial\theta^2}\right)_{\theta=\theta_0}\end{aligned}$$

$$B_2 = \frac{1}{n} \sum_{i=1}^{n} H(x_i).$$

It is necessary to demonstrate that a root $\theta$, $\theta_0 - \delta \leq \theta \leq \theta_0 + \delta$, exists for (9–63) with probability tending to 1 as $n \longrightarrow \infty$ for arbitrarily small $\delta$. The existence of this root, designated as $\hat{\theta}$, will be postulated rather than proved. The precise proof requires a lengthy argument which is given by Cramér [31, p. 501] and sketched by Mood [103, p. 210].

From (9–57), (9–55), and (9–52),

$$\begin{aligned} B^2(\theta) &= -\int \left(\frac{\partial^2}{\partial\theta^2} \ln f_n\right) f_n \, d\boldsymbol{x} \\ &= -\int \left[\frac{1}{f_n}\frac{\partial^2 f_n}{\partial\theta^2} - \left(\frac{1}{f_n}\frac{\partial f_n}{\partial\theta}\right)^2\right] f_n \, d\boldsymbol{x} \\ &= -\int \left(\frac{\partial \ln f_n}{\partial\theta}\right)^2 f_n \, d\boldsymbol{x} \\ &= \mathrm{E}\left\{\left(\frac{\partial \ln f_n}{\partial\theta}\right)^2\right\}. \end{aligned} \tag{9–64}$$

If we assume the existence of the root $\hat{\theta}$, (9–63) can be written as

$$Bn^{1/2}(\hat{\theta} - \theta_0) = -\frac{B^{-1} n^{-1/2} \sum_{i=1}^{n} \left(\frac{\partial \ln f(x_i;\theta)}{\partial\theta}\right)_{\theta=\theta_0}}{B^{-2} B_1 + \frac{1}{2}\beta B^{-2} B_2 \cdot (\hat{\theta} - \theta_0)}. \tag{9–65}$$

Using (9–64) and (9–63), the denominator on the right is

$$\begin{aligned} \frac{B_1 + \frac{1}{2}\beta B_2 \cdot (\hat{\theta} - \theta_0)}{B^2} = \frac{1}{\mathrm{E}\left\{\left(\frac{\partial \ln f_n}{\partial\theta}\right)^2\right\}} &\left[\frac{1}{n} \sum_{i=1}^{n} \left(\frac{\partial^2 \ln f_i}{\partial\theta^2}\right)_{\theta=\theta_0}\right. \\ &\left. + \frac{1}{2}\beta(\hat{\theta} - \theta_0)\frac{1}{n} \sum_{i=1}^{n} H(x_i)\right]. \end{aligned} \tag{9–66}$$

It can be argued that this term converges in probability to 1 [31].

The numerator term consists of a variable $\partial(\ln f)/\partial\theta$ which, referring to (9–64), has zero mean value and variance $B^2$. According to the Lindberg-Lévy version of the central limit theorem [31], the sum of these $n$ variates in (9–65) will be asymptotically normal, $N(0, B^2 n)$. Therefore, the right-hand side of (9–65) will be asymptotically normal, $N(0, 1)$. Finally, we can say that, since $Bn^{1/2}(\hat{\theta} - \theta_0)$ is asymptotically normal, $N(0, 1)$, $\hat{\theta}$ is asymptotically normal, $N(\theta_0, B^{-2} n^{-1})$.

As a final property, it will be shown that an MLE is both a consistent estimator and asymptotically efficient.

Suppose that $\tilde{\theta}$ is a biased estimator for the true value $\theta_0$, and the bias is $b_n(\theta_0)$, as defined in (9–36). From the definition of consistency (Section 2.7), if $\tilde{\theta}$ is to be a consistent estimate, then

$$\lim_{n\to\infty} \Pr\{[\tilde{\theta} - b_n(\theta_0) - \theta_0] = 0\} = 1. \tag{9–67}$$

To obtain an estimate for the lower bound of the variance $\sigma^2(\tilde{\theta}_n \mid \theta_0)$, an equivalent form of (9–41) is required for the case in which the variates $x_i$ are independent. This result is quickly obtained from (9–37) and the subsequent arguments by making the substitution

$$f_n(x_1, \ldots, x_n; \theta) = \prod_{i=1}^{n} f(x_i; \theta). \tag{9–68}$$

Corresponding to (9–41), we find (Problem 9.8) that, for the case of $n$ independent samples

$$\sigma^2(\tilde{\theta}) \geq \frac{[1 + b'_n(\theta_0)]^2}{nB^2(\theta_0)}. \tag{9–69}$$

Hence, we can write

$$\begin{aligned} \sigma^2(\sqrt{n}\,\tilde{\theta} \mid \theta_0) &= \mathrm{E}\{n[\tilde{\theta} - b_n(\theta_0) - \theta_0]^2 \mid \theta_0\} \\ &\geq \frac{[1 + b'_n(\theta_0)]^2}{B^2(\theta_0)}. \end{aligned} \tag{9–70}$$

Because the inequality (9–70) holds for each $n$, if

$$\lim_{n \to \infty} b'_n(\theta_0) = 0, \tag{9–71}$$

then the limiting operation yields

$$\lim_{n \to \infty} \sigma^2(\sqrt{n}\,\tilde{\theta} \mid \theta_0) \geq \frac{1}{B^2(\theta_0)}. \tag{9–72}$$

For an MLE, we have shown that the asymptotic variance is $nB^{-2}$, or that

$$\lim_{n \to \infty} \sigma^2(\sqrt{n}\,\hat{\theta} \mid \theta_0) = \frac{1}{B^2(\theta_0)}. \tag{9–73}$$

Because $Bn^{1/2}(\hat{\theta} - \theta_0)$ was shown to be asymptotically normal, $N(0, 1)$, $\hat{\theta}$ is a consistent estimator for $\theta_0$.

The *limiting* or *asymptotic efficiency* of $\theta$ is defined as [31, 154]

$$\mathrm{leff}(\hat{\theta} \mid \theta_0) = \lim_{n \to \infty} \frac{\sigma^2(\sqrt{n}\,\hat{\theta} \mid \theta_0)}{\sigma^2(\sqrt{n}\,\tilde{\theta} \mid \theta_0)}. \tag{9–74}$$

If leff $(\hat{\theta} \mid \theta_0) = 1$, the estimator is called asymptotically efficient. Replace the numerator in (9–74) by its value from (9–73),

$$\begin{aligned} \mathrm{leff} &= \lim_{n \to \infty} \left[\frac{1}{\sigma^2(\sqrt{n}\,\tilde{\theta} \mid \theta_0) \cdot B^2(\theta_0)}\right] \\ &= 1. \end{aligned} \tag{9–75}$$

Hence, as conjectured, the MLE $\hat{\theta}$ for $\theta_0$ is both consistent and asymptotically efficient for independent samples.

The characteristics of an MLE that have been discussed for a one-parameter distribution can be fairly readily extended to the case of $n$

parameters in the likelihood function. Most of these generalizations can be generated in an almost formal manner and are omitted [116, 154].

Because of the fact that, for independent samples, the MLE is asymptotically normal, it is apparent that many of the theoretical properties of these estimators for large sample sizes will be similar to the properties of normal distribution theory. There have been several published papers concerning MLE for large sample sizes. A good survey of this theory is contained in key papers by Neyman [110] and Wald [149]. Neyman introduced the concept of BAN estimates (*b*est *a*symptotically *n*ormal) for situations in which the distribution has multinomial characteristics. The BAN estimates were motivated by the fact that even for such *relatively simple* distributions MLE may be very difficult to find. Neyman points out that the BAN estimates have asymptotic behavior very similar to that of the MLE. The BAN estimates are based upon the principle of minimizing a quantity asymptotically distributed as $\chi^2$, which has the same asymptotic properties as those of maximum likelihood.

LeCam in a survey paper on the asymptotic theory of estimation and testing hypothesis [90] made the following comments on the difference between Neyman's BAN and Wald's approach.

Wald considered classes of densities that are restricted only by regularity conditions. In these cases, sufficient statistics of fixed dimension do not usually exist, and in this respect Wald's methods must, by necessity, differ from the BAN estimates of Neyman. A fundamental result of Wald's is that, under certain conditions, the MLE are asymptotically sufficient. Further, by means of suitable set transformations, it is possible to associate with each test problem on the original distributions a closely related, though not equivalent, problem on normal distributions.

LeCam [90] has described a method by which results similar to Wald's are obtained. Yet he was able to retain a large amount of freedom in the choice of the estimates.

The *nice* formulations of MLE generally follow from the hypotheses that the sample values are independent and that each is identically distributed. Unfortunately but frequently in real life, either or both of these hypotheses are not valid. The validity of certain statistical procedures in this connection depends upon the classical properties of the method of maximum likelihood associated with the two simple hypotheses, the method's consistency, and the fact that it leads to an estimator whose asymptotic variance can be derived easily from the likelihood function. Silvey [138] has considered the extension of the theory of MLE to the case of dependent random variables. He examined the extent to which the theory of the consistency and asymptotic normality of MLE, well established for independent identically distributed samples, carries over to more general stochastic processes. These extensions are based upon the behavior of martingales and semimartingales.

## 9.7

### *SOLUTION OF THE LIKELIHOOD EQUATION*

Many theories are typified by the characteristic that the implicit solution of a problem can be readily formulated, yet the explicit solution of the formulations may be exceedingly difficult. This situation is also true of MLE. Although frequently it is fairly straightforward to formulate the likelihood equations in particular problems, it doesn't necessarily follow that the solutions will be either straightforward or even possible to obtain in *closed forms*.

Solutions of the likelihood equation can be approximated by iteration techniques similar in principle to those described in Chapter 7. The question of convergence is better resolved in the case of the likelihood equation than in the general estimator formulation. Kale [76] examined the convergence of several iteration processes and has given sufficient conditions under which the processes are justifiable for large sample sizes. If $\hat{\theta}_1$ is selected as the initial estimate of the solution to the likelihood equation, if $\hat{\theta}_j$ is the $j$th iterate, and if $\hat{\theta}$ is the *true* MLE estimate, then the iteration process converges if $|\hat{\theta}_j - \hat{\theta}|$ decreases as $j$ increases and tends to zero as $j \longrightarrow \infty$.

Kale defined the iteration process in the following fashion: Let $g(\theta)$ be a differentiable function which has no zero in the neighborhood of the root $\hat{\theta}$ for the likelihood equation. The existence of $\hat{\theta}$ is postulated. Define

$$h(\theta) = \theta - g(\theta)\frac{\partial}{\partial\theta}\ln L. \tag{9–76}$$

The general iteration process is then

$$\begin{aligned}\hat{\theta}_{j+1} &= [h(\theta)]_{\theta=\hat{\theta}_j} \\ &= \hat{\theta}_j - g(\hat{\theta}_j)\left(\frac{\partial}{\partial\theta}\ln L\right)_{\theta=\hat{\theta}_j}.\end{aligned} \tag{9–77}$$

If

$$\epsilon_j = |\hat{\theta}_j - \hat{\theta}| \tag{9–78}$$

is the estimation error at the $j$th iteration, then $g(\theta)$ must be chosen such that $\epsilon_{j+1} < \epsilon_j$ and $\epsilon_j \longrightarrow 0$ as $j \longrightarrow 0$. This condition assures us that the iteration process defined by (9–77) will converge to $\hat{\theta}$.

Householder [71] has shown that two conditions are sufficient to satisfy the requirements on the error $\epsilon_j$.

(i) There exists a $\rho$ neighborhood of $\hat{\theta}$, $N_\rho(\hat{\theta})$, such that, if $\theta'$ and $\theta'' \in N_\rho(\hat{\theta})$, we have for some $k \geq 0$, $|h(\theta') - h(\theta'')| \leq k$, $0 \leq k < 1$. If $h(\theta)$ is differentiable, $|h'(\hat{\theta})| < 1$ ensures the existence of $N_\rho(\hat{\theta})$.

(ii) The initial estimate $\hat{\theta}_1 \in N_\rho(\hat{\theta})$.

Kale used the asymptotic characteristics of MLE for large sample sizes to show that three commonly used iteration techniques satisfy Householder's conditions and thus the convergence of the processes is assured.

(a) Newton-Raphson Method: Equation (9–77) becomes the *well-known* Newton-Raphson iteration method by the particular choice

$$g(\theta) = \left(\frac{\partial^2}{\partial \theta^2} \ln L\right)^{-1}. \tag{9–79}$$

(b) Scoring for Parameters: Rao's method of scoring for parameters [122] uses the following choice for (9–77),

$$\begin{aligned} g(\theta) &= -\frac{1}{nI(\theta)}, \qquad 0 < I(\theta) < \infty \\ I(\theta) &= \mathrm{E}\left\{-\frac{\partial^2}{\partial \theta^2} \ln L\right\}, \end{aligned} \tag{9–80}$$

where $n$ is the sample size.

(c) Constant Weighting: A convenient form for numerical calculations results from the choice $g(\theta) = -k/n$ for a suitable constant $k$. The practical problem, of course, is to select a *suitable* value for $k$. Another possibility is to use (9–77) in the form

$$\hat{\theta}_{j+1} + \hat{\theta}_j + \frac{a_j}{n}\left(\frac{\partial \ln L}{\partial \theta}\right)_{\theta=\hat{\theta}_j}, \tag{9–81}$$

where the $a_j$ are a sequence of real numbers somehow chosen so that the required conditions on the estimate errors are met.

Kale points out that, in comparison, only the Newton-Raphson process is of second order, while the others are of first order and as such are less rapidly convergent. The method of scoring for parameters is applicable if, as is usually the case, $I(\theta)$ is differentiable. The third choice of constant weights $a_j/n$ is not always applicable because of the difficulty of selecting a sequence $\{a_j\}$ so that the convergence proceeds, but not too slowly. The selection is governed to some extent by the behavior of $\partial(\ln L)/\partial\theta$. Frequently the choices of $k/j$ or $k/j^2$ will suffice.

The solutions of the likelihood equations in the general case, for which there are $n$ parameters, parallel those used for the single-parameter situation. If one or more of the parameters to be estimated are known or found by an independent calculation, the problem of finding the remaining roots can be materially simplified, as pointed out by Richards [125]. He has developed a method of obtaining MLE in the $n$-dimensional case, as well as the asymptotic covariance matrix, by capitalizing on the fact that one or more of the parameters are known.

## 9.8
## *CONNECTION BETWEEN METHODS OF MOMENTS AND MAXIMUM LIKELIHOOD*

Motivated by the practical difficulties encountered from the fact that, except for almost special cases, the likelihood equations are complicated and not easily solved, Shenton investigated approximations to the likelihood equations based upon expressions containing the sample and distribution moments [132, 133, 134]. His approach is based upon the expansion of the probability distributions in terms of orthogonal polynomials generated by the distribution function [31, 40]. The method will be illustrated for the simplified case of independent samples drawn from a common distribution.

Let $x_1, \ldots, x_n$ be samples drawn from a family and let $f(x; \theta)$ represent the common probability density function for these samples. $\theta$ is the family parameter, which is to be estimated by a maximum likelihood estimator.

A set of orthogonal polynomials $q_k(x)$ of degree $k$ in $x$ can be generated from the given density function by means of the defining relation

$$\int q_k(x; \theta) q_l(x; \theta) f(x; \theta)\, dx = \delta_{kl}\, \phi_k(\theta). \tag{9–82}$$

Since $q_k(x; \theta)$ is a polynomial, we can write

$$q_k(x; \theta) = \sum_{j=0}^{k} a_{kj}(\theta) x^j; \qquad k = 0, 1, \ldots \qquad a_{kk} \neq 0. \tag{9–83}$$

For independent samples, the likelihood equation is (9–22)

$$\frac{\partial}{\partial \theta} \ln L(\theta) = \sum_{i=1}^{n} \frac{\partial}{\partial \theta} \ln f(x_j; \theta) = 0. \tag{9–84}$$

By using the orthogonal polynomials generated by (9–82), the derivati of the density function can be approximately expressed by the generaliz Fourier series

$$\frac{\partial f(x; \theta)}{\partial \theta} = \sum_{p=0}^{N} A_p q_p(x; \theta) f(x; \theta), \tag{9–85}$$

where

$$A_k \phi_k(\theta) = \int q_k(x; \theta) \frac{\partial f(x; \theta)}{\partial \theta}\, dx. \tag{9–86}$$

Combine (9–84) and (9–85) to express the likelihood equation as

$$\begin{aligned} \sum_{i=1}^{n} \frac{\partial}{\partial \theta} \ln f(x_i; \theta) = 0 &= \sum_{i=1}^{n} \frac{1}{f(x_i; \theta)} \frac{\partial f(x_i; \theta)}{\partial \theta} \\ &= \sum_{i=1}^{n} \sum_{p=1}^{N} A_p q_p(x_i; \theta). \end{aligned} \tag{9–87}$$

Since (9–87) must hold for all values of $i$, it follows that

$$\sum_{p=0}^{N} A_p q_p(x_i;\theta) = 0. \tag{9–88}$$

We can now show that the expansion coefficients $A_p$ can be calculated from the moments of the sample distribution. Starting with (9–88),

$$\sum_{p=0}^{N} A_p q_p(x;\theta) f(x;\theta) = 0$$

$$\sum_{p=0}^{N} A_p \left[\frac{\partial q_p(x;\theta)}{\partial\theta} f(x;\theta) + q_p(x;\theta)\frac{\partial f(x;\theta)}{\partial\theta}\right] = 0, \tag{9–89}$$

$$\frac{\partial q_p}{\partial\theta} f(x;\theta) = -q_p \frac{\partial f(x;\theta)}{\partial\theta}.$$

Insert (9–89) into (9–86) to find

$$A_k \phi_k(\theta) = -\int \frac{\partial q_k(x;\theta)}{\partial\theta} f(x;\theta)\,dx. \tag{9–90}$$

Because $\partial q_k/\partial\theta$ is a polynomial in $x$, (9–90) implies that $A_k$ is a function of the first $k$ moments of the distribution. Thus the likelihood equation can be approximated as a function of these $k$ moments in the form

$$\sum_{i=1}^{n} \frac{\partial}{\partial\theta} \ln f(x_i;\theta) = 0 \approx \sum_{i=1}^{n}\sum_{p=0}^{k} A_p q_p(x_i;\theta). \tag{9–91}$$

## Problems

**9.1** Suppose that a sequence of samples $x_1, x_2, \ldots, x_n$ are drawn from a population having a uniform distribution. That is, the probability density function has the form

$$f(x;A) = \frac{1}{A}, \qquad 0 < x < A$$
$$= 0 \qquad \text{elsewhere.}$$

Find the maximum likelihood estimate $\hat{A}$ of $A$.

**9.2** Let

$$\Pr\{x = 1\} = p$$
$$\Pr\{x = 0\} = 1 - p,$$

where $\frac{1}{3} \le p \le \frac{2}{3}$. Find the MLE $\hat{p}$ of $p$.

**9.3** Let $x_1, \ldots, x_n$ be independent samples drawn from a distribution and such that

$$\Pr\{X = x;\theta\} = \frac{\theta^x e^{-\theta}}{x!}.$$

Find the MLE $\hat{\theta}$ for $\theta$ and compute the lower bound of the variance of an *unbiased* estimate of $\theta$.

**9.4** For independent samples $x_1, \ldots, x_n$ having a normal distribution

$$f(x_i; \sigma^2) = \frac{1}{\sqrt{2\pi\sigma^2}} e^{-x^2/2\sigma^2},$$

find the lower bound of the variance of the estimate $\hat{\sigma}^2$.

**9.5** If $x_1, \ldots, x_n$ are samples drawn from an arbitrary distribution such that $\mathrm{E}\{x^k\} < \infty$, show that

$$\frac{1}{n} \sum_{i=1}^{n} x_i^k$$

is a consistent estimator for $\mathrm{E}\{x^k\}$.

**9.6** If $x_1, \ldots, x_n$ are samples drawn from a distribution having the density function

$$f(x; \lambda) = \frac{\lambda^{k+1} x^k e^{-\lambda x}}{\Gamma(k+1)},$$

$x > 0$, $\lambda > 0$, $k$ a constant; show that the MLE $\hat{\lambda} = (k+1)/\bar{x}$. Demonstrate that this estimate is biased but consistent, and show that its asymptotic distribution for large $n$ is $N(\lambda, \lambda^2/[n(k+1)])$ [154, p. 391].

**9.7** Extending the arguments of Section 9.2, derive $\mu_3(\bar{x})$ and $\mu_4(\bar{x})$ given in (9–14).

**9.8** Verify Eq. (9–69).

**9.9** Suppose that sample values are drawn from a distribution which is known to be unimodal and bell-shaped. In this case, it is known that the probability density function can be approximated by a series of Hermite polynomials generated by (9–82) with a suitable weighting function [31; p. 77, 40]. Define

$$\phi(x) = \frac{1}{\sqrt{2\pi}} e^{-x^2/2},$$

then the $j$th derivative is related as follows to the Hermite polynomial:

$$\phi^{(j)}(x) = \frac{d^j}{dx^j}\left[\frac{1}{\sqrt{2\pi}} e^{-x^2/2} H_j(x)\right].$$

It can be verified that $\phi^{(j)}$ and $H_j$ are orthogonal and satisfy the relation

$$\int_{-\infty}^{\infty} H_i(x)\phi^{(j)}(x)\,dx = \delta_{ij}(-1)^j j!.$$

In place of (9–85), we now have

$$\frac{\partial f(x:\theta)}{\partial\theta} = \sum_{p=0}^{N} A_p \phi^{(p)}(x) f(x:\theta).$$

Continue the derivation to show how the first four sample moments can be used to estimate the distribution mean and variance.

**9.10** Prove the assertions in the last paragraph of Section 9.2. That is, if a set of samples $x_1, \ldots, x_n$ is drawn from a distribution having mean $\mu$ and variance $\sigma^2$, then

$$\bar{x} = \frac{1}{n} \sum_{i=1}^{n} x_i$$

will be the minimum variance linear estimator for $\mu$. Further, show that the sample variance $s^2$ is the minimum variance quadratic estimator for the variance $\sigma^2$ of the parent population distribution.

# Chapter 10

# ESTIMATION ERRORS

## 10.1
## *ERROR SOURCES*

It is almost axiomatic that any estimate of a set of system parameters obtained by processing a sequence of observations will be in error. The exact values of these parameters is knowledge that is denied us if we seek these values by means of an estimator. However, acknowledging that we cannot judge the exact parameter values does not imply that our experimental techniques and data reduction processes should not be meticulously planned and executed to reduce the errors in estimated quantities. Before explicitly defining the dual concepts of estimation errors and the confidence that can be placed in estimates, it is desirable to examine some of the controllable factors that can be varied during the experimental design phase of a measurement and estimation process for a set of system parameters.

Biased estimates can result from poor or inadequate instrument adjustment and calibration. Such biases can be eliminated or greatly reduced by taking the proper precautions of adjusting and calibrating all instruments prior to any precision set of measurements.

At times there may be other sources of bias errors which are beyond the full control of the observer. For example, if one wishes to measure the angles delineating a space vehicle's position by means of a telescope, the measurements will err because the line of sight as indicated by the instrument does not account for the refraction of the electromagnetic waves during their passage through the atmosphere.

By means of appropriate prediction formulas or charts, some of the ray-bending effects can be predicted and compensated. In spite of all possible precautions, even including recent upper-atmospheric rocket soundings, there will be a residue of uncompensated angular errors which act as a bias on the experiments. Uncompensated biases, or residuals, can sometimes be treated as one of the unknown system parameters to be estimated from the processing of the set of observations if a mathematical model can be constructed to yield the necessary prediction function.

Bias can also be introduced by the formulation of the estimator itself. It has already been demonstrated that sample moments are biased if the sum of the powers of the sampled variates are merely averaged by dividing by the number of samples. Maximum likelihood estimators are also, in many instances, biased estimates. If it is known a priori that the estimator has a theoretical bias, then the bias correction should be obtained, whenever possible, and used to yield final unbiased estimates.

The terms accuracy and precision as applied to the measurement and estimation of parameters have all too frequently been confused and even interchanged. *Accuracy*, in our sense, is a measure of how close the outcome of a measurement, or a sequence of observations, approaches the *true value* of a specified parameter. *Precision* is a measure of how close the outcome of a measurement, or a sequence of observations, clusters about some *estimated value* of a specified parameter. Notice that the most precise measurement techniques need not necessarily lead to a *good* estimate of the true value of a parameter. Precision implies repeatability of the observations and does not imply accuracy. Measurement controversies are not uncommon in which the disputes arise from the confusion between accuracy and precision.

Let $\boldsymbol{b}$ be the true value of a set of parameters and $\hat{\boldsymbol{b}}$ be the corresponding estimates. The measure of accuracy is defined by the risk function

$$R_a(\boldsymbol{b}) = [\mathrm{E}\{(\hat{\boldsymbol{b}} - \boldsymbol{b})^T(\hat{\boldsymbol{b}} - \boldsymbol{b})\}]^{1/2}. \tag{10–1}$$

Theoretical arguments have been made which show that, although the true value of $\boldsymbol{b}$ can occur in the sampled values furnished by a sequence of measurements, there is no way in which $\boldsymbol{b}$ can be unequivocally selected from the available samples. The true value of a measured parameter is *never* known to the observer if this knowledge must be inferred from his observations [158]. Because $\boldsymbol{b}$ may not be known, the measure of precision is defined by the risk function

$$R_p(\hat{\boldsymbol{b}}) = [\mathrm{E}\{\|\hat{\boldsymbol{b}} - \mathrm{E}\{\hat{\boldsymbol{b}}\}\|^2\}]^{1/2}. \tag{10–2}$$

Both measures $R_a$ and $R_p$ have been defined as standard deviations. The ideal measurement techniques would be one for which

$$\mathrm{E}\{\mathrm{E}\{\hat{\boldsymbol{b}}\} - \boldsymbol{b}\} = \boldsymbol{0}. \tag{10–3}$$

In other words, experimental accuracy is achieved by increasing the measurement precision and at the same time reducing the bias error to zero or at least to a minimal value.

Although it is not really necessary for our objectives in the exposition of estimation theory, it is perhaps of some importance to investigate the factors which influence measurement precision. Rather than being explicit in the sense of considering individual instrument sensitivity, response, calibration, etc., we shall limit ourselves to describing the manner in which certain fundamental quantities influence the measure of precision. Of course, such sweeping generalities must be accompanied by an almost equal loss in explicitness.

One can, with some justification, almost categorically state that the precision of an observation is limited only by the *signal-to-noise* ratio that exists in the measurement, or observation, system. This statement is undoubtedly an extremely broad generalization, but it has been found to be applicable to almost any type of observation, *provided* that an appropriate definition, or interpretation, is conferred on the concepts of *signal* and *noise*.

The exact form and scale factors that govern the precision of a particular physical measurement can be formulated only when one is willing to assume a priori knowledge of the probability distributions of the observables [6, 158]. Fortunately, aside from the magnitude of scale factors, a *universal* expression for a precision measure can be derived by means of heuristic arguments. While the arguments used are certainly not rigorous, they serve to provide an almost intuitive insight into a facet of measurement theory.

Let $z$ be a sample drawn from a population with mean value $\bar{z} = \mathrm{E}\{z\}$ and variance $\sigma_z^2$. The linear transformation

$$y = g(z) = c_1 + c_2 z \tag{10–4}$$

yields a random variable $y$ with mean value

$$\bar{y} = \mathrm{E}\{g(z)\} = c_1 + c_2 \bar{z} \tag{10–5}$$

and variance

$$\begin{aligned} \sigma_y^2 &= \mathrm{E}\{(y - \bar{y})^2\} = c_2^2 \mathrm{E}\{(z - \bar{z})^2\} \\ &= c_2^2 \sigma_z^2. \end{aligned} \tag{10–6}$$

Therefore, for a *linear transformation*, the relation between the new and original standard deviations is

$$\begin{aligned} \sigma_y &= |c_2| \sigma_z \\ &= \left|\frac{dg(z)}{dz}\right| \sigma_z \overset{d}{=} |g'(z)| \sigma_z. \end{aligned} \tag{10–7}$$

A central point in Chapter 13 is that the existence of a decision threshold is fundamental in a theory of signal detection. In the present context we relate the term signal to whatever we designate to be an observable. A little reflection based upon our everyday experiences, indicates that *almost all* quantitative (not comparison) physical measurements are implemented by transforming the phenomenon under observation to a displacement of a a suitable indicating instrument, or meter. A typical arrangement is shown in Figure 10–1. It is left as one more *classic* exercise for the reader to find a quantitative physical measurement which does not require, at some stage, the observable to be converted to a displacement.

If we accept the hypotheses of the fundamental aspects of a threshold in signal detection and a displacement for signal measurement, then the generalized measurement problem can be diagrammed as indicated in Figure 10–2. The generalized measurement problem has been posed as one of determining the value of the measurement $x_0$, corresponding to the point at which the signal-plus-noise displacement curve crosses a particular decision threshold $y_t$. For example, the signal-plus-noise curve in Figure 10–2 might represent the displacement law governing the pointer rotation of an electrical meter. The decision threshold, in this case, would be any particular scale calibration mark, while $x_0$ would be the observer's judgement of the scale reading. An even more graphic example of a measurement displacement curve is furnished by the situation in which the observable has been translated into a repetitive displacement of the beam of a cathode-ray oscilloscope.

The signal-plus-noise function of the observables is denoted by

$$\begin{aligned} y &= \text{signal} + \text{noise} \\ &= s + n. \end{aligned} \tag{10–8}$$

With no loss of generality, the noise is postulated to have zero mean value and variance $\sigma_n^2$. Suppose that the observations are related to the measurements by a continuous differentiable function

$$y = h(x). \tag{10–9}$$

Let $\Delta x$ represent a small error; then, in the neighborhood of $x_0$, the linear terms of a Taylor series expansion are

$$h(x_0 + \Delta x) = h(x_0) + h'(x_0)\,\Delta x + \cdots. \tag{10–10}$$

The observation error at the decision threshold can be approximated as

$$\begin{aligned} \epsilon_t = |y_t - (y_t + \Delta y_t)| &= |h(x_0) - h(x_0 + \Delta x)| \\ &= |h(x_0) - h(x_0) - h'(x_0)\,\Delta x| \\ &= |h'(x_0)\,\Delta x|. \end{aligned} \tag{10–11}$$

If it is assumed that the error $\Delta x$ can be equivalent to the standard deviation, then, by analogy to (10–7), an approximate conclusion is

$$\sigma_{y_t} = |h'(x_0)|\,\sigma_{x_0}. \tag{10–12}$$

$h'(x_0)$ is the slope of the signal-plus-noise displacement curve referenced to

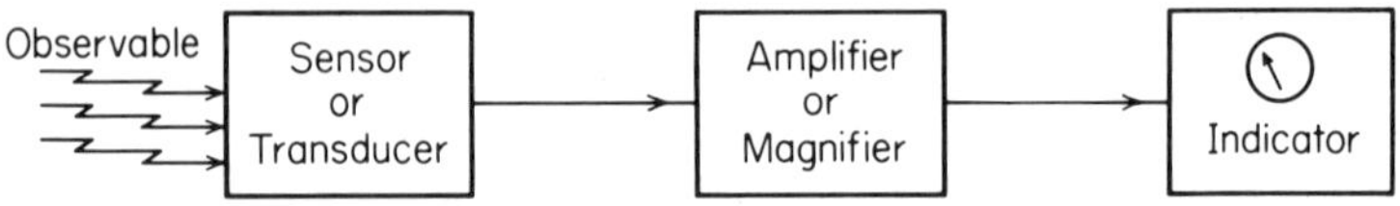


**Fig. 10-1** Measurement system

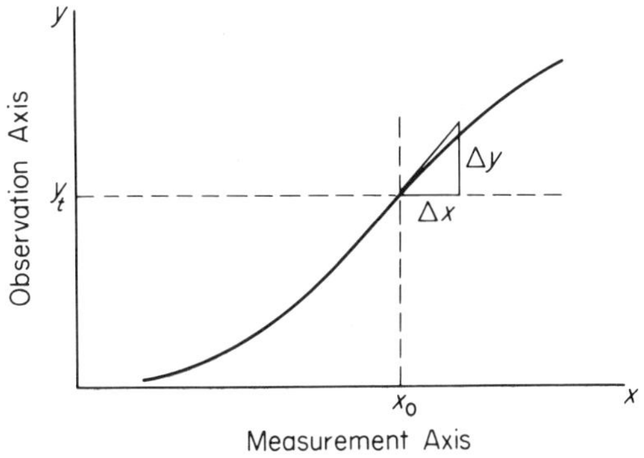


**Fig. 10-2** Measurement threshold

the decision threshold $y_t$. The slope of this curve is proportional to a quantity $\beta$, which, in communication theory, is called the *bandwidth* of the measurement system [12]. For a specified transfer function and system bandwidth, the slope of the curve at the decision point is also proportional to the signal amplitude $s$. Thus we can write

$$|h'(x_0)| = k\beta s, \tag{10–13}$$

where $k$ is the proportionality constant.

Combine (10–13) and (10–12) to obtain

$$\sigma_{x_0} = \frac{1}{k\beta}\left(\frac{s^2}{\sigma_{y_t}^2}\right)^{-1/2} \stackrel{d}{=} \frac{1}{k\beta}\left(\frac{S}{N}\right)^{-1/2}, \qquad \begin{aligned} S &= s^2 \ \text{ signal power} \\ N &= \sigma_{y_t}^2 \ \text{ noise power.} \end{aligned} \tag{10–14}$$

Equation (10–14) is an almost universal result embodying the fundamental property that the measurement error varies inversely with the response (sensitivity) $k\beta$ of the measurement system and also varies inversely with the square root of the signal-to-noise *power* ratio $S/N$.

As long as an experiment is designed to measure the magnitude of a *single* variable, a relation similar in form to (10–14) will be applicable, keeping in mind that the terms signal, noise, and bandwidth must be properly collated for particular cases. Depending upon a variety of factors, which include the particular nature of the observables and the method employed for combining the results of a sequence of measurements, the scale factor $k$ must be expected to vary in each specific situation.

If an attempt is made to use the results of a single observation to estimate two parameters, an additional theoretical constraint on the individual precisions may occur for each parameter estimate. For instance, it is *well known* in the theory of optics and quantum mechanics that the position and momentum (velocity) errors associated with an object are not independent. In fact, Heisenberg's uncertainty principle is a statement of the fact that the product of the uncertainties of an object's position and momentum is a constant. Any experiment designed to reduce the error in one component must be accompanied by increased uncertainties in the magnitude of the conjugate component. A similar phenomenom occurs in the operation of radio and radar tracking systems [6, 139, 146, 158]. The product of the uncertainties in range, line-of-sight velocity, and line-of-sight accelerations is bounded by a constant depending upon the product of the bandwidth $\beta$ and the effective time duration of the signal. Any increase in measurement precision for one of the measured system parameters must be accompanied by a compensating decrease in the measurement precision for the remaining parameters *if they are measured simultaneously from the same identical set of information data*. Unlike the quantum-mechanical-uncertainty principle, the uncertainty-limiting constant is under the control of the system designer. The bandwidth-signal duration product can be varied within practical bounds to help in the simultaneous measurement of parameters.

Equation (10–14) is most useful as an order of magnitude expression, especially when applied to parameters which are known to be either statistically dependent or bound together by an uncertainty relation.

## 10.2
## *CONFIDENCE REGIONS*

Most of the topics discussed in the previous chapters and sections have been primarily concerned with *point estimation*. That is, we were interested in the determination of a *good* estimate of a set of parameters based upon processing a sequence of observations. Although in many instances we have formulated expressions for the covariance matrix of the estimate error, we did not assign any quantitative probability statement to the estimates which expressed our confidence in these values. We shall now turn our attention to the selection of a region in the parameter space and the specification of the probability that the estimated values of a set of parameters will lie within the selected region. In this fashion, we shall be able to label our estimates with a measure of confidence.

Before describing the theory of confidence intervals, an example will be used to demonstrate that a method that appears to be almost intuitively obvious can lead to conceptual difficulties [31, 103]. Suppose that five samples (3, 2, 1.5, 0.5, 2.1) are drawn from a normal population having an unknown mean value $m$ and a known standard deviation $\sigma = 3$. From (9–32), the MLE of the mean value is

$$\bar{x} = \frac{1}{n}\sum_{i=1}^{n} x_i = \frac{1}{5}(3 + 2 + 1.5 + 0.5 + 2.1) = 1.82. \tag{10–15}$$

Our task is to determine the upper and lower limits of an interval such that it is certain that the true mean value of the distribution will lie in the interval.

In Section 9.6 it was shown that the MLE of $(x - m)n^{1/2}\sigma^{-1}$ would be asymptotically normal, $N(0, 1)$. Therefore, assuming asymptotic conditions for the limited sample, (9–73)

$$z = (\bar{x} - m)\frac{\sqrt{5}}{3} \tag{10–16}$$

will be normal, $N(0, 1)$, or has the probability density

$$f(z) = \frac{1}{\sqrt{2\pi}} \exp\left(-\frac{1}{2} z^2\right). \tag{10–17}$$

Suppose we specify that the probability that $z$ lie in an interval $(-z_1, z_1)$ be equal to 0.95. From published tables of the cumulative normal distribution [103], we find that

$$\Pr(-1.96 < z < 1.96) = \int_{-1.96}^{1.96} f(z)\, dz = 0.95, \tag{10–18}$$

or

$$\begin{aligned} &\Pr(\bar{x} - 2.63 < m < \bar{x} + 2.63) = 0.95 \\ &\Pr(-0.81 < m < 4.45) = 0.95. \end{aligned} \tag{10–19}$$

Formally, it has been computed that the probability is 0.95 that the true distribution mean $m$ will lie in the interval $(-0.81, 4.45)$. But is this statement meaningful? The mean $m$ is a fixed number, and it either lies in the interval or it does not. This is a dichotomy, and there is no intermediate possibility. In place of (10–19), we can only state that

$$\Pr(-0.81 < m < 4.45) = 1, \tag{10–20}$$

if $m$ actually lies in the interval $(-0.81, 4.45)$; if not, then

$$\Pr(-0.81 < m < 4.45) = 0. \tag{10–21}$$

What meaning shall be attributed to the calculation results embodied in (10–19)? Equation (10–19) simply states that the probability that the *random interval* $(\bar{x} - 2.63, \bar{x} + 2.63)$ covers the distribution's mean value $m$ is 0.95. The measure of confidence is 0.95 because, before drawing our samples, this was the probability we assigned to the random interval which was to be constructed so that it covers the true mean value.

Let us place the concepts illustrated by the preceding example in a more general and precise form. Suppose that $x_1, \ldots, x_n$ are drawn from a population having a known probability density function $f_n(x_1, \ldots, x_n; \theta)$. $\theta$ is the parameter of the population which is to be estimated on the basis of the sample values. Further, suppose that $\underline{\theta}(x_1, \ldots, x_n)$ and $\bar{\theta}(x_1, \ldots, x_n)$ are two functions of the sample values such that $\underline{\theta} < \bar{\theta}$. $\underline{\theta}$ and $\bar{\theta}$ will both be random variables. The interval $(\underline{\theta}, \bar{\theta})$ is called a $100\,\gamma$ per cent confidence limit for an estimate $\hat{\theta}$ if $\underline{\theta}$ and $\bar{\theta}$ can be selected such that

(10–22) $$\Pr(\underline{\theta} < \hat{\theta} < \bar{\theta}) = \gamma = \int_{\underline{\theta}}^{\bar{\theta}} g(\hat{\theta}; \theta)\, d\theta,$$

where $g(\hat{\theta}; \theta)$ is the probability density function of the estimates. It is assumed that $g(\hat{\theta}; \theta)$ is derivable from the given density function $f_n(x_1, \ldots, x_n; \theta)$. $\bar{\theta}$ and $\underline{\theta}$ are called the *upper* and *lower confidence limits* for $\theta$; $\gamma$ is called the *confidence coefficient*. The confidence interval $(\underline{\theta}, \bar{\theta})$ is a two-dimensional random variable with the assigned property that $\gamma$ is the probability that the interval contains the true value of $\theta$ in the population density function $f_n(x_1, \ldots, x_n; \theta)$.

In 1814, Laplace first introduced the formality of a confidence interval in connection with the estimation of the parameter of a binomial distribution [154]. Laplace regarded the confidence interval as a fixed constant and regarded the true value of the estimate as a random variable. Wilson, in 1927, essentially rediscovered Laplace's concept of the confidence interval [155]. However, Wilson improved upon Laplace's concept by attaching to the theory the correct interpretation of the interval as a random variable. The development of the contemporary theory and terminology of confidence intervals is due to Neyman [109].

It should be noted that the method of constructing confidence intervals does not depend upon whether or not the estimated parameter $\theta$ is a random variable. The price of this generality is that the constructions do not allow us to make probability statements which give the probability $\gamma$ that the parameter $\theta$ lies between given fixed limits. Such probability statements are, in fact, meaningless unless $\theta$ is a random variable. At best, confidence intervals only permit statements of the type which give the probability $\gamma$ that *such* and *such* limits (which may vary between successive samples) include the parameter corresponding to the actual sample.

The concepts of a confidence interval can also be applied to the case in which the given population is composed of discrete elements involving a single unknown parameter $\theta$ [31, 154]. There is one modification that must be made in the general formulation, because it cannot be expected, except in fortuitous instances, that confidence intervals can now be selected which have confidence coefficients exactly equal to $\gamma$. Instead, we choose $\underline{\theta}$ and $\bar{\theta}$ such that

(10–23) $$\Pr(\underline{\theta} < \theta < \bar{\theta}) \geq \gamma.$$

## 10.3
## *CALCULATION OF CONFIDENCE REGIONS*

In keeping with the almost universal practical plague, it is often much easier to discuss the theory of confidence regions than it is to calculate specific cases. A few *standard* examples are given to illustrate some of the practical difficulties as well as the schemes that have been formulated for circumventing some of these difficulties. It is almost self-evident that, because of the manner of defining confidence regions, the regions cannot be explicitly calculated unless one has specific knowledge of the probability distribution of the estimates as well as the parent population.

(i) *Mean of a Normal Distribution*: The method used in Section 10.2 to obtain the confidence interval for the mean of a normal distribution depended upon a priori knowledge of the distribution's standard deviation. But, suppose that the standard deviation is not known to the observer. This is a *classic problem*, and the lack of knowledge of the standard deviation is avoided by recourse to the *Student's distribution.*

Let $x_1, \ldots, x_n$ be a set of sample values drawn from a normal distribution with unknown mean $m$ and variance $\sigma^2$. The first two sample moments are

$$\begin{aligned} \bar{x} &= \frac{1}{n}\sum_{i=1}^{n} x_i \\ s^2 &= \frac{1}{n-1}\sum_{i=1}^{n}(x_i - \bar{x})^2. \end{aligned} \tag{10–24}$$

Define the variate $t$ in terms of these quantities as

$$t = \sqrt{n-1}\,\frac{\bar{x} - m}{s}. \tag{10–25}$$

$t$ is distributed according to the Student's distribution and has the probability density function

$$f_{n-1}(t) = [(n-1)\pi]^{-1/2}\,\frac{\Gamma\left(\frac{n}{2}\right)}{\Gamma\left(\frac{n-1}{2}\right)}\left(1 + \frac{t^2}{n-1}\right)^{-n/2}. \tag{10–26}$$

This is the Student's distribution with $n - 1$ degrees of freedom. From (10–26) we can find the interval bounds $\underline{t}$ and $\bar{t}$ such that

$$\Pr(\underline{t} < t < \bar{t}) = \int_{\underline{t}}^{\bar{t}} f_{n-1}(t)\,dt = \gamma \tag{10–27}$$

or

$$\Pr\left(\bar{x} - \bar{t}\,\frac{s}{\sqrt{n-1}} < m < \bar{x} - \underline{t}\,\frac{s}{\sqrt{n-1}}\right) = \gamma. \tag{10–28}$$

Equation (10–28) permits us to estimate the mean value $m$, without knowledge of the original distribution's variance, from a sequence of sample values.

(ii) *Variance of a normal distribution*: Consider the calculation of a confidence interval for the variance $\sigma^2$ of a normal distribution estimated from a sequence of samples drawn from a population having an unknown mean value. In this situation, the lack of knowledge of the mean value is circumvented by using the properties of the *chi-square distribution.*

Let the first sample moment be defined by (10–24), and define

$$\chi^2 = \frac{1}{\sigma^2}\sum_{i=1}^{n}(x_i - \bar{x})^2. \tag{10–29}$$

It is well known in statistical theory [31, 103] that the variate $\chi^2$ is distributed according to the chi-square distribution with $n - 1$ degrees of freedom. Its frequency function is, therefore,

$$\begin{aligned} f_{n-1}(\chi^2) &= \frac{1}{\Gamma\left(\frac{n-1}{2}\right)} 2^{-\frac{1}{2}(n-1)} (\chi^2)^{\frac{1}{2}(n-1)-1} e^{-\frac{1}{2}\chi^2}; && \chi^2 > 0 \\ &= 0; && \chi^2 \leq 0. \end{aligned} \tag{10–30}$$

Since this density function does not include any unknown parameters, it can be used analogous to (10–27) in order to furnish the confidence interval for a given probability $\gamma$. Thus,

$$\Pr(\underline{\chi}^2 < \chi^2 < \bar{\chi}^2) = \int_{\underline{\chi}^2}^{\bar{\chi}^2} f_{n-1}(\chi^2)\, d\chi^2 = \gamma, \tag{10–31}$$

or, inserting the definition (10–29),

$$\Pr\left(\frac{1}{\bar{\chi}^2}\sum_{i=1}^{n}(x_i - \bar{x})^2 < \sigma^2 < \frac{1}{\underline{\chi}^2}\sum_{i=1}^{n}(x_i - \bar{x})^2\right) = \gamma. \tag{10–32}$$

The preceding examples depended upon the ability to obtain functions of the sample values and unknown distribution parameters such that the function values were distributed independently of the parameters. It cannot always be anticipated that, even when such functions can be constructed, one will be able to write an explicit function for the probability density of the constructed function. Mood [103, p. 229] describes a general procedure for constructing confidence limits for these situations based upon a geometrical interpretation of confidence intervals. Wilks strengthens this construction by supplying an analytical proof for the existence of the procedure [154, p. 366].

## 10.4
## *MULTIDIMENSIONAL CONFIDENCE REGIONS*

The concept of confidence intervals can readily, and almost formally, be extended to the case of several parameters which are estimated [154]. In many of the applications of multidimensional confidence regions, it is either postulated or demonstrated by means of asymptotic arguments, that our estimates $\hat{\boldsymbol{\theta}} = [\theta_1\ \theta_2\ \ldots\ \theta_q]$ of an unknown parameter vector $\boldsymbol{\theta}$ are normally distributed. We shall, therefore, limit our discussion of $n$-dimensional confidence regions to normal distributions.

As an example, suppose that from a set of sample values $x_1, \ldots, x_n$, an MLE estimate $\hat{\boldsymbol{\theta}}^{[q\times 1]} = [\theta_1\ \theta_2 \ldots \theta_q]$ is made. It has been demonstrated in Section 9.6 that $\hat{\boldsymbol{\theta}}$ will be asymptotically normally distributed with some mean value $\bar{\boldsymbol{\theta}} = \mathrm{E}\{\hat{\boldsymbol{\theta}}\}$ and covariance matrix $\boldsymbol{\Psi}$, where

$$\boldsymbol{\Psi}^{[q\times q]} = \left[\frac{1}{nB_{ij}^2(\theta_0, \theta_0)}\right] = \mathrm{E}\{(\hat{\boldsymbol{\theta}} - \bar{\boldsymbol{\theta}})(\hat{\boldsymbol{\theta}} - \bar{\boldsymbol{\theta}})^T\}$$

$$S_i(\boldsymbol{x}, \theta_0) = \frac{\partial}{\partial\theta_i} \ln f_n(\boldsymbol{x}; \boldsymbol{\theta}) \tag{10–33}$$

$$B_{ij}^2(\theta_0, \theta_0) = \int S_i(\boldsymbol{x}, \theta_0) S_j(\boldsymbol{x}, \theta_0) f_n(\boldsymbol{x}; \boldsymbol{\theta})\, d\boldsymbol{x}$$

$$= \mathrm{E}\{S_i(\boldsymbol{x}, \theta_0) S_j(\boldsymbol{x}, \theta_0)\}.$$

Thus, the asymptotic probability density function of the MLE $\hat{\boldsymbol{\theta}}$ is

$$f(\hat{\boldsymbol{\theta}}) = (2\pi)^{-q/2} |\boldsymbol{\Psi}|^{-1/2} \exp\{-\tfrac{1}{2}(\hat{\boldsymbol{\theta}} - \bar{\boldsymbol{\theta}})^T \boldsymbol{\Psi}^{-1} (\hat{\boldsymbol{\theta}} - \bar{\boldsymbol{\theta}})\}. \tag{10–34}$$

This normal distribution is characterized by the quadratic form

$$Q = (\hat{\boldsymbol{\theta}} - \bar{\boldsymbol{\theta}})^T \boldsymbol{\Psi}^{-1} (\hat{\boldsymbol{\theta}} - \bar{\boldsymbol{\theta}}). \tag{10–35}$$

$Q$ can be shown to have a chi-square distribution with $q$ degrees of freedom, where $q$ is the number of elements in the matrix $\boldsymbol{\theta}$. Because $\boldsymbol{\Psi}$ is a covariance matrix, it is symmetric. Thus, there exists a nonsingular matrix $\mathbf{H}$ such that

$$\mathbf{H}\boldsymbol{\Psi}\mathbf{H}^T = \mathbf{I} \tag{10–36}$$

or

$$\boldsymbol{\Psi} = (\mathbf{H}^T\mathbf{H})^{-1}. \tag{10–37}$$

Introduce a new random variable $\boldsymbol{z}^{[q\times 1]}$ by means of the relation

$$\boldsymbol{z} = \mathbf{H} \cdot (\hat{\boldsymbol{\theta}} - \bar{\boldsymbol{\theta}}). \tag{10–38}$$

The mean and variance of $\boldsymbol{z}$ are

$$\mathrm{E}\{\boldsymbol{z}\} = \boldsymbol{O}$$

$$\boldsymbol{\Lambda} = \mathrm{E}\{\boldsymbol{z}\boldsymbol{z}^T\} = \mathrm{E}\{\mathbf{H}(\hat{\boldsymbol{\theta}} - \bar{\boldsymbol{\theta}})(\hat{\boldsymbol{\theta}} - \bar{\boldsymbol{\theta}})^T\mathbf{H}^T\} \tag{10–39}$$

$$= \mathbf{H}\boldsymbol{\Psi}\mathbf{H}^T = \mathbf{I}.$$

Since $\boldsymbol{z}$ was defined as a linear transformation of a normal vector, it follows that $\boldsymbol{z}$ will also be a normal vector characterized by $N(\boldsymbol{O}, \boldsymbol{\Lambda})$. We note that, because we can write

$$\boldsymbol{z}^T\boldsymbol{z} = \sum_{i=1}^{q} z_i^2, \tag{10–40}$$

$\boldsymbol{z}^T\boldsymbol{z}$ will have a chi-square distribution with $q$ degrees of freedom. Finally, our desired contention is verified from the observation

$$\boldsymbol{z}^T\boldsymbol{z} = (\hat{\boldsymbol{\theta}} - \bar{\boldsymbol{\theta}})^T \mathbf{H}^T\mathbf{H}(\hat{\boldsymbol{\theta}} - \bar{\boldsymbol{\theta}})$$

$$(10\text{–}41) \qquad = (\hat{\boldsymbol{\theta}} - \bar{\boldsymbol{\theta}})^T \boldsymbol{\Psi}^{-1}(\hat{\boldsymbol{\theta}} - \bar{\boldsymbol{\theta}})$$

$$= Q.$$

Once it has been established that $Q$ is a chi-square variate, the confidence interval

$$(10\text{–}42) \qquad \Pr\{Q_1 < Q < Q_2\} = \gamma$$

can be computed with the aid of the density function given in (10–30).

Notice that if (10–40), (10–41), and (10–34) are inspected as a whole. the inequality

$$(10\text{–}43) \qquad \boldsymbol{z}^T\boldsymbol{z} = \sum_{i=1}^{q} z_i^2 \leq g$$

defines a $q$-dimensional *closed* ellipsoid with a center at $\bar{\boldsymbol{\theta}}$. This ellipsoid is called the *ellipsoid of probabilities* associated with the quadratic form $Q$.

The formulation of (10–34) fiom the asymptotic properties of the MLE requires the inverse of the matrix $\boldsymbol{\Psi}$. In this particular case, the calculation of the inverse can be replaced by the calculation of two determinants. Let

$$(10\text{–}44) \qquad Q = (\hat{\boldsymbol{\theta}} - \bar{\boldsymbol{\theta}})^T \boldsymbol{\Psi}^{-1}(\hat{\boldsymbol{\theta}} - \bar{\boldsymbol{\theta}}) = \boldsymbol{h}^T\boldsymbol{\Psi}^{-1}\boldsymbol{h}.$$

The reader can verify (Problem 10.7) that

$$(10\text{–}45) \qquad \boldsymbol{h}^T\boldsymbol{\Psi}^{-1}\boldsymbol{h} = \frac{|\boldsymbol{\Psi} + \boldsymbol{h}\boldsymbol{h}^T|}{|\boldsymbol{\Psi}|} - 1.$$

## 10.5
## *COMPUTATION OF ERROR ELLIPSOID*

As a result of a series of observations, suppose that an estimate $\hat{\boldsymbol{b}}$ is made of the parameter set $\boldsymbol{b}$. If $\hat{\boldsymbol{b}}$ is a normal vector with zero mean value, then the estimate error

$$(10\text{–}46) \qquad \boldsymbol{q} = \hat{\boldsymbol{b}} - \boldsymbol{b}$$

is also a normal vector. The error ellipsoid can be computed using a form similar to (10–34) if the estimate-error covariance matrix

$$(10\text{–}47) \qquad \boldsymbol{\Psi} = \mathrm{E}\{\boldsymbol{q}\boldsymbol{q}^T\}$$

is known.

The detailed calculation will be illustrated for a slightly more general situation in which we desire to construct the error ellipsoid corresponding to parameters which may not be system observables and which may not even be identical with the original estimated parameters $\hat{\boldsymbol{b}}$. A situation of this variety occurs, for instance, in problems of orbital dynamics of a space vehicle when a radar is used to track the vehicle. The satellite's orbital elements, which are not directly observable, can be estimated from radar observations of range and line-of-sight angles. Instead of the orbital elements themselves, one might wish to estimate other nonobservables which are functionally related to the elements, such as future positions and velocities.

The vector $\hat{\boldsymbol{b}}^{[m\times 1]}$ will represent the estimates of an *original* set of system parameters $\boldsymbol{b}$. The desired parameters $\boldsymbol{g}^{[n\times 1]}$ are obtained by a given relation

$$\boldsymbol{g} = \boldsymbol{g}(\hat{\boldsymbol{b}}). \tag{10–48}$$

Notice that $\boldsymbol{b}$ and $\boldsymbol{g}$ are not restricted to having the same number of component elements. While $\boldsymbol{g}$ may not be an observable, for the moment we adopt the mathematical fiction that it is an observable. Thus the fictional *true* observation value, corresponding to (10–48) in the absence of any measurement errors, can be written as

$$\boldsymbol{G} = \boldsymbol{G}(\boldsymbol{b}) = \boldsymbol{g}(\boldsymbol{b}). \tag{10–49}$$

The prediction error is

$$\begin{aligned} &\text{Prediction error} = \text{predicted value} - \text{true value} \\ &\boldsymbol{z} = \boldsymbol{g}(\hat{\boldsymbol{b}}) - \boldsymbol{G}(\boldsymbol{b}). \end{aligned} \tag{10–50}$$

The problem is to construct the confidence region for the prediction error $\boldsymbol{z}$.

Assume that the prediction function is based upon a *reasonably good* estimate of $\hat{\boldsymbol{b}}$. That is, $\hat{\boldsymbol{b}} - \boldsymbol{b}$ is sufficiently small so that $\boldsymbol{g}$ can be expanded in a neighborhood of the true values and only the linear terms need be kept in the approximation. Thus,

$$\begin{aligned} \boldsymbol{g}(\hat{\boldsymbol{b}}) &\approx \boldsymbol{g}(\boldsymbol{b}) + \mathrm{U}(\boldsymbol{b}) \cdot (\hat{\boldsymbol{b}} - \boldsymbol{b}) \\ &= \boldsymbol{g}(\boldsymbol{b}) + \mathrm{U}(\boldsymbol{b}) \cdot \boldsymbol{q}, \end{aligned} \tag{10–51}$$

where

$$\mathrm{U}^T(\boldsymbol{b}) = \nabla_b \boldsymbol{g}^T(\boldsymbol{b}). \tag{10–52}$$

Combine (10–50) and (10–52) to obtain

$$\begin{aligned} \boldsymbol{z} &= \boldsymbol{g}(\boldsymbol{b}) + \mathrm{U}(\boldsymbol{b})\boldsymbol{q} - \boldsymbol{G}(\boldsymbol{b}) \\ &= \mathrm{U}(\boldsymbol{b})\boldsymbol{q}. \end{aligned} \tag{10–53}$$

A postulate that the measurement errors $\boldsymbol{q}$ are normally distributed is equivalent to stating that $\boldsymbol{z}$ is also a normal vector because, by (10–53), $\boldsymbol{z}$ is approximated by a linear transformation of a normal vector. Assume $\mathrm{E}\{\boldsymbol{q}\} = \boldsymbol{0}$, then $\boldsymbol{z}$ will also have zero mean value and covariance matrix

$$\begin{aligned} \Lambda &= \mathrm{E}\{\boldsymbol{z}\boldsymbol{z}^T\} = \mathrm{UE}\{\boldsymbol{q}\boldsymbol{q}^T\}\mathrm{U}^T \\ &= \mathrm{U}\Psi\mathrm{U}^T, \end{aligned} \tag{10–54}$$

where,

$$\Psi = \mathrm{E}\{\boldsymbol{q}\boldsymbol{q}^T\}. \tag{10–55}$$

We can, at this stage, write the quadratic form $Q$ corresponding to the distribution of the prediction errors $\boldsymbol{z}$ as

$$Q = \boldsymbol{z}^T \boldsymbol{\Lambda}^{-1} \boldsymbol{z} = \frac{|\boldsymbol{\Lambda} + \boldsymbol{z}\boldsymbol{z}^T|}{|\boldsymbol{\Lambda}|} - 1. \tag{10–56}$$

The latter form of the quadratic form *may be easier* to evaluate because the inverse of the matrix $\boldsymbol{\Lambda}$ given by (10–54) cannot readily be formulated; in the general case $\mathbf{U}$ need not be a square matrix.

$\boldsymbol{\Lambda}$ was defined as a covariance matrix, therefore it is at least positive semidefinite [42]. For such a matrix, there will exist an orthogonal matrix $\mathbf{B}$ such that

$$\boldsymbol{\Lambda}' = \mathbf{B}^{-1}\boldsymbol{\Lambda}\mathbf{B} \tag{10–57}$$

is a diagonal matrix. The diagonal moment matrix $\boldsymbol{\Lambda}'$ can be explicitly determined from the solution of the secular equation

$$|\lambda\mathbf{I} - \boldsymbol{\Lambda}| = 0. \tag{10–58}$$

For convenience in treating our illustrative problem, let us assume that the roots $\lambda_i$ of (10–58) are all distinct. These roots are called the *eigenvalues.* Cases for which the eigenvalues are not all distinct, can also be treated by further arguments [15, 104].

Although it is feasible to calculate the error ellipsoid for the quadratic form $Q$ without the intermediate step of finding the corresponding eigenvalues and eigenvectors, it is desirable to obtain these quantities in an illustrative problem because of their geometrical significance. The semiaxes of the error ellipsoid will have lengths equal to the square roots of the eigenvalues, while the orientation of these axes in the prediction space will be governed by the eigenvectors.

Select any root, say $\lambda_k$ of the secular equation (10–58), and form the set of linear equations

$$\boldsymbol{\Lambda}\boldsymbol{y} = \lambda_k \boldsymbol{y}. \tag{10–59}$$

This is a system of homogeneous linear equations which can be solved for the ratio of the components of the eigenvector $\boldsymbol{y}_k$ which correspond to the selected eigenvalue $\lambda_k$. Using each of the remaining eigenvalues in turn, the set of corresponding eigenvectors can be determined in the same manner. The eigenvectors are orthogonal; i.e.,

$$\boldsymbol{y}_i^T \boldsymbol{y}_i = \delta_{ij}. \tag{10–60}$$

The matrix $\mathbf{B}$ is formed by using the eigenvectors of $\boldsymbol{\Lambda}$ as columns,

$$\mathbf{B} = [\boldsymbol{y}_1\, \boldsymbol{y}_2 \cdots \boldsymbol{y}_n]. \tag{10–61}$$

Thus the set of equations (10–59) can be written as

$$\mathbf{\Lambda B} = \mathbf{B} \cdot [\lambda_j \delta_{ij}] = \mathbf{B} \cdot \begin{bmatrix} \lambda_1 & 0 & \cdots & 0 \\ 0 & \lambda_2 & & \vdots \\ \vdots & & \ddots & \vdots \\ 0 & 0 & \cdots & \lambda_n \end{bmatrix}. \tag{10–62}$$

Hence, we have accomplished the desired diagonalization because (10–62) is equivalent to

$$\begin{aligned} \mathbf{\Lambda B} &= \mathbf{B\Lambda}' \\ \mathbf{B}^{-1}\mathbf{\Lambda B} &= \mathbf{\Lambda}'. \end{aligned} \tag{10–63}$$

The diagonal $\mathbf{\Lambda}'$ matrix is unique except for the order in which the eigenvalues occur along the diagonal.

Since $\boldsymbol{z}$ has $n$ elements, $Q$ will have a chi-square distribution with $n$ degrees of freedom. The probability density function of $Q$ is

$$\begin{aligned} f_n(Q) &= \frac{1}{2^{n/2}\Gamma(n/2)} Q^{(n/2)-1} e^{-Q/2}; \qquad Q > 0 \\ &= 0; \qquad Q \leq 0. \end{aligned} \tag{10–64}$$

The last step is to compute the confidence interval for $Q$ as defined in (10–42). The probability that the error $\boldsymbol{z}$ lies within an error ellipsoid corresponding to $Q \leq Q_1$ is

$$\begin{aligned} \Pr(Q_1, n) &= \frac{1}{2^{n/2}\Gamma(n/2)} \int_0^{Q_1} Q^{(n/2)-1} e^{-Q/2}\, dQ \\ &= \frac{2 \cdot 2^{(n/2)-1}}{2^{n/2}\Gamma(n/2)} \int_0^{Q_1/2} u^{(n/2)-1} e^{-u}\, du \\ &= \frac{\gamma(n/2, Q_1/2)}{\Gamma(n/2)}, \end{aligned} \tag{10–65}$$

where $\gamma(n/2, Q_1/2)$ is the incomplete gamma function. The remainder of the calculation is left as an exercise (Problem 10.8).

There are occasions in which one might not wish to carry out the complete computations of the confidence regions. This may be true when many cases must be considered in a system design. Instead of the confidence region, an approximate figure of merit for the error ellipsoid can be defined. Schlegel has proposed a rather simple figure of merit [130] ,which we shall generalize.

Let us recall that the elements of $\mathbf{\Lambda}'$ (10–62) are the eigenvalues of the original covariance matrix $\mathbf{\Lambda}$. Combine (10–57) and (10–56) and, using the properties of an orthogonal matrix, we find that

$$\begin{aligned} Q &= \boldsymbol{z}^T \mathbf{B\Lambda}'^{-1}\mathbf{B}^{-1}\boldsymbol{z} \\ &= \boldsymbol{z}^T \mathbf{B\Lambda}'^{-1}\mathbf{B}^T\boldsymbol{z} \\ &= \boldsymbol{z}'^T \mathbf{\Lambda}'^{-1}\boldsymbol{z}', \end{aligned} \tag{10–66}$$

where the transformed random vectors

$$\mathbf{z}' = \mathbf{B}^T \mathbf{z} \tag{10–67}$$

have $\Lambda'$ as their covariance matrix. The key point is that the determinant of the diagonal matrix $|\Lambda'|$ determines the volume of an ellipsoid corresponding to the quadratic form $Q$. This volume $V$ is

$$V = \frac{4\pi}{3} |\Lambda'|^{1/2}. \tag{10–68}$$

Note that if $\Lambda$ is positive semidefinite and not positive definite, then at least one of the eigenvalues must be zero, implying that in this case $V = 0$. The ellipsoid is aligned with the *primed* axes $\mathbf{z}'$ and has semiaxes equal to the square roots of the eigenvalues of $\Lambda'$.

The volume of the error ellipsoid is a confidence measure, because we can assign probabilities for which it can be expected that the estimates will lie within these ellipsoids. Similarly, it is permissible to interpret $|\Lambda'|$ as a fundamental figure of merit for the *goodness* of an estimate. Because $\Lambda'$ is obtained by a similarity transformation with orthogonal matrices, it is not necessary to diagonalize $\Lambda$ to compute the determinant $|\Lambda'|$. Since $B$ is orthogonal,

$$\begin{gathered} \mathbf{B}^T\mathbf{B} = \mathbf{I} \\ \mathbf{B}^T = \mathbf{B}^{-1} \\ |\mathbf{B}| = |\mathbf{B}^{-1}| = +1. \end{gathered} \tag{10–69}$$

Hence,

$$\begin{gathered} |\mathbf{B}^{-1}\Lambda\mathbf{B}| = |\Lambda'| \\ |\mathbf{B}^{-1}||\Lambda||\mathbf{B}| = |\Lambda'| \\ |\Lambda| = |\Lambda'|. \end{gathered} \tag{10–70}$$

The property stated in (10–70) permits us to use $\Lambda$ in computing the figure of merit. On the other hand, because $\Lambda'$ is a diagonal matrix, it is far easier to compute $|\Lambda'|$ than it is to compute $|\Lambda|$. Schlegel investigated the size of the error introduced by approximating $|\Lambda|$ by the product of the diagonal elements of $\Lambda$. He demonstrated that, for a covariance matrix, the product of the diagonal elements is always greater than or equal to the value of the determinant of the matrix. While Schlegel restricted his proof to three dimensions, it can readily be shown that the same inequality is valid in $n$ dimensions. Our extension is a direct by-product of Wegner's theorem [15, p. 80]. This theorem states that, if a positive definite matrix $\Lambda$ is partitioned into matrices $\Lambda_{ij}$,

$$\Lambda = [\Lambda_{ij}]; \qquad i = 1, \ldots, r, \tag{10–71}$$

where the diagonal matrices $\Lambda_{ii}$ are restricted to being square, then

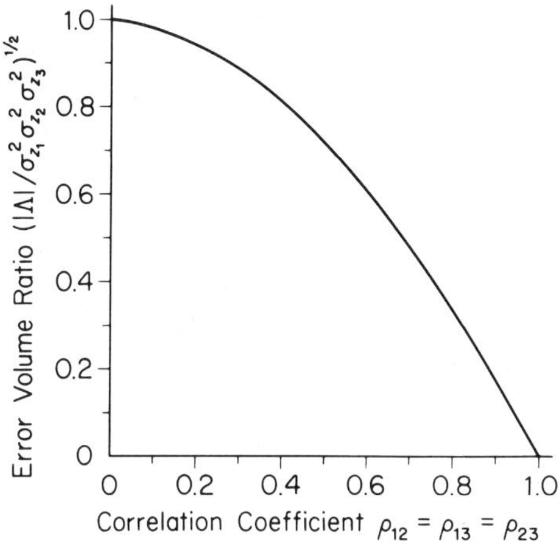


**Fig. 10-3** Effect of correlation on error volume approximation.

(10–72)
$$\det \boldsymbol{\Lambda} = |\boldsymbol{\Lambda}| \leq \prod_{i=1}^{r} |\boldsymbol{\Lambda}_{ii}|.$$

Let us now restrict $\boldsymbol{\Lambda}$ to being a positive definite matrix. Since the diagonal elements of the covariance matrix $\boldsymbol{\Lambda}$ now satisfy the hypotheses of the theorem, it follows that

(10–73)
$$|\boldsymbol{\Lambda}| \leq \lambda_{11}\,\lambda_{22}\,\ldots\,\lambda_{nn}$$

where

(10–74)
$$\lambda_{ii} = \mathrm{E}\{\boldsymbol{z}_i^2\} = \sigma_{z_i}^2.$$

Figure 10–3 illustrates the manner in which the off-diagonal terms $\mathrm{E}\{z_i z_j\}/\sigma_{z_i}\sigma_{z_j}$ affect the error values. Schlegel plotted the ratio

$$|\boldsymbol{\Lambda}|^{1/2}/(\sigma_{z_1}^2\sigma_{z_2}^2\sigma_{z_3}^2)^{1/2}$$

for a three-dimensional case as a function of the correlation coefficient. These ratios are equivalent to the ratios of the error ellipsoid volumes calculated with and without the off-diagonal terms included in the covariance matrix. For simplicity, the curve was plotted for the case in which the three paired correlation coefficients were all set equal; the effect of unequal coefficients can be roughly inferred from these results.

## 10.6
## *NUMERICAL ERRORS*

The realistic experimenter and data processor is well aware of the inherent numerical errors that are introduced in almost any lengthy sequence of computations. We are all too aware of the obvious *human errors* that plague us. These errors are first encountered in the faulty reading of measurement instruments. The errors are often compounded by the mistakes introduced during the arithmetical operations used to process the data by either hand or desk-machine computation. The computational errors, at first thought, might be completely eliminated by the use of automatic computers. One is tempted to believe that, once the automatic computers have been properly programmed for a particular sequence of operations, we no longer need consider the problems of computational error and can concentrate only on the problems introduced by approximations to the estimators. Obviously this may not be a safe assumption. While the probability of an incorrect computation, once a computer program has been fully tested, is very small, this is not equivalent to the statement that automatic digital computers provide error-free calculations. For a long sequence of calculations, these machines, if not programmed from the point of view of a careful numerical analysis, may yield results containing significant errors. The two most common error sources are those caused by *round-off* and *truncation*. A digital machine is constructed with a given word length, or number of significant digits $n$. Thus, after a multiplication of two full words, it is necessary that the product be rounded off by deleting the least significant digits until the result is equal to the machine's normal word length. For a few multiplication steps, the round-off error may be insignificant. However, in some system applications which use estimation techniques, hundreds of multiplication steps may not be unusual and the round-off errors can accumulate and may even influence the significant digits of the final answers. The problem of round-off errors is particularly significant in the evaluation of large-order determinants as well as in the computation of matrix inverses. In these cases, considerable effort has been made to develop algorithms that reduce the number of multiplications (and divisions) and thereby reduce the effects of round-off errors.

Truncation errors are those introduced by terminating long or infinite series after a finite number of terms. These errors are most commonly encountered in estimators which rely upon the numerical integration of a differential equation to evaluate the prediction function $\boldsymbol{w}(\boldsymbol{b})$. Numerical integration on digital machines requires that the integrals be replaced by sums; differential equations must be replaced by difference equations. These substitutions become better with decreasing lengths of the integration steps. But, as the steps are refined to decrease the truncation error, the number of steps must be increased, which in turn increases the round-off errors. Evidently some balance must be made between the truncation and round-off errors. The astronomers have been plagued by these problems and seem to have been the first to seriously consider unavoidable numerical errors in a sequence of calculations [17, 121, 131].

## 10.7
## *ERROR SENSITIVITY*

While confidence regions are an effective method of describing the reliance that one can place on values of estimated parameters, the practical difficulties involved in computing the dimensions and axes orientations of $n$-dimensional error ellipsoids often dampens one's enthusiasm. Several alternative measures of confidence have been proposed, which lack theoretical elegance, but are easier to compute than are confidence regions. The most commonly used alternative technique is that of error sensitivity [61, 63, 89]. We used this technique in Section 10.1 to establish the factors that influence measurement precision. The error-sensitivity method is one in which the variations in the state of a system are investigated as a function of small or infinitesimal changes in the values of the estimated parameters. In this respect, the sensitivity of a system to the state variables is a perfectly legitimate concept. Unfortunately, the concept of parameter sensitivity has frequently been loosely extended to be interpreted as an error sensitivity to which a probabilistic statement is attached or inferred. For example, suppose that the observations $x$ are related to a state parameter $b$ by the relation

$$x = f(b). \tag{10–75}$$

The derivative relation is

$$dx = f'(b)\, db, \tag{10–76}$$

which can also be expressed as a first-order sensitivity equation in the form

$$\Delta x = f'(b)\, \Delta b. \tag{10–77}$$

It is tempting to interpret $\Delta x$ and $\Delta b$ as standard deviations and then use (10–77) as an error-sensitivity transformation. This interpretation is only strictly valid in limited regions for which $f(b)$ can be linearized. In spite of the fact that these conditions may not be satisfied, Equation (10–77) is frequently used as a relation between standard deviations because small variations of $\Delta b$ are usually implied, so that $f(b)$ can be readily linearized in the regions of interest [61, 63, 89, 147].

Error-sensitivity calculations are a very common analysis tool, and, although they are not really a facet of estimation theory based upon probabilistic models, their widespread use and acceptance warrants some comments.

Error sensitivities are intimately related to perturbation theories of classical mechanics and, of course, celestial mechanics. The following discussion is based upon a general exposition of sensitivity analysis which has recently been used by Danby for application to the calculation and analysis of orbits [33, 34, 35].

Let us consider a system for which the output variables $\boldsymbol{z}$ are related to a set of state variables (system parameters) $\boldsymbol{b}$ by means of a known prediction function $\boldsymbol{w}$. That is,

$$\boldsymbol{z}^{[p\times 1]} = \boldsymbol{w}^{[p\times 1]}(\boldsymbol{b}^{[n\times 1]}). \tag{10–78}$$

Moreover, let us assume that the variation in $\boldsymbol{z}$ induced by a small change in a state element $b_i$ can be written as

$$\frac{\partial \boldsymbol{z}}{\partial b_i} = k_i \boldsymbol{g}^{[p\times 1]}(\boldsymbol{z}; \boldsymbol{b}), \tag{10–79}$$

where $k_i$ is a small constant parameter. The system *unperturbed* case corresponds to $k_i = 0$. The undisturbed solution for $k_i = 0$ is $\boldsymbol{z} = \boldsymbol{z}^{(0)}$ and is assumed to be known from (10–78). Expand $\boldsymbol{g}$ in a neighborhood of the unperturbed solution $\boldsymbol{z}^{(0)}$ by means of a Taylor series. Retaining only the constant and linear terms, we find

$$\boldsymbol{g}(\boldsymbol{z}) = \boldsymbol{g}(\boldsymbol{z}^{(0)}) + \nabla_z \boldsymbol{g}^T(\boldsymbol{z}^{(0)}) \cdot (\boldsymbol{z} - \boldsymbol{z}^{(0)}). \tag{10–80}$$

The output $\boldsymbol{z}$ can be written as a sum of $n$th-order perturbations in the form

$$\boldsymbol{z} = \boldsymbol{z}^{(0)} + k\boldsymbol{z}^{(1)} + k^2\boldsymbol{z}^{(2)} + \cdots, \tag{10–81}$$

where the superscripts denote the order of the perturbation and $k$ is a small constant parameter. Substitute (10–80) and (10–81) into (10–79). We find that

$$\frac{\partial \boldsymbol{z}^{(0)}}{\partial b_i} + k_i \frac{\partial \boldsymbol{z}^{(1)}}{\partial b_i} + \cdots = k_i \boldsymbol{g}(\boldsymbol{z}^{(0)}) + k_i \nabla_z \boldsymbol{g}^T(\boldsymbol{z}^{(0)}) \cdot [k_i \boldsymbol{z}^{(1)} + k_i^2 \boldsymbol{z}^{(2)} + \cdots]. \tag{10–82}$$

Equate terms of corresponding order of $k_i$ to obtain

$$\frac{\partial \boldsymbol{z}^{(0)}}{\partial b_i} = \boldsymbol{0}, \tag{10–83}$$

and

$$\frac{\partial \boldsymbol{z}^{(1)}}{\partial b_i} = \boldsymbol{g}(\boldsymbol{z}^{(0)}). \tag{10–84}$$

Integrate these equations to yield expressions for the first two orders of perturbations:

$$\boldsymbol{z}^{(0)} = \text{constant}; \qquad \text{undisturbed case,} \tag{10–85}$$

$$\boldsymbol{z}^{(1)} = \int \boldsymbol{g}(\boldsymbol{z}^{(0)}; \boldsymbol{b})\, db_i; \qquad \text{first-order perturbation.} \tag{10–86}$$

Equation (10–86) demonstrates that an error-sensitivity analysis is equivalent to the solution of first-order perturbations for the given system.

Consider the system of $n$ first-order differential equations defined in (10–79). Suppose a first-order solution $\boldsymbol{z}^{(1)} = \boldsymbol{z}_R(\boldsymbol{b})$ of (10–79) is known, with the initial condition $\boldsymbol{z}_R(\boldsymbol{b} = \boldsymbol{b}_0) = \boldsymbol{z}_0$. Substitute this solution into (10–84) to find

$$\frac{\partial}{\partial b_i}[\boldsymbol{z}^{(1)} + \delta\boldsymbol{z}] = \frac{\partial}{\partial b_i}[\boldsymbol{z}_R + \delta\boldsymbol{z}] = \boldsymbol{g}(\boldsymbol{z}^{(0)} + \delta\boldsymbol{z})$$

(10–87)

$$\frac{\partial \boldsymbol{z}_R}{\partial b_i} + \frac{\partial(\delta\boldsymbol{z})}{\partial b_i} = \boldsymbol{g}(\boldsymbol{z}^{(0)}) + \boldsymbol{\nabla}_z\, \boldsymbol{g}^T(\boldsymbol{z}^{(0)}) \cdot \delta\boldsymbol{z},$$

where $\delta\boldsymbol{z}$ is a small change in the system's output. Apply (10–84) to (10–87) to yield

(10–88)
$$\frac{\partial(\delta\boldsymbol{z})}{\partial b_i} \overset{d}{=} \delta\boldsymbol{z}' = \boldsymbol{\nabla}_z\, \boldsymbol{g}^T(\boldsymbol{z}^{(0)}) \cdot \delta\boldsymbol{z} \overset{d}{=} \mathbf{A} \cdot \delta\boldsymbol{z}.$$

Each of the partial derivatives, which are the elements of $\mathbf{A}$, are evaluated for the unperturbed or reference value $\boldsymbol{z}_0$. Thus $\mathbf{A}$ is a given function of $\boldsymbol{z}$ and is also a function of $\boldsymbol{b}$ through (10–78). Because higher-order terms have been neglected, (10–87) is only valid for small variations. The set of linear equations (10–88) can be solved if $p$ linearly independent integrals can be found. Denote the solutions by the separate columns of the matrix

(10–89)
$$\mathbf{Z} = [z_{ij}(b_i)].$$

Since any linear combinations of the columns of $\mathbf{Z}$ will also be a solution, the columns of the matrix defined as

(10–90)
$$\boldsymbol{\Omega} = \boldsymbol{\Omega}(b_i, b_0) = \mathbf{Z}(b_i) \cdot \mathbf{Z}^{-1}(b_0)$$

are also solutions. Notice that by construction

(10–91)
$$\boldsymbol{\Omega}(b_0, b_0) = \mathbf{I}.$$

The matrix $\boldsymbol{\Omega}$ is known as the *fundamental solution* and is called the *matrizant* by Danby. Because each column of $\boldsymbol{\Omega}$ satisfies the system differential equation (10–88), it necessarily follows that $\boldsymbol{\Omega}$ itself must also satisfy the same equation, or

(10–92)
$$\boldsymbol{\Omega}' = \frac{\partial}{\partial b_i}\boldsymbol{\Omega} = \mathbf{A}\boldsymbol{\Omega}.$$

Our system is perturbed from its normal state by adding a forcing function $\boldsymbol{B}(b_i)$ to (10–88). We now have

(10–93)
$$\delta\boldsymbol{z}' = \mathbf{A}\,\delta\boldsymbol{z} + \boldsymbol{B}(b_i)$$

with the corresponding general solution

(10–94)
$$\delta\boldsymbol{z}(b_i) = \boldsymbol{\Omega}(b_i, b_0)\,\delta\boldsymbol{z}_0 + \boldsymbol{\Omega}(b_i, b_0)\int_{b_0}^{b_i} \boldsymbol{\Omega}^{-1}(b_0, \beta) \cdot \boldsymbol{B}(\beta)\, d\beta.$$

Equation (10–94) is the solution of (10–93) with the initial condition $\delta\boldsymbol{z}(b_0) \equiv \delta\boldsymbol{z}_0$. Therefore, $\boldsymbol{\Omega}(b_0, b_i) \cdot \boldsymbol{\Omega}^{-1}(b_0, \beta)$ is the Green's function of the differential equation (10–88). This is the property of matrizants that can be exploited in error-sensitivity analyses. The first term on the right-hand side of (10–94) is called the *complementary function* and contains the constants of integration that embody the initial conditions. The second term reflects the perturbations that have been inserted by the perturbing function $\boldsymbol{B}(b_i)$.

The matrix $\boldsymbol{\Omega}$, for our purposes, can be placed on more familiar grounds. Suppose that the initial conditions are $\delta\boldsymbol{z}(b_i) = \delta\boldsymbol{z}(b_0)$; then the solution of (10–94) would be

$$\delta\boldsymbol{z}(b_i) = \boldsymbol{\Omega}(b_i, b_0) \cdot \delta\boldsymbol{z}_0. \tag{10–95}$$

In this form, it is *evident* that $\boldsymbol{\Omega}$ is nothing more than the Jacobian of the transformation between the variables $\delta\boldsymbol{z}(b_i)$ and $\delta\boldsymbol{z}(b_0)$. Jacobians satisfy the relations

$$\begin{aligned}\boldsymbol{\Omega}(b_i, b_0) &= \boldsymbol{\Omega}(b_i, \beta) \cdot \boldsymbol{\Omega}(\beta, b_0)\\ &= \boldsymbol{\Omega}(b_i, \beta) \cdot \boldsymbol{\Omega}^{-1}(b_0, \beta);\end{aligned} \tag{10–96}$$

$$\boldsymbol{\Omega}(b_i, b_0)\boldsymbol{\Omega}^{-1}(\beta, b_0) = \boldsymbol{\Omega}(b_i, b_0)\boldsymbol{\Omega}(b_0, \beta) = \boldsymbol{\Omega}(b_i, \beta). \tag{10–96a}$$

From these relations, the values of the Jacobian at any value $b_j$ can be found from $\boldsymbol{\Omega}(b_i, b_0)$ without recomputing the entire matrices. The importance of this observation lies in the property that, although a solution for the error sensitivity may have been formulated in some given component of the state vector, the results are readily extended to the computation of variations in any other component.

## Problems

**10.1** Obtain the 92 per cent confidence interval for the mean of a normally distributed population based upon the sample values 5, $-1.2$, $-0.8$, 3, 1.75, $-6$ if the standard deviation is known to be $\sigma = 2$. What would be this confidence interval if $\sigma$ were not known?

**10.2** For the samples in Problem **10.1**, compute the 90 per cent confidence interval for the variance, assuming $\sigma$ is unknown.

**10.3** Derive the expressions for the confidence interval corresponding to the estimate of the ratio of the variances of two distinct, normal distributions based upon sampled values.

**10.4** Find the eigenvalues and eigenvectors of the three-dimensional rotation matrix

$$\mathbf{R} = \begin{bmatrix} 1 & 0 & 0 \\ 0 & \cos\theta & \sin\theta \\ 0 & -\sin\theta & \cos\theta \end{bmatrix}.$$

Is $\mathbf{R}$ an orthogonal matrix?

**10.5** Compute the eigenvalues and eigenvectors of the matrix

$$\mathbf{A} = \begin{bmatrix} 2 & -2 & 2 \\ 3 & 3 & 1 \\ 1 & 5 & 7 \end{bmatrix}.$$

Find the orthogonal matrix $\mathbf{B}$ such that $\mathbf{A}' = \mathbf{B}^{-1}\mathbf{A}\mathbf{B}$ is a diagonal matrix.

**10.6** Suppose that the covariance matrix of a three-dimensional normal vector $\boldsymbol{x}$ is

$$\boldsymbol{\Psi} = \begin{bmatrix} x_{11} & x_{12} & x_{13} \\ x_{21} & x_{22} & x_{23} \\ x_{31} & x_{32} & x_{33} \end{bmatrix},$$

$$x_{ij} = x_{ji}.$$

Show that

$$x_{11}\, x_{22}\, x_{33} \geq |\boldsymbol{\Psi}|$$

without using Wegner's theorem (10–72).

**10.7** Verify Equation (10–45). Demonstrate that the relation holds for a three-dimensional vector.

**10.8** Complete the calculation of the confidence interval for a quadratic form by continuing from (10–65).

# Chapter 11

# LINEAR LEAST SQUARES SMOOTHING AND PREDICTION

## 11.1
## *INTRODUCTION*

The copious present-day theories for smoothing and prediction of time series, with few exceptions, owe their genesis to the original papers of Wiener [152] and Kolmogorov [85, 86]. These papers appeared during World War II, a period during which many serious and urgent smoothing and prediction problems were being attacked by military systems designers. Kolmogorov's basic paper, unfortunately, was published in the Russian language in a journal with a rather limited circulation. Wiener's work, on the other hand, was available as a United States government report and received wide distribution. It was known as the *yellow peril* because of its rather difficult reading and yellow report cover. Although the mathematical treatments in these papers were serious stumbling blocks, engineers were willing to overcome these hurdles because they quickly realized that for the first time an analytical synthesis technique was available for the systematic design of filters to be used for the separation of desired signals in an environment of undesired noise. Unfortunately, the abstract formalisms coupled with almost unsurmountable difficulties of solving a certain basic integral equation, deterred many readers from a full understanding of the rather simple underlying principles of the W-K (Wiener-Kolmogorov) theory. On the other hand, the seemingly formidable presentations of both Wiener and Kolmogorov were also a mixed blessing because several analysts were sufficiently motivated to develop simplified and more easily assimilated versions of the theory based upon slightly different approaches which still reflect the original mathematical fundamentals of the W-K theory.

The number of papers which have generalized, modified, interpreted, and extended the original W-K theory is far too large to even permit us to list an adequate reference list. Extensive bibliographies on this subject are given in References 5, 143, and 165. Some extensive developments of the W-K theory are contained in the publications of Darlington [36], Bendat [7], Wainstein and Zubakov [148], Yaglom [159], and Laning and Battin [87].

In contrast to most of the previous chapters, we shall take this opportunity to restrict the discussions to continuous functions of time rather than to discrete samples. Moreover, in keeping with the majority of applications, the theory will be restricted to one-dimensional formulations. These restrictions are imposed solely for economical and pedagogical reasons so that the presentation can be contained within reasonable bounds.

The W-K theory was formulated to treat the problem of the *optimal* separation, by the use of a linear filter, of a signal which has been perturbed by the addition of noise, or a random process. The input data, for our purposes, will be a time function $y(t)$ consisting of a signal $s(t)$ and noise $n(t)$,

(11–1) $$y(t) = s(t) + n(t).$$

It is postulated that $s(t)$ and $n(t)$ are typical members drawn from ensembles of these functions, which have certain known statistical characteristics. The central problem of the W-K theory is to derive an estimate $y_d(t)$ of $s(t)$ in the form

(11–2) $$y_d(t) = s(t + \alpha),$$

for the three following cases:

(i) If $\alpha > 0$, then $y_d(t)$ is called a *smoothed prediction* of $s(t)$.

(ii) If $\alpha > 0$ and $n(t) = 0$, then $y_d(t)$ is called a *prediction* of $s(t)$.

(iii) If $\alpha \leq 0$, then $y_d(t)$ is called a *smoothed replica* of $s(t)$, or an estimate of the signal at a time $\alpha$ before the present time $t$.

Instead of (11–2), one has the liberty of choosing a wide variety of linear functions. For instance, a common problem in the application of the W-K theory is to estimate the derivative,

(11–3) $$y_d(t) = \frac{d}{dt} s(t)\Big|_{t+a}, \qquad \alpha > 0.$$

Equation (11–3) would provide a smoothed prediction of the derivative of the original signal $s(t)$.

One cannot expect that the prediction $y_d(t)$ of $s(t + \alpha)$ will be errorless. Therefore, to be realistic, (11–2) should be replaced by

(11–4) $$y_d(t) = s(t + \alpha) + \epsilon(t),$$

where $\epsilon(t)$ is the estimation error. The objective of the W-K theory is to determine specific conditions and operations which will minimize the estimation error $\epsilon(t)$. Before these conditions and operations can be investigated, we shall have to define the sense in which $y_d(t)$ is to be an *optimal* estimate of $s(t + \alpha)$.

## 11.2
## *LINEAR FILTERS*

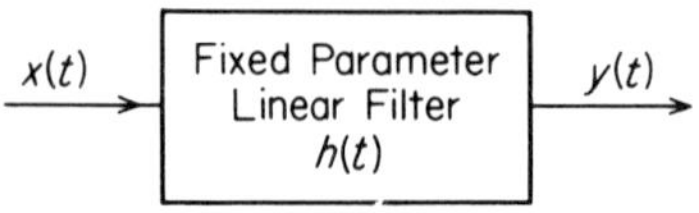


**Fig. 11.1** Linear system.

A brief summary of some properties of linear filters is desirable as an introduction to the main theory of signal prediction [38, 87, 91]. Suppose in Figure 11–1 that $x(t)$ is the input signal to a fixed parameter linear system and $y(t)$ is the output after the system transformation. The system, represented by the transformation $h$, is called linear if, for all input signals $x(t)$, the output $y(t) = h[x(t)]$ satisfies the two linearity conditions:

(i) $h$ is additive,

$$y_{12}(t) = h[x_1(t) + x_2(t)] = h[x_1(t)] + h[x_2(t)], \tag{11–5}$$

(ii) $h$ is homogeneous; for a constant $a$,

$$h[ax(t)] = ah[x(t)]. \tag{11–6}$$

In addition, for the majority of linear filters used in physical systems, we impose the further restriction that they constitute a *fixed parameter* system. Such systems are time-independent. That is, if

$$y(t) = h[x(t)], \tag{11–7}$$

then

$$y(t + \tau) = h[x(t + \tau)]. \tag{11–8}$$

The restriction to fixed parameter systems is frequently omitted because its physical significance may be overlooked. Consider a special input signal $x(t) = A \exp{(i\omega t)}$ which has been applied to a fixed-parameter stable linear filter since time $t = -\infty$. It is certainly safe to assume that all transients have been damped out and steady-state conditions exist. The output signal, from (11–8), is

$$y(t + \tau) = h[A\, e^{i\omega t} e^{i\omega \tau}]. \tag{11–9}$$

Apply the homogeneity property (11–6) to write

$$\begin{aligned} y(t + \tau) &= A\, e^{i\omega \tau} h[e^{i\omega t}] \\ &= A\, e^{i\omega \tau} y(t). \end{aligned} \tag{11–10}$$

In particular, if we let $t = 0$, then

$$y(\tau) = A\, e^{i\omega\tau} y(0) \tag{11–11}$$

is the response of the given system to a signal $A \exp (i\omega\tau)$. Notice that for the particular input signal $x(t) = A \exp (i\omega t)$, the output of a fixed-parameter linear system exhibits the desirable characteristic that the output signal has the same form as the original input signal. This characteristic is the foundation for further developments.

Let the system input signal now have the more general form

$$x(t) = X(i\omega)e^{i\omega t}. \tag{11–12}$$

Equation (11–11) is applicable; thus the steady-state output signal corresponding to (11–12) is

$$\begin{aligned} y(t) &= y(0)X(i\omega)e^{i\omega t} \\ &\overset{d}{=} Y(i\omega)e^{i\omega t}. \end{aligned} \tag{11–13}$$

The *system function*, or *filter response*, is defined to be the ratio of the amplitude of the output signal to the amplitude of the input signal. Corresponding to (11–12) and (11–13), the filter response is

$$H(i\omega) = \frac{Y(i\omega)}{X(i\omega)}. \tag{11–14}$$

We shall soon demonstrate that the filter response is the Fourier transform of the system transfer function, $h(t)$.

### 11.2.1 *DIRAC-DELTA FUNCTION*

The Dirac-delta function, $\delta(t)$, can be formally introduced by the four characteristic properties, $f(x)$ continuous at $x = x_0$,

$$\begin{aligned} &\int_{-\infty}^{\infty} f(x)\,\delta(x - x_0)\,dx = f(x_0) = \int_{-\infty}^{\infty} f(x)\,\delta(x_0 - x)\,dx; \\ &\int_{x_1}^{x_2} f(x)\,\delta(x - x_0)\,dx = \tfrac{1}{2} f(a_0); \qquad \text{if} \quad x_0 = x_1 \quad \text{or} \quad x_0 = x_2, \\ &\int_{-\infty}^{\infty} \delta(x - x_0)\,dx = 1, \\ &\int_{-\infty}^{x_0} \delta(x - x_0)\,dx = \int_{x_0}^{\infty} \delta(x - x_0)\,dx = \tfrac{1}{2}. \end{aligned} \tag{11–15}$$

The Fourier transform of the Dirac-delta function is

$$\mathscr{F}\{\delta(x)\} = \int_{-\infty}^{\infty} \delta(x)e^{-i\omega x}\,dx = 1. \tag{11–16}$$

One must use caution in the application of these formal relations as many pitfalls exist. For example,

$$\begin{aligned}\int_{-\infty}^{\infty} f(x)\,\delta(ax-b)\,dx &\neq f(b)\\ &\neq f\left(\frac{b}{a}\right).\end{aligned} \tag{11–17}$$

The reason is that (11–17) is not in the same form as the defining relation (11–15). The integration variable must exactly correspond to the same variable that appears in the delta function. The correct procedure is to make an appropriate change of variables and multiply the integral by the Jacobian of the transformation. We use a change of variables to evaluate

$$\begin{aligned}\int_{-\infty}^{\infty} f(x)\,\delta(ax-b)\,dx &= \int_{-\infty}^{\infty} f\left(\frac{u}{a}\right)\delta(u-b)\,\frac{du}{a}\\ &= \frac{1}{a}f\left(\frac{b}{a}\right).\end{aligned} \tag{11–18}$$

#### 11.2.2 *FILTER RESPONSE TO IMPULSE SIGNAL*

A periodic input signal $x(t)$ can be expressed as a Fourier series:

$$\begin{aligned}x(t) &= \sum_{n=-\infty}^{\infty} a(in\omega_0)\,e^{in\omega_0 t}\\ a(in\omega_0) &= \frac{1}{T_0}\int_{-T_0/2}^{T_0/2} x(t)\,e^{-in\omega_0 t}\,dt,\end{aligned} \tag{11–19}$$

where $T_0 = 1/f_0 = 2\pi/\omega_0$ is the period of the signal. From (11–13) and (11–14), the output signal corresponding to the $n$th component of the input signal $x(t)$ is

$$\begin{aligned}y_n(t) &= Y(in\omega_0)\,e^{in\omega_0 t}\\ &= a(in\omega_0)\,H(in\omega_0)\,e^{in\omega_0 t}.\end{aligned} \tag{11–20}$$

We now make use of the additivity property of a linear filter to write the total output signal as

$$\begin{aligned}y(t) &= \sum_{n=-\infty}^{\infty} y_n(t)\\ &= \sum_{n=-\infty}^{\infty} a(in\omega_0)\,H(in\omega_0)\,e^{in\omega_0 t}.\end{aligned} \tag{11–21}$$

As the next step, we let $x(t)$ be a signal for which a Fourier transform $X(i\omega)$ exists;

$$x(t) = \mathscr{F}\{X(i\omega)\} = \frac{1}{2\pi}\int_{-\infty}^{\infty} X(i\omega)\,e^{i\omega t}\,d\omega. \tag{11–22}$$

Analogous to (11–20), in this case the output signal is

$$\begin{aligned}y(t) &= \frac{1}{2\pi}\int_{-\infty}^{\infty} X(i\omega)\,H(i\omega)\,e^{i\omega t}\,d\omega\\ &= \mathscr{F}\{X(i\omega)\,H(i\omega)\},\end{aligned} \tag{11–23}$$

and its transform is

(11–24) $$Y(i\omega) = \mathscr{F}\{y(t)\} = X(i\omega)H(i\omega).$$

Of particular importance in the theory of linear filters is the response, or output, of a filter subjected to an impulse signal $x(t) = \delta(t)$. For an impulse input signal

(11–25) $$\mathscr{F}\{x(t)\} = \mathscr{F}\{\delta(t)\} = 1.$$

Combine (11–25) with (11–24) to find the output spectrum $Y(i\omega)$ for an impulse input signal,

(11–26) $$Y(i\omega) = 1 \cdot H(i\omega).$$

Finally, the output signal is obtained from (11–26) combined with (11–23),

(11–27) $$y_\delta(t) = \frac{1}{2\pi}\int_{-\infty}^{\infty} H(i\omega)e^{i\omega t}\,d\omega.$$

The important conclusion drawn from (11–27) is that

(11–28) $$h(t) = y_\delta(t) = \frac{1}{2\pi}\int_{-\infty}^{\infty} H(i\omega)e^{i\omega t}\,d\omega.$$

The inverse relation is

(11–29) $$H(i\omega) = \int_{-\infty}^{\infty} h(t)e^{-i\omega t}\,dt.$$

If the unit impulse response of a filter is zero for negative values of $t$, $[h(t) = 0, t < 0]$, then the linear system is said to be physically realizable.

### 11.2.3 *LINEAR FILTER RESPONSE*

The response of a fixed-parameter linear filter (or system) to a signal $x(t)$ can be expressed by substituting (11–29) into (11–23). We find that the output signal is

(11–30) $$y(t) = \int_{-\infty}^{\infty} h(\tau)\,d\tau \frac{1}{2\pi}\int_{-\infty}^{\infty} X(i\omega)e^{i\omega(t-\tau)}\,d\omega.$$

Observe that the second integral is simply the Fourier transform of $X(i\omega)$ evaluated at $t - \tau$. Therefore, we can write

(11–31) $$\begin{aligned} y(t) &= \int_{-\infty}^{\infty} h(\tau)x(t-\tau)\,d\tau; \qquad h(\tau) = 0,\ \tau < 0 \\ &= \int_{0}^{\infty} h(\tau)x(t-\tau)\,d\tau \end{aligned}$$

or, in the equivalent form,

(11–32) $$\begin{aligned} y(t) &= \int_{-\infty}^{\infty} h(t-\tau)x(\tau)\,d\tau \\ &= \int_{-\infty}^{t} h(t-\tau)x(\tau)\,d\tau. \end{aligned}$$

## 11.3
## *WIENER-KOLMOGOROV THEORY*

The W-K theory is presented in a fashion closely resembling that used by Wiener. Thus, the theory emphasizes a time-domain analysis. The covariance function for the signal $s(t)$, for example, was given the time-domain definition

$$\Psi_s(\tau) = \lim_{T\to\infty} \frac{1}{T} \int_{-T/2}^{T/2} s(t)s(t-\tau)\,d\tau. \tag{11–33}$$

However, because we shall restrict ourselves to signals and noise which are real stationary ergodic processes [114], Equation (11–33) can be replaced by the ensemble, or statistical average,

$$\Psi_s(\tau) = \mathrm{E}\{s(t)s(t-\tau)\}. \tag{11–34}$$

It will be slightly more convenient to use definitions analogous to (11–34) than the forms analogous to (11–33) that appear in Wiener's original publication.

Let $y(t) = s(t) + n(t)$ be applied to a linear fixed-parameter filter having an impulse response, or *weighting function*, $h(t)$. The output signal $y_d(t)$ can be written immediately by applying (11–31);

$$y_d(t) = \int_{-\infty}^{\infty} h(\tau)y(t-\tau)\,d\tau. \tag{11–35}$$

The error that exists in the output, which attempts to reproduce the translated original signal, is

$$\epsilon(t) = y_d(t) - s(t+\alpha). \tag{11–36}$$

The criterion for an *optimum filter* is selected as the linear fixed-parameter filter which minimizes the mean squared risk function

$$\begin{aligned} R &= \mathrm{E}\{\epsilon^2(t)\} = \mathrm{E}\{[y_d(t) - s(t+\alpha)]^2\} \\ &= \mathrm{E}\{y_d^2(t)\} + \mathrm{E}\{s^2(t+\alpha)\} - 2\mathrm{E}\{y_d(t)s(t+\alpha)\}. \end{aligned} \tag{11–37}$$

Each element of (11–37) is examined in turn so that it can be expressed in terms of the signal and noise statistical parameters, which are assumed to be known. The first element in (11–37) can be written as

$$\mathrm{E}\{y_d^2(t)\} = \mathrm{E}\left\{\int_{-\infty}^{\infty}\int_{-\infty}^{\infty} h(\tau)h(\sigma)y(t-\tau)y(t-\sigma)\,d\tau\,d\sigma\right\}. \tag{11–38}$$

Assume that the orders of integration can be interchanged so that the expected value is performed first. This expected value can be written as follows by utilizing the hypotheses of stationarity:

$$\begin{aligned} \mathrm{E}\{y(t-\tau)y(t-\sigma)\} &= \mathrm{E}\{y(\tau)y(\sigma)\} \\ &= \mathrm{E}\{[s(\tau)+n(\tau)][s(\sigma)+n(\sigma)]\} \\ &= \Psi_s(\tau-\sigma) + \Psi_n(\tau-\sigma), \end{aligned} \tag{11–39}$$

where

$$\begin{aligned} \Psi_s(\tau - \sigma) &= \mathrm{E}\{s(\tau)s(\sigma)\} \\ \Psi_n(\tau - \sigma) &= \mathrm{E}\{n(\tau)n(\sigma)\} \\ \Psi_{sn}(\tau - \sigma) &= \mathrm{E}\{s(\tau)n(\sigma)\} = 0. \end{aligned} \tag{11–40}$$

The last statement in (11–40) is an additional hypothesis; i.e., the signal and noise are assumed to be stochastically independent. The theory can also be developed without the independence hypothesis, but this additional refinement is omitted.

Combine (11–38) and (11–39) to obtain

$$\mathrm{E}\{y_d^2(t)\} = \iint h(\tau)h(\sigma)[\Psi_s(\tau - \sigma) + \Psi_n(\tau - \sigma)]\, d\tau\, d\sigma. \tag{11–41}$$

In the same fashion we consider the expansions

$$\begin{aligned} \mathrm{E}\{y_d(t)s(t+\alpha)\} &= \mathrm{E}\left\{s(t+\alpha)\int h(\tau)y(t-\tau)\,d\tau\right\} \\ &= \mathrm{E}\left\{s(t+\alpha)\int h(\tau)[s(t-\tau) + n(t-\tau)]\,d\tau\right\} \\ &= \int h(\tau)\Psi_s(\tau+\alpha)\,d\tau. \end{aligned} \tag{11–42}$$

Finally,

$$\mathrm{E}\{s^2(t+\alpha)\} = \Psi_s(0). \tag{11–43}$$

Therefore, the risk function $R$ can be written in the following equivalent form:

$$\begin{aligned} R = \Psi_s(0) &- 2\int h(\tau)\Psi_s(\tau+\alpha)\,d\tau \\ &+ \iint h(\tau)h(\sigma)[\Psi_s(\tau-\sigma) + \Psi_n(\tau-\sigma)]\,d\tau\,d\sigma. \end{aligned} \tag{11–44}$$

Because it is convenient not to write out explicitly the integration limits, it should be recalled that it is implicit that these limits reflect the physical realizability restriction $h(t) = 0$ for $t < 0$.

Equation (11–44) is in a form that explicitly symbolizes the problem of finding a minimum risk for a choice of the linear filter weighting function $h(t)$. In particular, notice that the minimization *does not* depend directly on the signal process $s(t)$ or the noise process $n(t)$, but only depends upon their respective covariance functions. This is probably one of the most important points in the W-K theory because it implies that the design of the optimum filter does not depend upon the exact nature of the input time series, but rather depends upon a limited knowledge of their statistical properties. In fact, the optimum linear filter can accommodate a limitless class of signals and noise as long as the respective covariances are the same as those for which the filter is optimum.

Suppose that $R_m$ is a minimum value of the risk $R$, which is attained by some particular choice of the weighting function $h(t)$. Then, if we replace

$h(t)$ in the risk function by $h(t) + \eta M(t)$, where $\eta$ is a real number and $M(t)$ is an arbitrary time function, it necessarily follows that

$$R_m[h(t)] \leq R[h(t) + \eta M(t)]. \tag{11–45}$$

Replace $h$ by $h + \eta M$ in (11–44) to obtain

$$\begin{aligned} R[h + \eta M] = R[h] &- 2\eta \int M(\tau)\Psi_s(\tau + \alpha)\, d\tau \\ &+ 2\eta \iint M(\tau)h(\sigma)[\Psi_s(\tau - \sigma) + \Psi_n(\tau - \sigma)]\, d\tau\, d\sigma \\ &+ \eta^2 \iint M(\tau)M(\sigma)[\Psi_s(\tau - \sigma) + \Psi_n(\tau - \sigma)]\, d\tau\, d\sigma. \end{aligned} \tag{11–46}$$

Equation (11–46) can be written in the abbreviated form

$$R[h + \eta M] = R[h] - 2\eta J_1 + \eta^2 J_2, \tag{11–47}$$

by defining the two integrals

$$\begin{aligned} J_1 &= \int M(\tau)\left\{\Psi_s(\tau + \alpha) - \int h(\sigma)[\Psi_s(\tau - \sigma) + \Psi_n(\tau - \sigma)]\, d\sigma\right\} d\tau \\ J_2 &= \iint M(\tau)M(\sigma)[\Psi_s(\tau - \sigma) + \Psi_n(\tau - \sigma)]\, d\tau\, d\sigma. \end{aligned} \tag{11–48}$$

It is apparent from (11–45) and (11–47) that (11–47) will be a minimum for $\eta = 0$. Differentiate $R[h + \eta M]$ with respect to $\eta$; the result will vanish at $\eta = 0$, if $J_1 = 0$. But, since this result must be valid for an arbitrary function $M(\tau)$, then (11–48) yields the minimizing condition

$$\Psi_s(\tau + \alpha) - \int h(\sigma)[\Psi_s(\tau - \sigma) + \Psi_n(\tau - \sigma)]\, d\sigma = 0. \tag{11–49}$$

Equation (11–49) provides the necessary condition that the risk $R$ be equal to the minimum risk $R_m$. We shall now show that (11–49) is also the sufficient condition for attaining the minimum of the risk function. If $J_1 = 0$, Equation (11–47) will reduce to

$$R[h + \eta M] = R[h] + \eta^2 J_2. \tag{11–50}$$

Note that in the definition of $J_2$, $\Psi_s$ and $\Psi_n$ are covariance functions and are, therefore, positive semidefinite functions. Thus, because the arbitrary function $M$ appears as a square, we conclude that $J_2 \geq 0$. This conclusion, when argued with (11–50), demonstrates that $R[h + \eta M] \geq R[h]$ and, thereby, establishes the conjectured sufficiency of (11–49) as the minimizing condition for the risk function.

Equation (11–49) is commonly called the *Wiener-Hopf equation* in many papers dealing with the filtering of time series. Strictly speaking, (11–49) should be called the Wiener-Hopf equation of the first kind. For the original form of the Wiener-Hopf equation, the kernel $\Psi = \Psi_s + \Psi_n$ must be exponentially small in magnitude. When integral transforms are taken of this equation, the kernel restriction assures one that there will exist a strip in the complex plane with which to match up the parameters. In the equation of the first kind, as we shall see, no such strip is available and factorization as a method of solution will be limited to the real axis of the complex plane.

## 11.4
## *WIENER-HOPF EQUATION WITHOUT PHYSICAL REALIZABILITY*

A criterion for the physical realizability of a linear filter can be stated in terms of either the weighting function $h(t)$ or its transform $H(i\omega)$.

In terms of the weighting function $h(t)$, physical realizability requires that $h(t) = 0$ for $t < 0$. Thus, the filter cannot respond to an impulse signal before the impulse arrives. Furthermore, $h(t)$ must approach zero with reasonable rapidity as $t \to +\infty$. This condition assures us that the effect produced by applying an impulse signal to the linear filter will eventually vanish.

In terms of the filter frequency response $H(i\omega)$, the condition for physical realizability is that $H$, considered as a function of the complex variable $\omega$, must be an analytic function in the half-plane defined by $\mathcal{I}m(\omega) < 0$. Moreover, $H$ must be sufficiently well behaved on the real frequency axis so that it satisfies the Paley-Wiener criterion [113, 148, 152],

$$\int_0^\infty \frac{|\ln|H(i\omega)||}{1+\omega^2}\, d\omega < \infty. \tag{11–51}$$

The fundamental difficulty in solving the Wiener-Hopf equation of the first kind (11–49) lies in imposing the restriction that the filter weighting function $h(t)$ be physically realizable. Without first verifying this source of theoretical difficulty, we shall, for the moment, drop the restriction that the linear filter be physically realizable. The results which are obtained under these conditions will serve to motivate the rather involved solution techniques required for practical problems. Moreover, our immediate results are directly applicable to problems arising in the design of spatial filters in physical optics. Spatial filters in optical systems do not have the cumbersome restriction of physical realizability, in the sense that has been defined, and, therefore, the methods of this section can be readily modified to the two-dimensional optical spatial filters [111].

Dropping the restriction that $h(t) = 0$, $t < 0$, take the Fourier transform of the Wiener-Hopf equation in the form of (11–49). The following sequence of equations are obtained:

$$\int \Psi_s(\tau + \alpha) e^{-i\omega\tau}\, d\tau = \iint h(\sigma)[\Psi_s(\tau - \sigma) + \Psi_n(\tau - \sigma)] e^{-i\omega\tau}\, d\sigma\, d\tau$$

$$\text{(11–52)} \quad e^{i\omega\alpha} \int \Psi_s(u) e^{-i\omega u}\, du = \int h(\sigma) e^{-i\omega\sigma}\, d\sigma \int [\Psi_s(v) + \Psi_n(v)] e^{-i\omega v}\, dv$$

$$e^{i\omega\alpha}\Phi_s(\omega) = H(i\omega)\,[\Phi_s(\omega) + \Phi_n(\omega)],$$

where, by definition,

$$\text{(11–53)} \quad \begin{aligned} \Phi_s(\omega) &= \mathscr{F}\{\Psi_s(t)\} = \int \Psi_s(t) e^{-i\omega t}\, dt \\ \Phi_n(\omega) &= \mathscr{F}\{\Psi_n(t)\} = \int \Psi_n(t) e^{-i\omega t}\, dt. \end{aligned}$$

Hence, under the given conditions, the frequency response of the optimum linear filter is

$$\text{(11–54)} \qquad H(i\omega) = \frac{\Phi_s(\omega) e^{i\omega\alpha}}{\Phi_s(\omega) + \Phi_n(\omega)}.$$

The next step is to find the value of the risk function for the minimizing filter given by (11–54). For this purpose, it is convenient to transform each element of (11–44) to a frequency domain form by inserting the Fourier transform pairs in the following fashion:

$$\begin{aligned} R &= \frac{1}{2\pi}\int \Phi_s(\omega)\, d\omega - \frac{2}{2\pi}\int h(\tau) \int \Phi_s(\omega) e^{i\omega(\tau+\alpha)}\, d\omega\, d\tau \\ &\quad + \frac{1}{2\pi}\iint h(\tau)h(\sigma) \int [\Phi_s(\omega) + \Phi_n(\omega)] e^{-i\omega(\sigma-\tau)}\, d\omega\, d\sigma\, d\tau \\ \text{(11–55)} \quad &= \frac{1}{2\pi}\int \Phi_s(\omega)\, d\omega - \frac{2}{2\pi}\int h(\tau) e^{i\omega\tau}\, d\tau \int \Phi_s(\omega) e^{i\omega\alpha}\, d\omega \\ &\quad + \frac{1}{2\pi}\int h(\tau) e^{i\omega\tau}\, d\tau \int h(\sigma) e^{-i\omega\sigma}\, d\sigma \int [\Phi_s(\omega) + \Phi_n(\omega)]\, d\omega \\ &= \frac{1}{2\pi}\int \{\Phi_s(\omega)[1 - 2H^*(i\omega)e^{i\omega\alpha}] + |H(i\omega)|^2[\Phi_s(\omega) + \Phi_n(\omega)]\}\, d\omega, \end{aligned}$$

or

$$\text{(11–56)} \qquad R = \frac{1}{2\pi}\int [\Phi_s(\omega)\,|e^{i\omega\alpha} - H(i\omega)|^2 + |H(i\omega)|^2 \Phi_n(\omega)]\, d\omega.$$

Substitute (11–54) into (11–56) to find the minimum value of the risk,

$$\text{(11–57)} \quad \begin{aligned} R_m &= \frac{1}{2\pi}\int \left[\Phi_s(\omega)\left| e^{i\omega\alpha} - \frac{e^{i\omega\alpha}\Phi_s(\omega)}{\Phi_s(\omega) + \Phi_n(\omega)}\right|^2 \right. \\ &\qquad \left. + \frac{\Phi_s^2(\omega)\Phi_n(\omega)}{[\Phi_s(\omega) + \Phi_n(\omega)]^2}\right] d\omega \\ R_m &= \frac{1}{2\pi}\int \frac{\Phi_s(\omega)\Phi_n(\omega)}{\Phi_s(\omega) + \Phi_n(\omega)}\, d\omega. \end{aligned}$$

As an illustrative example, consider a signal $s(t)$ having the power density spectrum

$$\Phi_s(\omega) = \mathscr{F}\{\Psi_s(t)\} = \frac{1}{1+\omega^2}. \tag{11–58}$$

The signal is additively mixed with *white noise*, which is characterized by a constant power-spectral density

$$\Phi_n(\omega) = N, \qquad \text{a constant.} \tag{11–59}$$

Let $\alpha = 0$, then for the optimum filter we apply (11–54) to obtain

$$H(\omega) = \frac{1/(1+\omega^2)}{1/(1+\omega^2)+N} = \frac{1/N}{(1+1/N)+\omega^2}. \tag{11–60}$$

The linear filter weighting function corresponding to (11–60) is

$$\begin{aligned} h(t) &= \frac{1}{2\pi}\int H(i\omega)e^{i\omega t}\,d\omega \\ &= \frac{1}{2[N(N+1)]^{1/2}}\exp\left\{-|t|\left(\frac{N+1}{N}\right)^{1/2}\right\}. \end{aligned} \tag{11–61}$$

It should be emphasized that this particular weighting function $h(t)$ is not physically realizable.

## 11.5
## *THE FACTORIZATION PROBLEM*

The principal developments in this section depend upon the following two theorems from the theory of functions [91, 102, 113, 148, 152, 159].

THEOREM 11.1: If $A(\omega)$ is a positive and real-valued function defined for real values of $\omega$ for which

$$\int_{-\infty}^{\infty}\frac{|\ln|A(\omega)||}{1+\omega^2}\,d\omega < \infty,$$

then there exist two functions of a complex variable, $A_1(\omega)$ and $A_2(\omega)$, such that

$$A(\omega) = A_1(\omega)A_2(\omega)$$

holds for real values of $\omega$. Furthermore, $A_1(\omega)$ is analytic, bounded, and free from zeros and singularities in the upper half-plane. Similarly $A_2(\omega)$ is analytic, bounded, and free from zeros and singularities in the lower half-plane. Also, $A_1(\omega) = A_2^*(\omega)$.

THEOREM 11.2: Let $f(t)$ be an integrable function which vanishes over the range $(-\infty, 0)$ and possesses a Fourier transform $F(\omega)$. Then

$$F(\omega) = \int_{-\infty}^{\infty} f(t)e^{-i\omega t}\,dt = \int_0^{\infty} f(t)e^{-i\omega t}\,dt$$

is an analytic and bounded function of the complex variable $\omega$ in the lower half of the complex plane. Conversely, let $F(\omega)$ be an analytic and bounded function of the complex variable $\omega$ in the lower half of the complex plane. Then, if $F(\omega)$ is the Fourier transform of a function $f(t)$ so that

$$f(t) = \frac{1}{2\pi} \int_{-\infty}^{\infty} F(\omega) e^{i\omega t}\, d\omega,$$

it is also true that $f(t)$ vanishes over the range $(-\infty, 0)$. A similar statement also is valid if the range $(-\infty, 0)$ is replaced by $(0, \infty)$ and if the word "lower" is replaced by "upper."

By means of these theorems, we can now proceed with the solution of the Wiener-Hopf equation.

Define an auxiliary function $g(\tau)$ by the relations

$$(11\text{–}62) \qquad \begin{aligned} g(\tau) &= \int_{-\infty}^{\infty} h(\sigma) \Psi_{s+n}(\tau - \sigma)\, d\sigma - \Psi_s(\tau + \alpha), \\ \Psi_{s+n}(\tau) &= \Psi_s(\tau) + \Psi_n(\tau). \end{aligned}$$

Equation (11–49) implies that, if $h(\sigma) = 0$ when $\sigma < 0$, then $g(\tau) = 0$ when $\tau \geq 0$.

Let $G(\omega)$ denote the Fourier transform of the auxiliary function $\mathbf{g}(\tau)$;

$$(11\text{–}63) \qquad G(\omega) = \int_{-\infty}^{\infty} g(\tau) e^{-i\omega\tau}\, d\tau.$$

Then the Fourier transform of (11–62) is

$$(11\text{–}64) \qquad \begin{aligned} G(\omega) &= \iint h(\sigma) \Psi_{s+n}(\tau - \sigma) e^{-i\omega\tau}\, d\sigma\, d\tau \\ &\quad - \int \Psi_s(\tau + \alpha) e^{-i\omega\tau}\, d\tau \\ &\overset{d}{=} I_1 + I_2. \end{aligned}$$

Theorem 11.2, coupled with the defining relation (11–62), implies that $G(\omega)$ is an analytic and bounded function of $\omega$ in the upper half of the complex plane. The component integrals $I_1$ and $I_2$ can be replaced by more convenient expressions. Thus, by definition,

$$(11\text{–}65) \qquad \begin{aligned} I_2 &= -\int \Psi_s(\tau + \alpha) e^{-i\omega\tau}\, d\tau \\ &= -e^{i\omega\alpha} \Phi_s(\omega). \end{aligned}$$

Similarly,

$$(11\text{–}66) \qquad \begin{aligned} I_1 &= \iint h(\sigma) \Psi_{s+n}(\tau - \sigma) e^{-i\omega\tau}\, d\sigma\, d\tau \\ &= \int h(\sigma) e^{-i\omega\sigma}\, d\sigma \int \Psi_{s+n}(u) e^{-i\omega u}\, du \\ &= H(i\omega) \Phi_{s+n}(\omega). \end{aligned}$$

Substitute (11–65) and (11–66) into (11–64) to obtain

$$G(\omega) = H(i\omega)\Phi_{s+n}(\omega) - e^{i\omega\alpha}\Phi_s(\omega). \tag{11–67}$$

Let us postulate that $\Phi_{s+n}(\omega)$ satisfies the hypotheses of Theorem 11.1. This being assumed, we can write

$$\Phi_{s+n}(\omega) = \Phi^+_{s+n}(\omega)\Phi^-_{s+n}(\omega), \tag{11–68}$$

where $\Phi^+_{s+n}(\omega)$ is analytic, bounded, and has no zeros or singularities in the upper half-plane while $\Phi^-_{s+n}(\omega)$ has analogous properties in the lower-half plane. From (11–67) and (11–68), we find

$$\frac{G(\omega)}{\Phi^+_{s+n}(\omega)} = H(i\omega)\Phi^-_{s+n}(\omega) - \frac{\Phi_s(\omega)}{\Phi^+_{s+n}(\omega)}e^{i\omega\alpha}. \tag{11–69}$$

Theorem 11.1 allows us to conclude that the ratio on the left-hand side of (11–69) is an analytic function of $\omega$ in the upper half-plane. If, in addition, this ratio is also bounded in the upper half-plane, then Theorem 11.2 leads us to the conclusion that the Fourier transform of the ratio $G(\omega)/\Phi^+_{s+n}(\omega)$ must vanish for $0 \leq t < \infty$. Therefore, if the Fourier transform is taken of (11–69), for $t > 0$, we have

$$\frac{1}{2\pi}\int_{-\infty}^{\infty} H(\omega)\Phi^-_{s+n}(\omega)e^{i\omega t}\,d\omega = \frac{1}{2\pi}\int_{-\infty}^{\infty}\frac{\Phi_s(\omega)}{\Phi^+_{s+n}(\omega)}e^{i\omega(t+\alpha)}\,d\omega. \tag{11–70}$$

We know that both $H(i\omega)$ and $\Phi^-_{s+n}(\omega)$ are analytic and bounded in the lower half-plane. Thus, Theorem 11.2 permits us to conclude that the Fourier transform $\mathscr{F}\{H(i\omega)\Phi^-_{s+n}(\omega)\} = 0$ for $t \leq 0$, or, in equation form,

$$\begin{aligned} b(t) &= \frac{1}{2\pi}\int_{-\infty}^{\infty} H(i\omega)\Phi^-_{s+n}(\omega)e^{i\omega t}\,d\omega \\ &= 0, \qquad t \leq 0. \end{aligned} \tag{11–71}$$

Hence, taking the inverse transform of (11–71),

$$\begin{aligned} H(i\omega)\Phi^-_{s+n}(\omega) &= \int_{-\infty}^{\infty} b(t)e^{-i\omega t}\,dt \\ &= \int_0^{\infty} b(t)^{-i\omega t}\,dt \\ &= \frac{1}{2\pi}\int_0^{\infty} e^{-i\omega t}\int_{-\infty}^{\infty} H(i\omega')\Phi^-_{s+n}(\omega')e^{i\omega' t}\,d\omega'\,dt. \end{aligned} \tag{11–72}$$

Equation (11–70) is valid for $t > 0$; therefore it can be inserted into (11–72) to yield the form of the optimal filter:

$$H(i\omega) = \frac{1}{2\pi\Phi^-_{s+n}(\omega)}\int_0^{\infty} e^{-i\omega t}\int_{-\infty}^{\infty}\frac{\Phi_s(\omega')}{\Phi^+_{s+n}(\omega')}e^{i\omega'(t+\alpha)}\,d\omega'\,dt. \tag{11–73}$$

The real problem in finding the optimal filter is to perform the factorization of the functions indicated in (11–68). Moreover, the real difficulties in the mathematical proof leading to (11–73) lie in the existence proof for the functions in (11–68).

In certain classes of linear filtering problems, the factorization of (11–68) offers no problem. For example, Wiener [152] illustrated the application of (11–73) for the particular power spectral-density functions

$$\Phi_n(\omega) = 0$$

$$\Phi_{s+n}(\omega) = \Phi_s(\omega) = \frac{1}{1+\omega^2}. \tag{11–74}$$

This particular spectral density factors into the two functions

$$\Phi_s^+(\omega) = \frac{1}{\omega + i}$$

$$\Phi_s^-(\omega) = \frac{1}{\omega - i}. \tag{11–75}$$

Insert (11–74) and (11–75) into (11–73) to compute

$$H(i\omega) = \frac{1}{2\pi[1/(\omega - i)]}\int_0^\infty e^{-i\omega t}\int_{-\infty}^{\infty}\frac{1/(1+\omega'^2)}{1/(\omega'+i)}e^{i\omega'(t+\alpha)}\,d\omega'\,dt$$

$$= \frac{\omega - i}{2\pi}\int_0^\infty e^{-i\omega t}\int_{-\infty}^{\infty}\frac{1}{\omega' - i}e^{i\omega'(t+\alpha)}\,d\omega'\,dt \tag{11–76}$$

$$= e^{-\alpha}.$$

Thus, we conclude that the optimum prediction of $s(t+\alpha)$ is obtained by the product $s(t)\exp(-\alpha)$. This result, as Wiener stated, implies that the *predictable* part of $s(t)$ tends to zero as $\alpha \to \infty$ and that, roughly, the *unpredictable* part of $s(t)$ is as equally likely to be positive as to be negative. That is, $s(t+\alpha)$ will be distributed about $s(t)\exp(-\alpha)$ as a mean value.

## 11.6
## *SOLUTIONS OF THE WIENER-HOPF EQUATION*

Because very few filtering problems can be solved by means of the factorization technique of Section 11.5, alternative solution methods have been formulated for the Wiener-Hopf equation which are applicable in special, but practical, situations. Two special solution techniques are described in this section as being representative of some of the more commonly employed schemes.

The Wiener-Hopf equation can be written in the general form

$$\Psi_s(t) = \int_0^T h(\sigma)\Psi(|t-\sigma|)\,d\sigma. \tag{11–77}$$

If the spectral density function $\Phi(\omega)$ corresponding to $\Psi(t)$ is rational in $\omega^2$, then we can demonstrate that an explicit solution can be formulated for the Wiener-Hopf equation [87, 140, 159, 160, 161, 162, 163].

The first technique is to transform the Wiener-Hopf integral equation to an equivalent differential equation. In some cases one is able to find solutions to the differential equation while little hope is seen for a solution to the integral equation. The reduction to the differential equation is always possible when the signal-plus-noise spectral density function $\Phi_{s+n}(\omega)$ can be expressed as a rational function in $\omega^2$, or equivalently as the ratio of two polynomials in $\omega^2$. The spectral density

$$\Phi(\omega) = \int \Psi(\tau)e^{-i\omega\tau}\,d\tau \tag{11-78}$$

is postulated to be a rational function of $\omega^2$. Therefore, it can be written as the quotient of two polynomials $P_m/Q_n$; $P_m$ is of degree $m$, and $Q_n$ is of degree $n$; $n > m$. Hence,

$$\Phi(\omega) = \frac{P_m(\omega^2)}{Q_n(\omega^2)} = \frac{a_0 + a_2\omega^2 + \cdots + a_{2m}\omega^{2m}}{b_0 + b_2\omega^2 + \cdots + b_{2n}\omega^{2n}}; \qquad n > m. \tag{11-79}$$

The finite power condition

$$\int_{-\infty}^{\infty} \Phi(\omega)\,d\omega < \infty \tag{11-80}$$

is satisfied only if $P_m$ is at least 2 degrees less than the polynomial $Q_n$. Insert (11–79) into (11–77) in the following fashion:

$$\begin{aligned}\Psi_s(t) &= \int_0^T h(\sigma)\,d\sigma \cdot \frac{1}{2\pi}\int_{-\infty}^{\infty} \Phi(\omega)e^{i\omega(t-\sigma)}\,d\omega \\ &= \int_0^T h(\sigma)e^{-i\omega\sigma} \cdot \frac{1}{2\pi}\int_{-\infty}^{\infty} \Phi(\omega)e^{i\omega t}\,d\sigma\,d\omega \\ &= \frac{1}{2\pi}\int_{-\infty}^{\infty} \frac{P_m(\omega^2)}{Q_n(\omega^2)}\bar{H}(i\omega)e^{i\omega t}\,d\omega,\end{aligned} \tag{11-81}$$

where

$$\bar{H}(i\omega) \stackrel{d}{=} \int_0^T h(\sigma)e^{-i\omega\sigma}\,d\sigma. \tag{11-82}$$

Introduce the differential operators

$$\begin{aligned}D_Q &= b_0 - b_2D^2 + b_4D^4 + \cdots + (-1)^nD^{2n} \\ D_P &= a_0 - a_2D^2 + a_4D^4 + \cdots + (-1)^mD^{2m} \\ D &\stackrel{d}{=} \frac{d}{dt}.\end{aligned} \tag{11-83}$$

Operate on (11–81) by $D_Q$ to find

$$\begin{aligned}D_Q\{\Psi_s(t)\} &= \frac{1}{2\pi}D_Q\left\{\int_{-\infty}^{\infty} \frac{P_m(\omega^2)}{Q_n(\omega^2)}\bar{H}(i\omega)e^{i\omega t}\,d\omega\right\} \\ &= \frac{1}{2\pi}D_P\left\{\int_{-\infty}^{\infty} \bar{H}(i\omega)e^{i\omega t}\,d\omega\right\} \\ &= D_P\{h(t)\}.\end{aligned} \tag{11-84}$$

The important result contained in (11–84) is that the integral equation which is satisfied by the frequency response of the optimal linear filter has been replaced by a differential equation for the filter's impulse response $h(t)$. However, all solutions of (11–84) are not necessarily solutions of the integral equation (11–77); only those which satisfy the proper boundary conditions are admissible solutions. These boundary conditions will next be established.

Operate on (11–78) to obtain

$$\Psi(|t|) = \frac{1}{2\pi}\int_{-\infty}^{\infty} \Phi(\omega)e^{i\omega t}\,d\omega$$

$$D_Q\{\Psi(|t|)\} = D_Q\left\{\int_{-\infty}^{\infty} \frac{P_m(\omega^2)}{Q_n(\omega^2)}e^{i\omega t}\,d\omega\right\} \tag{11–85}$$

$$= \int_{-\infty}^{\infty} P_m(\omega^2)e^{i\omega t}\,d\omega = 0, \qquad t \neq 0.$$

Therefore, a covariance function corresponding to a spectral-density function which is expressible as a rational function of two polynomials must satisfy a differential equation of the form

$$\left\{b_0 - b_2\frac{d^2}{dt^2} + b_4\frac{d^4}{dt^4} + \cdots + (-1)^n\frac{d^{2n}}{dt^{2n}}\right\}\Psi(|t|) = 0. \tag{11–86}$$

Youla [160] illustrated the application of these results by considering the Picard kernel

$$\Psi(|t|) = e^{-k|t|}. \tag{11–87}$$

The corresponding spectral-density function is

$$\Phi(\omega) = \int_{-\infty}^{\infty} \Psi(|t|)e^{-i\omega t}\,dt$$

$$= \int_{-\infty}^{\infty} e^{-k|t|}e^{-i\omega t}\,dt \tag{11–88}$$

$$= \frac{k}{k^2+\omega^2}.$$

By comparing (11–88) with (11–79), we find the polynomial coefficients

$$a_0 = k$$

$$b_0 = k^2 \tag{11–89}$$

$$b_2 = 1.$$

With these coefficients, the appropriate form of the differential equation (11–83) for the illustrative example is

$$k^2\Psi_s(t) - \frac{d^2\Psi_s(t)}{dt^2} = kh(t). \tag{11–90}$$

In practice, $\Psi_s(t)$ and $\Psi_{s+n}(t)$ are known, and $h(t)$ can be solved from (11–90).

The second technique is to use the hypothesis that $\Phi_{s+n}(\omega)$ is a rational function to obtain the factorizations (11–73). Let $\omega_{pi}$ denote zeros of

$P_m(\omega^2)$ in the upper half-plane ($\mathscr{I}m\,\omega_{pi} > 0$) and let $-\omega_{pi}$ denote zeros in the lower half-plane. A similar convention is chosen for the roots $\omega_{qi}$ of the polynomial $Q_n(\omega^2)$. Then (11–79) can be written in the equivalent form

(11–91)
$$\Phi(\omega) = c^2 \frac{\prod_{i=1}^{m} (\omega^2 - \omega_{pi}^2)}{\prod_{i=1}^{n} (\omega^2 - \omega_{qi}^2)}$$
$$= (-1)^g c^2 \frac{\prod (\omega_{pi}^2 - \omega)}{\prod (\omega_{qi}^2 - \omega)}; \; g = n - m.$$

It should be noted that since $\Phi(\omega)$ is real for all real $\omega$, all complex roots $\omega_{pi}$ and $\omega_{qi}$ must be present in conjugate pairs. Furthermore, because by definition $\Phi(\omega) \geq 0$, it follows that all real roots of the numerator must occur with even multiplicity or the expression would change sign. Finally the desired factorization can be written as

(11–92)
$$\Phi(\omega) = \Phi^+(\omega)\,\Phi^-(\omega)$$
$$\Phi^+(\omega) = i^g c \frac{\prod (\omega_{pi} + \omega)}{\prod (\omega_{qi} + \omega)}$$
$$\Phi^-(\omega) = i^g c \frac{\prod (\omega_{pi} - \omega)}{\prod (\omega_{qi} - \omega)}.$$

Wong and Thomas [157] extended the W-K theory for $n$-dimensional processes and expressed the formulations in matrix equations. They were able to obtain the matrix counterparts to the solution of the Wiener-Hopf equation by generalizations of the method of factorizations as well as the method of rational spectral-density functions.

The difficulties involved in solving the Wiener-Hopf equation for arbitrary kernels has motivated investigators to search for appropriate approximation solution methods. An example of one such approach is the technique proposed by Carrier [23]. Carrier suggested that the kernel in the given Wiener-Hopf equation be replaced by a substitute kernel which duplicates the *important* features of the original kernel and at the same time, the solution of the modified integral equation duplicates the dominant features of the original problem. Carrier found that, although no firm rules could be formulated for selecting the substitute kernel, it should have the same singularities in the integration domain, the same area, and the same first moment corresponding to the original kernel. Some examples of the use of substitute kernels are contained in Reference 23.

## 11.7
### *FREQUENCY DOMAIN ANALYSIS*

The frequency domain analysis techniques for the synthesis of optimum linear filters are commonly known as the method of Bode and Shannon to acknowledge the original contributions of these men [14]. Bode and Shannon simplified the derivation of the optimum filter formulation by using *conventional* electrical circuit theory concepts to interpret the mathematical operations in physically *intuitive* terms. Whether or not the reader will find their approach intuitive will, to a large extent, depend upon his familiarity with linear filter theory. The reliance upon physical interpretations of the operations has been found to provide a very powerful tool for nonmathematicians who are faced with the real-life problem of designing optimal linear filters. However, the Bode-Shannon method does have some disadvantages. In particular, the method does not lend itself readily to generalizations of practical interest without increased complications which soon lead directly to problems in numerical manipulations. Darlington has generalized the Bode-Shannon method and has both extended and rigorized the original theory [36].

The key point in the Bode-Shannon method lies in the recognition of the fact that the mean square error for a linear system is dependent solely upon the power density spectrums of the signal and of the noise. Because of this characteristic, we can replace the true signal $s(t)$ by an equivalent signal $\tilde{s}(t)$, provided that they both have identical spectral density functions

$$\begin{aligned} \Phi_s(\omega) &= \mathscr{F}\{\mathrm{E}\{s(t)s(t-\tau)\}\} = \mathscr{F}\{\mathrm{E}\{\tilde{s}(t)\tilde{s}(t-\tau)\}\} \\ &= \mathscr{F}\{\Psi_s(\tau)\} = \mathscr{F}\{\Psi_{\tilde{s}}(\tau)\}. \end{aligned} \tag{11–93}$$

The equivalent signal $\tilde{s}(t)$ is introduced to simplify certain manipulations in the theoretical development.

The optimum filter is conceptually decomposed into two parts. The first part is designed to convert the equivalent signal $\tilde{s}(t)$ into a *white* noise process. The second part of the optimum filter is selected as one which, when transforming a white noise process, yields a *best* prediction of the equivalent signal. These concepts will now be developed and demonstrated to produce the desired optimum filter.

The equivalent signal $\tilde{s}(t)$ is formed by using white noise $\tilde{n}(t)$ as an input to a linear filter having a frequency response $A(i\omega)$ which bears the following relation to the original signal $s(t)$:

$$|A(i\omega)|^2 = \Phi_s(\omega) = \int_{-\infty}^{\infty} \Psi_s(t)e^{-i\omega t}\,dt. \tag{11–94}$$

Define

$$a(t) = \mathscr{F}\{A(i\omega)\} = \frac{1}{2\pi}\int_{-\infty}^{\infty} A(i\omega)e^{i\omega t}\,d\omega; \tag{11–95}$$

then, by definition, we can write the equivalent signal as

$$\tilde{s}(t) = \int_{-\infty}^{\infty} n(\tau)a(t-\tau)\,d\tau; \qquad a(t-\tau) = 0,\ \tau > t. \tag{11–96}$$

Assume that $E\{\tilde{s}(t)\} = 0$; then the covariance function of the equivalent signal is

$$\begin{aligned} \Psi_{\tilde{s}}(\tau) &= E\{\tilde{s}(t)\tilde{s}(t-\tau)\} \\ &= \int_{-\infty}^{\infty}\int_{-\infty}^{\infty} E\{\tilde{n}(\sigma)\tilde{n}(\eta)a(t-\sigma)a(t-\tau-\eta)\}\,d\sigma\,d\eta \\ &= \int_{-\infty}^{\infty}\int_{-\infty}^{\infty} \Psi_{n}(\sigma-\eta)a(t-\sigma)a(t-\tau-\eta)\,d\sigma\,d\eta. \end{aligned} \tag{11–97}$$

We postulated that $\tilde{n}(t)$ was a white noise process; therefore, its covariance function must be of the Dirac-delta form

$$\Psi_{\tilde{n}}(\tau) = N\,\delta(\tau), \tag{11–98}$$

where $N$ is a constant. Insert (11–98) into (11–97) to obtain

$$\Psi_{\tilde{s}}(\tau) = N\int_{-\infty}^{\infty} a(t-\eta)a(t-\tau-\eta)\,d\eta. \tag{11–99}$$

If the Fourier transform is taken of both sides of (11–99), we find

$$\begin{aligned} \Phi_{\tilde{s}}(\omega) = \mathscr{F}\{\Psi_{\tilde{s}}(\tau)\} &= N\int_{-\infty}^{\infty}\int_{-\infty}^{\infty} a(t-\eta)a(t-\tau-\eta)e^{-i\omega\tau}\,d\eta\,d\tau \\ &= N\int_{-\infty}^{\infty}\int_{-\infty}^{\infty} a(u)a(u-\tau)e^{i\omega(u-\tau)}e^{-i\omega u}\,du\,d\tau \\ &= N\,|A(i\omega)|^2 \\ &= N\Phi_s(\omega). \end{aligned} \tag{11–100}$$

The constant $N$ is arbitrary and at our disposal to set equal to unity. Thus, (11–100) proves that $\tilde{s}(t)$ and $s(t)$ have the same power density and covariance functions as required by the definition of an equivalent signal in (11–93). The conclusion is that the procedure for generating $\tilde{s}(t)$ from an appropriate transformation of a white noise process $\tilde{n}(t)$ satisfies our requirements.

An important fundamental question is whether or not the linear filter, having the required response $A(i\omega)$, is physically realizable. Two possibilities exist.

(i) If $\Phi_s(\omega)$ satisfies the Paley-Wiener criterion

$$\int_{-\infty}^{\infty} \frac{|\ln|\Phi_s(\omega)||}{1+\omega^2}\,d\omega < \infty, \tag{11–101}$$

then, according to Theorem 11.1, a function $A(i\omega)$ exists such that

(*a*) $|A(i\omega)|^2 = \Phi_s(\omega) = \Phi_s^{+}(\omega)\Phi_s^{-}(\omega) = A(i\omega)A(-i\omega)$.

(*b*) $a(t) = \mathscr{F}\{A(i\omega)\} = 0, \qquad \text{for } t < 0.$

(c) $A(i\omega)$ is analytic and can be selected so that it is nonzero in the right half-plane.

(d) $1/A(i\omega)$ is also analytic and nonzero in the right half-plane.

(ii) If $\Phi_s(\omega)$ fails to satisfy (11–101), then it can be shown that the future of the input signal $s(t)$ can be completely determined from knowledge of its past history. This condition is called the singular case and it will not be discussed.

### 11.7.1 *PURE PREDICTION*

The Bode-Shannon analysis method is diagrammed in Figure 11–2. The initial input signal is a white noise process $\tilde{n}(t)$ which is transformed to an equivalent signal $\tilde{s}(t)$ by means of a linear filter having the frequency response $A(i\omega)$. We have previously shown that, if (11–94) is satisfied, then $\tilde{s}(t)$ is equivalent to $s(t)$ in the sense of contributing the same mean-square-prediction error. This is a conceptual step used only to indicate a manner of generating the equivalent signal. The first filter is not part of the optimum filter which is contained within the dashed lines in Figure 11–2. The next step is to transform $\tilde{s}(t)$ back to $\tilde{n}(t)$ by passing it through a second linear filter having the response $H_1(i\omega) = A^{-1}(i\omega)$. Finally, the optimum filtering problem is embodied in the selection of a linear filter response $H_2(i\omega)$ which processes $\tilde{n}(t)$ to produce the *best* mean-square approximation to $\tilde{s}(t+\alpha)$. The combination of the two filters characterized by $H_1(i\omega)$ and $H_2(i\omega)$ will be shown to constitute the optimum prediction filter for the original true signal $s(t)$.

For the moment, in order to motivate the development, we shall neglect the problems imposed by the condition that the linear filters be physically realizable. Notice that, if white noise is applied to the input of the first filter, the output is the equivalent signal $\tilde{s}(t)$. Therefore, using (11–54), if $\tilde{n}(t)$ is transformed by a filter having the response

$$H_2'(i\omega) = \frac{H(i\omega)}{H_1(i\omega)} = \frac{1}{1/A(i\omega)}\frac{\Phi_s(\omega)}{\Phi_s(\omega)}e^{i\omega\alpha} = A(i\omega)e^{i\omega\alpha}, \tag{11–102}$$

then the output is

$$\begin{aligned} z(t) &= \frac{1}{2\pi}\int_{-\infty}^{\infty}\tilde{n}(\sigma)\,d\sigma\int_{-\infty}^{\infty}A(i\omega)e^{i\omega\alpha}e^{i\omega(t-\sigma)}\,d\omega \\ &= \int_{-\infty}^{\infty}\tilde{n}(\sigma)a(t+\alpha-\sigma)\,d\sigma \qquad (11\text{–}103) \\ &= \tilde{s}(t+\alpha). \end{aligned}$$

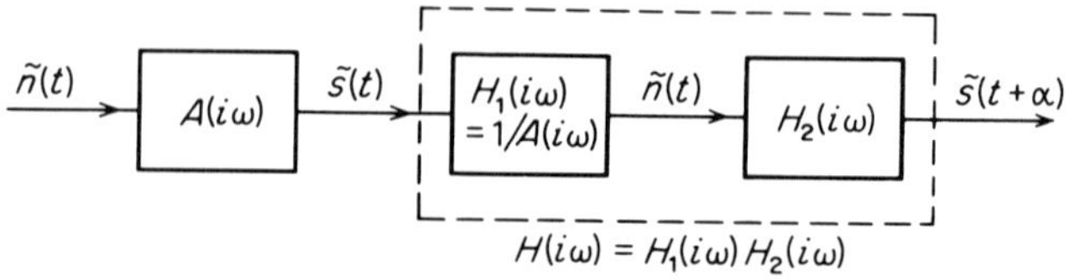


**Fig. 11-2** Bode-Shannon optimum filter factorization.

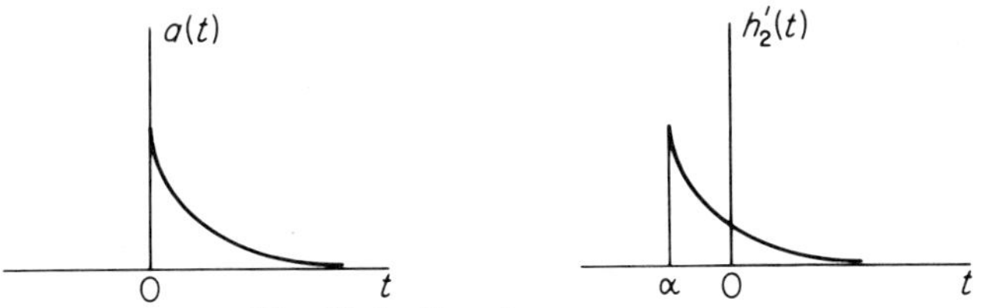


**Fig. 11-3** Impulse responses.

$\tilde{s}(t+\alpha)$ is the signal which is known to yield a zero mean-square error for the prediction problem. The impulse response corresponding to $H_2'(i\omega)$ is

$$
\begin{aligned}
h_2'(t) &= \mathscr{F}\{H_2'(i\omega)\} = \frac{1}{2\pi}\int_{-\infty}^{\infty} A(i\omega)e^{i\omega(t+\alpha)}\,d\omega \\
&\overset{d}{=} a(t+\alpha).
\end{aligned}
\tag{11–104}
$$

The impulse responses a$(t)$ and $h_2'(t)$ are sketched in Figure 11–3. It is evident that $h_2'(t)$ is unrealizable because it does not vanish for $t < 0$.

By comparing (11–103) with (11–104), we observe that one can write the equivalent signal in the alternate form

$$
\tilde{s}(t+\alpha) = \int_{-\infty}^{\infty} \tilde{n}(\tau)h_2'(t-\tau)\,d\tau. \tag{11–105}
$$

The conclusion drawn from (11–105) is that the contribution to $\tilde{s}(t)$ contributed by $\tilde{n}(t)$ for $\tau < t$ is exactly equivalent to that produced by transforming $\tilde{n}(t)$ by a linear filter having the impulse response $h_2(t)$, shown in Figure 11–4, in place of $h_2'(t)$. The substitution of $h_2(t)$ for $h_2'(t)$ is tantamount to ignoring the influence of future values of $\tilde{n}(\tau)$ for $\tau > t$. This is precisely what must be done in order to obtain a minimum mean-square-prediction error.

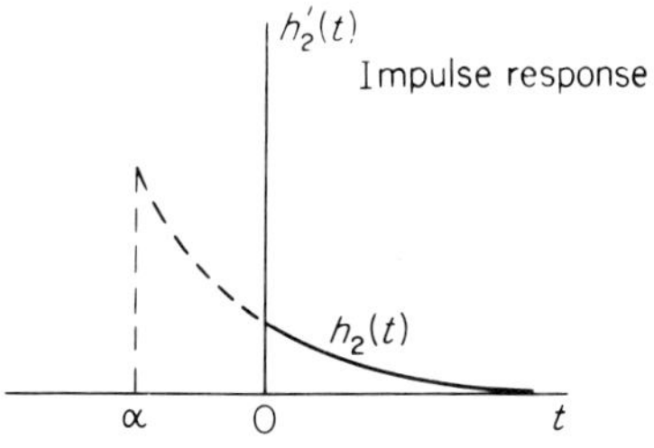


**Fig. 11-4** Impulse response.

The advantage of using the filter $H_1(i\omega)$ is that it allows us to work with a statistically simple white noise process $\tilde{n}(t)$, rather than work immediately with the equivalent signal $\tilde{s}(t)$. The important characteristic of white noise is that future samples of the process are stochastically independent of previous samples. If the original signal $s(t)$ is assumed to have zero mean value, then the expected value, as well as the most probable value, of $\tilde{s}(t)$ resulting from the transformation of $\tilde{n}(\tau)$, $\tau > t$, is zero. Successive future values are stochastically independent and can be treated one at a time.

Combining our results, we find the desired optimum realizable linear filter to be

(11–106)

$$H(i\omega) = H_1(i\omega)H_2(i\omega)$$

$$H(i\omega) = \frac{H_2(i\omega)}{A(i\omega)} = \frac{1}{A(i\omega)}\int_0^\infty h_2'(t)e^{-i\omega t}\,dt,$$

$$h_2'(t) = \frac{1}{2\pi}\int_{-\infty}^{\infty} A(i\omega)e^{i\omega(t+\alpha)}\,d\omega,$$

$$|A(i\omega)|^2 = \int_{-\infty}^{\infty} \Psi_s(t)e^{-i\omega t}\,dt.$$

The application of (11–106) can be illustrated with the example used in the preceding sections. Let the signal $s(t)$ have a power density spectral function

(11–107) $$\Phi_s(\omega) = \frac{1}{1+\omega^2} = \frac{1}{1+i\omega}\cdot\frac{1}{1-i\omega}.$$

In this case,

(11–108) $$A(i\omega) = \frac{1}{1+i\omega},$$

and

(11–109)

$$h_2'(t) = \frac{1}{2\pi}\int_{-\infty}^{\infty}\frac{1}{1+i\omega}e^{i\omega(t+\alpha)}\,d\omega$$

$$= \begin{cases} e^{-(t+\alpha)}, & t+\alpha > 0 \\ 0, & t+\alpha < 0; \end{cases}$$

(11–110)

$$H_2(i\omega) = \int_0^\infty e^{-(t+\alpha)}e^{-i\omega t}\,dt$$

$$= \frac{1}{1+i\omega}e^{-\alpha}.$$

Thus, for this example, the optimum filter is

(11–111) $$H(i\omega) = \frac{H_2(i\omega)}{A(i\omega)} = e^{-\alpha}.$$

This corresponds to the result obtained for the same example illustrated in Section 11.5.

### 11.7.2 *PREDICTION OF SIGNAL PERTURBED BY NOISE*

Suppose that the signal $s(t)$ is perturbed by adding a noise $n(t)$. The arguments employed in Section 11.7.1 can also be extended to include this situation.

The first step, as indicated in Figure 11–2, is to transform

$$y(t) = s(t) + n(t)$$

to a process $\tilde{n}(t)$ having a uniform, or constant, power density spectrum. Define

$$\Phi_s(\omega) = \int_{-\infty}^{\infty} \mathrm{E}\{s(t)s(t-\tau)\}e^{-i\omega\tau}\,d\tau$$

(11–112) $$\Phi_n(\omega) = \int_{-\infty}^{\infty} \mathrm{E}\{n(t)n(t-\tau)\}e^{-i\omega\tau}\,d\tau$$

$$\Phi_{s+n}(\omega) = \Phi_s(\omega) + \Phi_n(\omega).$$

From Theorem 11.1, assuming that the theorem hypotheses are satisfied, we can factor $\Phi_{s+n}(\omega)$ into

(11–113) $$\Phi_{s+n}(\omega) = \Phi_{s+n}^{+}(\omega)\Phi_{s+n}^{-}(\omega),$$

where $\Phi_{s+n}^{+}(\omega)$ is analytic, bounded, and has no zeros or singularities in the upper half-plane. Let $c(t)$ denote the Fourier transform of $\Phi_{s+n}^{+}(\omega)$. Theorem 11.2 then implies that $c(t) = 0$ for $t < 0$.

We have already shown that, if there were no restriction of physical realizability, the optimum filter would have the response, (11–54),

(11–114) $$H'(i\omega) = \frac{\Phi_s(\omega)}{\Phi_{s+n}(\omega)}e^{i\omega\alpha}.$$

If $y(t)$ is transformed by a linear filter having the response

$$H_1(i\omega) = \frac{1}{A_{sn}(i\omega)},$$

where

(11–115) $$|A_{sn}(i\omega)|^2 = \Phi_{s+n}(\omega) = A_{sn}(i\omega)A_{sn}(-i\omega),$$

then the resulting process $\tilde{n}(t)$ will have the required uniform, or white, spectral density function. It follows that, neglecting realizability, the best optimum filter to use is, by analogy with (11–102) and (11–114),

$$H_2'(i\omega) = \frac{H'(i\omega)}{H_1(i\omega)} = \frac{\Phi_s(\omega)}{\Phi_{s+n}(\omega)}A_{sn}(i\omega)e^{i\omega\alpha}$$

(11–116) $$= \frac{\Phi_s(\omega)}{\Phi_{s+n}^{+}(\omega)\Phi_{s+n}^{-}(\omega)}A_{sn}(i\omega)e^{i\omega\alpha} = \frac{\Phi_s(\omega)}{A_{sn}(i\omega)A_{sn}(-i\omega)}A_{sn}(i\omega)e^{i\omega\alpha}$$

$$= \frac{\Phi_s(\omega)}{A_{sn}(-i\omega)}e^{i\omega\alpha}.$$

The corresponding impulse response is

(11–117) $$h_2'(t) = \mathscr{F}\{H_2'(i\omega)\} = \frac{1}{2\pi}\int_{-\infty}^{\infty}\frac{\Phi_s(\omega)}{A_{sn}(-i\omega)}e^{i\omega(t+\alpha)}\,d\omega.$$

Let

(11–118) $$h_2(t) = \begin{cases} h_2'(t), & t \geq 0 \\ 0, & t < 0. \end{cases}$$

Then the desired optimum realizable filter will have the response

(11–119) $$\begin{aligned} H(i\omega) &= H_1(i\omega)H_2(i\omega) \\ &= H_1(i\omega)\mathscr{F}\{h_2(t)\}. \end{aligned}$$

An illustration of these formulations will be given by using the same example considered at the end of Section 11.4. We have the given spectral density functions

$$\Phi_s(\omega) = \frac{1}{1+\omega^2}$$

$$\Phi_n(\omega) = N \tag{11–120}$$

$$\Phi_{s+n}(\omega) = \frac{(1+N)+N\omega^2}{1+\omega^2}.$$

The spectral function can be factored into the form

$$\Phi_{s+n}(\omega) = \left[\frac{(1+N)^{1/2}+iN^{1/2}\omega}{1+i\omega}\right]\left[\frac{(1+N)^{1/2}-iN^{1/2}\omega}{1-i\omega}\right]. \tag{11–121}$$

Hence,

$$A_{sn}(-i\omega) = \frac{(1+N)^{1/2}-iN^{1/2}\omega}{1-i\omega}. \tag{11–122}$$

Insert (11–120) and (11–122) into (11–116) to obtain

$$\begin{aligned} H_2(i\omega) &= \frac{1}{1+\omega^2}\cdot\frac{1-i\omega}{(1+N)^{1/2}-iN^{1/2}\omega}e^{i\omega\alpha} \\ &= \frac{1}{(1+i\omega)[(1+N)^{1/2}-iN^{1/2}\omega]}e^{i\omega\alpha}. \end{aligned} \tag{11–123}$$

Define the auxiliary variable

$$\eta = \left(\frac{1+N}{N}\right)^{1/2}. \tag{11–124}$$

Calculate $h_2'(t)$ from (11–117), (11–123), and (11–124). The result is

$$h_2'(t) = \begin{cases} \dfrac{1}{N^{1/2}(1+\eta)}e^{-(t+\alpha)}, & t+\alpha > 0 \\ \dfrac{1}{N^{1/2}(1+\eta)}e^{\eta(t+\alpha)}, & t+\alpha < 0. \end{cases} \tag{11–125}$$

We simplify the illustrative problem by limiting ourselves to the case in which $\alpha = 0$.

In this case

$$h_2'(t) = \frac{1}{N^{1/2}(1+\eta)}e^{-t}, \tag{11–126}$$

and the corresponding transform is

$$H_2(i\omega) = \mathscr{F}\{h_2'(t)\} = \frac{[N^{1/2}(1+\eta)]^{-1}}{1+i\omega}. \tag{11–127}$$

Finally, the optimum filter is

$$H(i\omega) = H_1(i\omega)H_2(i\omega)$$

$$= \frac{1}{A_{sn}(i\omega)} \cdot \frac{[N^{1/2}(1+\eta)]^{-1}}{1+i\omega}$$

(11–128)
$$= \frac{1+i\omega}{N^{1/2}\{[(1+N)/N]^{1/2}+i\omega\}} \cdot \frac{[N^{1/2}(1+\eta)]^{-1}}{1+i\omega}$$

$$= \frac{[N(1+\eta)]^{-1/2}}{\eta+i\omega}.$$

## 11.8
## *A PROPERTY OF WIENER FILTERS*

Quite a few papers have been written on extensions of the W-K theory. In particular, it will concern us in this section that many authors have formally carried out the development for individual cases in which the desired output of the optimum filter is not the signal itself, but rather some particular linear transformation of the signal. Zakai has discovered a rather remarkable and useful property of *Wiener filters* (filters which are the optimal filters in the W-K theory) which provides a universal technique for treating what was previously considered as discrete special problems [167].

Let $s(t)$ be the original input signal, and let $H(i\omega; \alpha)$ be the physically realizable transfer function which yields a *best* mean least squares estimate of $s(t+\alpha)$. This is the fundamental problem. A generalization of the fundamental problem was given in Section 11.3. There we sought a transfer function $H_L(i\omega; \alpha)$ which produced the best least squares estimate of $y_d(t)$, where $y_d(t)$ was a linear transformation of $s(t)$. The W-K theory provides the method of solving for the optimum filter $H_L(i\omega; \alpha)$. Zakai showed that, once $H(i\omega; \alpha)$ is known for all real $\alpha$ and a given set of spectral density functions $\Phi_s(\omega)$, $\Phi_n(\omega)$, $\Phi_{sn}(\omega)$, it is possible to find $H_L(i\omega; \alpha)$ directly from $H(i\omega; \alpha)$ without any further references to the spectral density functions which determined $H(i\omega; \alpha)$.

Since we restrict ourselves to linear operations, the desired output after a linear operation can be written as

(11–129)
$$z(t) = L_\alpha[s(t+\alpha)],$$

where $L_\alpha$ denotes the linear operator transforming $s(t)$ to $z(t)$. The important contribution of Zakai is that the optimum filters $H(i\omega; \alpha)$ and $H_L(i\omega; \alpha)$ are related by the same linear operator $L_\alpha$. That is,

(11–130)
$$H_L(i\omega; \alpha) = L_\alpha[H(i\omega; \alpha)].$$

Although Zakai [167] has given a rigorous proof of (11–130), we shall obtain the same result by a formal sequence of arguments. The estimate error is defined as

(11–131)
$$\epsilon(t) = y_d(t) - L_\alpha[s(t+\alpha)].$$

The corresponding mean-square-risk function is

$$\begin{aligned} R &= \mathrm{E}\{\epsilon^2(t)\} = \mathrm{E}\{\| y_d(t) - L_\alpha[s(t+\alpha)] \|^2\} \\ &= \mathrm{E}\{y_d^2(t)\} + \mathrm{E}\{(L_\alpha[s(t+\alpha)])^2\} \\ &\quad -2\mathrm{E}\{y_d(t)\, L_\alpha[s(t+\alpha)]\}. \end{aligned} \tag{11–132}$$

Each element in (11–132) must be expressed in terms of known operations as well as the known signal and noise statistical parameters.

Because $L_\alpha$ is a linear transformation, it can be commuted with other linear operations, such as expected values and Fourier transforms. The first term on the right-hand side of (11–132) is the same as that given in (11–41), where $h(t)$ is replaced by $h_L(t)$ to signify that the optimal filter must yield a transformed value of the original signal.

The second term can be transformed in the following fashion:

$$\begin{aligned} \mathrm{E}\{L_\alpha[s(t+\alpha)]\, L_\alpha[s(t+\alpha)]\} &= L_\alpha L_\alpha \mathrm{E}\{s(t+\alpha)s(t+\alpha)\} \\ &= L_\alpha L_\alpha \Psi_s(0) \\ &= \Psi_s(0). \end{aligned} \tag{11–133}$$

The third term is treated in an analogous manner,

$$\begin{aligned} \mathrm{E}\{y_d(t)\, L_\alpha[s(t+\alpha)]\} &= \mathrm{E}\left\{\int h_L(\tau)[s(t-\tau) + n(t-\tau)] \cdot L_\alpha[s(t+\alpha)]\, d\tau\right\} \\ &= \int h_L(\tau)\, L_\alpha[\mathrm{E}\{s(t-\tau)s(t+\alpha)\}]\, d\tau \\ &= \int h_L(\tau)\, L_\alpha[\Psi_s(\tau+\alpha)]\, d\tau. \end{aligned} \tag{11–134}$$

Combining these results permits us to write the risk function as

$$\begin{aligned} R &= \Psi_s(0) - 2\int h_L(\tau)\, L_\alpha[\Psi_s(\tau+\alpha)]\, d\alpha \\ &\quad + \iint h_L(\tau) h_L(\sigma) \Psi_{s+n}(\tau-\sigma)\, d\tau\, d\sigma. \end{aligned} \tag{11–135}$$

The Wiener-Hopf equation can be written down immediately by inspection of (11–135), (11–44), and (11–49). The particular form of this equation for our present situation is, therefore,

$$L_\alpha[\Psi_s(\tau+\alpha)] = \int h_L(\sigma) \Psi_{s+n}(\tau-\sigma)\, d\sigma. \tag{11–136}$$

The simplest way to demonstrate (11–130) is to neglect the restriction of physical realizability. Hence, starting with (11–136) in place of (11–49), we find that, corresponding to (11–54), we now have

$$\begin{aligned} H_L(i\omega;\alpha) &= \frac{L_\alpha[\Phi_s(\omega)e^{i\omega\alpha}]}{\Phi_{s+n}(\omega)} \\ &= L_\alpha[H(i\omega;\alpha)]. \end{aligned} \tag{11–137}$$

As an example of the use of (11–130), suppose that we wish to obtain

$$\begin{aligned} z(t) &= \frac{\partial}{\partial \alpha} s(t+\alpha)\bigg|_{\alpha=0} \\ &\stackrel{d}{=} L_\alpha[s(t+\alpha)]. \end{aligned} \tag{11–138}$$

If $H(i\omega; \alpha)$ is known for the input signal $s(t)$, then the optimal filter for $z(t)$ is simply

$$\begin{aligned} H_L(i\omega; \alpha) &= L_\alpha[H(i\omega; \alpha)] \\ &= \frac{\partial}{\partial \alpha} H(i\omega; \alpha)\bigg|_{\alpha=0}. \end{aligned} \tag{11–139}$$

## 11.9
## *COMMENTS*

The W-K theory has not been universally accepted, and various criticisms have been directed at the theory. These criticisms have been partly directed at the underlying assumptions used in the theory and partly toward the often almost unsurmountable practical problems of actually synthesizing the optimal filters. These criticisms have been the motivations for several modifications as well as generalizations of the original concept. Almost invariably each valid criticism has spawned a new formulation of a modified filtering problem.

At first, before the theory had been well assimilated, almost everyone was content with the hypothesis that both the signal and noise be stationary processes. However, as engineering technology became more refined and systems became more complex, the stationarity hypothesis was questioned. For this reason the W-K theory has been extended to encompass nonstationary signals [37, 101, 106, 137]. The cases of sampled data systems with, and without, the nonstationarity hypothesis have also received their due share of attention [53]. Theories have also been formulated for situations in which the linear filters are permitted to have time varying elements [8, 16, 20, 22, 66].

The restriction to linear filters is not mandatory, and, moreover, it is certainly not as restrictive as one might be led to believe by various critics of the W-K theory. In Chapters 2 and 3 it was demonstrated that, if the signal is a normal process, then the optimum filter for a large class of loss functions is a linear filter, or linear transformation. Thus, the only real problems are those involving loss functions which are not symmetric and those of distribution functions, which may be neither symmetric nor convex. These are not valid criticisms of the W-K theory but rather are an outgrowth of the definition of *optimum*, which requires the minimization of a risk function.

General theorems for this minimization require the restrictive conditions discussed in Chapters 2 and 3.

The most severe problems encountered in the application of the W-K theory to specific applications arise from the problems in synthesizing the theoretically optimum filter responses. Except for a relatively few special and simple examples, the synthesis of the filter is an extremely laborious task and frequently one must resort to approximations and certain compromises [127]. Fortunately, experience has shown that the minimum of the risk function is frequently rather insensitive to changes in the filter characteristics. Even quite gross approximations to the optimum filter have led to only slightly increased errors. In fact, often *educated* guesses for the filter, based upon the system designers' intuition coupled with prior experience, provide results that vary by trivial amounts from the theoretical optimum filter. Mathematically this is to be expected because the minimization of the risk function was obtained by employing the calculus of variations. The minimum weighting function was thereby selected from a group of neighboring functions as that function yielding a minimum variation.

Circuit designers have been critical of the W-K methods of computing optimal filters because the transfer responses are dictated completely by a minimal-error criterion and the computation thus ignores the filter's transient response [102]. Wiener filters frequently result in underdamped systems which exhibit an oscillatory transient response that can be objectionable. At the present date there has not been a satisfactory theory proposed which will both provide an optimal filter in the W-K sense and have predetermined transient characteristics.

## Problems

**11.1** Sketch the impulse response given by (11–61). For the same problem, compute the impulse response for the smoothing case in which $\alpha \neq 0$, and sketch the function.

**11.2** Derive the optimum filter for a noise-free signal having the spectral density function

$$\Phi_s(\omega) = \frac{1}{(1 + \omega^2)^2}.$$

**11.3** Derive the optimum filter for $z(t) = d/d\alpha\,[s(t + \alpha)]|_{\alpha=0}$ for the same signal spectral density function given in Problem 11.2.

**11.4** Derive the optimum filter to separate a signal $s(t)$ from independent noise $n(t)$ when their respective spectral density functions are

$$\Phi_s(\omega) = \frac{1}{1 + \omega^2}$$

$$\Phi_n(\omega) = \frac{\omega^2}{1 + \omega^4}.$$

**11.5** Derive the optimum filter for

$$z(t) = \int_t^{t+\alpha} s(\tau)\, d(\tau)$$

for the same signal and noise processes of Problem 11.4.

**11.6** Fill in the details leading to Eq. (11–136).

**11.7** Prove that a linear filter (transformation) is the optimum filter for normally-distributed signals and noise, and a mean-square error criterion.

# Chapter 12

# DIFFERENTIAL EQUATION TECHNIQUES FOR FILTERING AND PREDICTION

The W-K theory has served both as an end in itself and as the motivation for related theories which are designed to avoid the problems encountered in solving the Wiener-Hopf equation as well as the practical problem of synthesizing the theoretically optimum filter from its impulse response. An alternative approach to signal filtering and prediction has been suggested, which essentially avoids the Wiener-Hopf integral equation by substituting an equivalent differential equation. Of more practical interest is the fact that the differential equation technique has the property that the optimum filter can be synthesized in a sequential fashion and, thus, is often readily implemented. Although these differential equation techniques were independently developed, they are in most instances equivalent or intimately related to the sequential estimator of Chapter 8.

The primary impetus for the current activity in the theory of sequential estimation stems from the work of Kalman and Bucy [77, 78, 79, 81]. Only portions of their work applicable to estimation theory will be discussed. In particular, this opportunity has been taken to present alternative derivations of the sequential estimator as well as to provide further insight into the significance of the Wiener-Hopf equation.

Both Kalman and Bucy independently recognized that, rather than attack the Wiener-Hopf equation directly with the attendant problems of factorization, it is frequently desirable to convert the integral equation into a nonlinear differential equation whose solution yields the covariance matrix of the minimum filtering error. In turn, this matrix contains all the necessary information for the design of the optimum filter.

## 12.1
## *KALMAN-BUCY METHOD*

The Kalman-Bucy method is characterized by the following five relations [81]:

(i) The differential equation governing the optimal filter, which is excited by the observed signals and generates the best linear estimate of the message.

(ii) The differential equations governing the error of the best linear estimate.

(iii) The time-varying gains of the optimal filter expressed in terms of the error variances.

(iv) The nonlinear differential equation governing the covariance matrix of the errors of the best linear estimate, called the *variance equation.*

(v) The formula for prediction.

A continuous time linear dynamical system can be described either by the integral equation formulation used in Chapter 11, or by a linear differential equation. For our present purposes we shall consider a linear system characterized by the differential equations:

$$\frac{d\mathbf{x}(t)}{dt} = \mathbf{F}(t)\mathbf{x}(t) + \mathbf{G}(t)\mathbf{u}(t) \tag{12–1}$$

$$\mathbf{y}(t) = \mathbf{H}(t)\mathbf{x}(t), \tag{12–2}$$

where $\mathbf{x}^{[n\times 1]} = [x_i]$: system state vector (if not a function of time, this would represent system parameters);

$x_i$: state variables, elements of $\mathbf{x}$;

$\mathbf{u}^{[m\times 1]}$: input, or control, function;

$\mathbf{y}^{[p\times 1]}$: system output vector

$\mathbf{F}^{[n\times n]}$: system dynamics function;

$\mathbf{G}^{[n\times m]}$: input constraints on system state;

$\mathbf{H}^{[p\times n]}$: constraints on observing the state of the system from the system output.

Equations (12–1) and (12–2) can be diagrammed as indicated in Figure 12–1.

The general solution of the linear differential equation (12–1) has the form [27, Chapter 3]

$$\mathbf{x}(t) = \mathbf{\Phi}(t, t_0)\mathbf{x}(t_0) + \int_{t_0}^{t} \mathbf{\Phi}(t, \tau)\mathbf{G}(\tau)\mathbf{u}(\tau)\, d\tau. \tag{12–3}$$

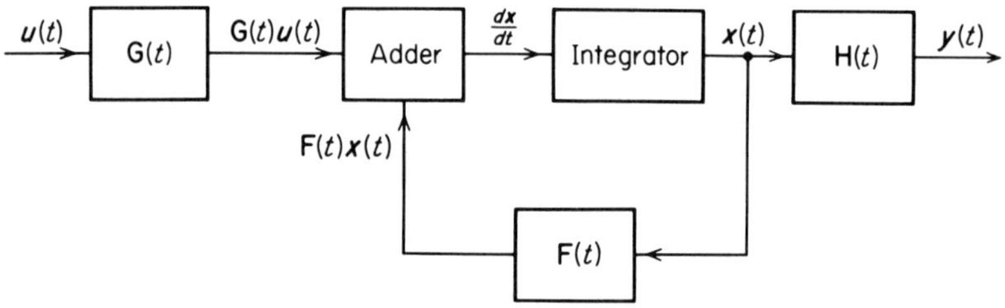


**Fig. 12-1** General linear dynamic system.

$\mathbf{\Phi}$ is known as the *transition*, or *fundamental*, matrix and satisfies the relations

$$\frac{d}{dt}\mathbf{\Phi}(t, t_0) = \mathbf{F}(t)\mathbf{\Phi}(t, t_0) \qquad (12\text{–}4)$$

$$\mathbf{\Phi}(t_0, t_0) = \mathbf{I}.$$

Further, as a consequence of postulating the existence and uniqueness of a solution to (12–1), one is led to the relations

$$\mathbf{\Phi}^{-1}(t_1, t_0) = \mathbf{\Phi}(t_0, t_1) \qquad (12\text{–}5)$$

$$\mathbf{\Phi}(t_2, t_0) = \mathbf{\Phi}(t_2, t_1)\mathbf{\Phi}(t_1, t_0). \qquad (12\text{–}6)$$

The property of $\mathbf{\Phi}$ symbolized in (12–6) justifies its being called a transition matrix. Because of the manner in which $\mathbf{\Phi}$ is defined, this matrix can never be singular. If the system function $\mathbf{F}$ is a constant matrix, then Equation (12–1) reduces to the familiar linear differential equation with constant coefficients. In this case [27], the transition matrix is known explicitly:

$$\mathbf{\Phi}(t, t_0) = \exp\{\mathbf{F} \cdot (t - t_0)\}. \qquad (12\text{–}7)$$

There is no general form for expressing $\mathbf{\Phi}$ when $\mathbf{F}$ is not constant.

All the preceding expressions can be formulated into equivalent relations for the situation in which the independent time variable $t$ is permitted to assume only discrete values. The discrete case has been developed by Kalman [77] but for our purposes can readily be obtained by analogy from the continuous case.

The original signal $\boldsymbol{x}(t)$ is assumed to be a random process generated by a mathematical model of the type described by (12–1). The observed signal $\boldsymbol{z}(t)$ is an additive combination of the output signal and a white noise process $\boldsymbol{v}(t)$;

$$\begin{aligned} \boldsymbol{z}(t) &= \boldsymbol{y}(t) + \boldsymbol{v}(t) \\ &= \mathbf{H}(t)\boldsymbol{x}(t) + \boldsymbol{v}(t), \end{aligned} \qquad (12\text{–}8)$$

where the signal and noise have the following statistical moments:

$$\begin{aligned} &\mathrm{E}\{\boldsymbol{u}(t)\} = \mathrm{E}\{\boldsymbol{v}(t)\} = \boldsymbol{0}, \\ &\mathrm{E}\{\boldsymbol{u}(t)\,\boldsymbol{v}(t-\tau)\} = \mathbf{0}, \\ &\boldsymbol{\Psi}_u(\tau) = \mathbf{Q}(t)\delta(t-\tau) = \mathrm{E}\{\boldsymbol{u}(t)\,\boldsymbol{u}^T(t-\tau)\}, \\ &\boldsymbol{\Psi}_v(\tau) = \mathbf{R}(t)\delta(t-\tau) = \mathrm{E}\{\boldsymbol{v}(t)\,\boldsymbol{v}^T(t-\tau)\}. \end{aligned} \tag{12–9}$$

$\mathbf{Q}(t)$ and $\mathbf{R}(t)$ are symmetric, positive definite matrices which are continuously differentiable in $t$.

Assume that the system has reached a steady-state condition after the application of $\boldsymbol{u}(t)$, then using (12–3) we can write

$$\boldsymbol{x}(t) = \int_{-\infty}^{t} \boldsymbol{\Phi}(t, \tau)\mathbf{G}(\tau)\boldsymbol{u}(\tau)\, d\tau. \tag{12–10}$$

If $\mathbf{F}$, $\mathbf{G}$, and $\mathbf{Q}$ are constant, then it follows that $\boldsymbol{x}(t)$ will be a stationary random process.

Kalman and Bucy relaxed the asymptotic stability requirement as imbodied in (12–10) and generalized this principal assumption of the original version of the W-K theory. They simply require that $\boldsymbol{x}(t)$ start at some fixed instant $t_0$ (which may be $-\infty$), at which time $\boldsymbol{\Psi}_x(0) = \mathrm{E}\{\boldsymbol{x}(t_0)\boldsymbol{x}^T(t_0)\}$ is known.

The optimal estimation problem for the multidimensional situation is one in which we are given known values of $\boldsymbol{z}(\tau)$, $t_0 \leq \tau \leq t$, and we wish to find an estimate $\hat{\boldsymbol{x}}(t_1 \,|\, t)$ of $\boldsymbol{x}(t_1)$ having the form

$$\hat{\boldsymbol{x}}(t_1 \,|\, t) = \int_{t_0}^{t} \mathbf{A}(t_1, \tau)\boldsymbol{z}(\tau)\, d\tau, \tag{12–11}$$

such that the risk function

$$R(\mathbf{A}) = \mathrm{E}\{\|\, \boldsymbol{x}(t_1) - \hat{\boldsymbol{x}}(t_1 \,|\, t)\,\|^2\} \tag{12–12}$$

is minimized as a function of $\mathbf{A}$.

Notice that (12–8), (12–10), and (12–11) imply that

$$\mathrm{E}\{\boldsymbol{x}(t_1)\} = \mathrm{E}\{\hat{\boldsymbol{x}}(t_1 \,|\, t)\} = \boldsymbol{0}, \tag{12–13}$$

or, that $\hat{\boldsymbol{x}}(t_1 \,|\, t)$ is an unbiased minimum variance linear estimator of $\boldsymbol{x}(t_1)$.

If $\boldsymbol{u}$ and $\boldsymbol{v}$ are both normal vectors, then, since $\boldsymbol{z}$ and $\boldsymbol{x}$ are linear transformations of these vectors, $\boldsymbol{z}$ and $\boldsymbol{x}$ will be normal vectors. Thus, we can immediately conclude from the discussions in Chapters 2, 3, and 11, that (12–11) will be the form of the optimal estimator, which must be a linear transformation of the observed process for a mean-squared risk function $R(\mathbf{A})$.

### 12.1.1 *WIENER-HOPF EQUATION*

The principal result of Chapter 3 is that, for mean-square risk functions of normal processes (or wide sense estimators), the optimal estimator is a projection on a Hilbert space generated from the observables. While all the necessary conditions for using this estimator characteristic existed in the development of the W-K theory presented in Chapter 11, no explicit mention or use was made of the projection property. The omission is now corrected.

An interesting and enlightening approach to optimal linear filtering theory was pointed out by Pugachev [118, 81]. Pugachev noted that the Wiener-Hopf equation is nothing more than a special case of the orthogonal-projection theorem (Chapter 3).

By analogy between our present problem and the results of Chapter 11, we can state the following theorem [81]:

THEOREM 12.1: A necessary and sufficient condition that $\hat{\boldsymbol{x}}(t_1 | t)$ be a minimum variance estimator for $\boldsymbol{x}(t_1)$ is that the matrix function $\mathbf{A}(t_1, \tau)$ satisfy the Wiener-Hopf equation

$$\boldsymbol{\Psi}_{xz}(t_1 - \sigma) = \int_{t_0}^{t} \mathbf{A}(t_1, \tau)\boldsymbol{\Psi}_z(\tau - \sigma)\, d\tau \tag{12–14}$$

or, equivalently,

$$\boldsymbol{\Psi}_{\epsilon z}(t_1 - \sigma | t) = \mathrm{E}\{[\hat{\boldsymbol{x}}(t_1 | t) - \boldsymbol{x}(t)]\boldsymbol{z}^T(\sigma)\} = \mathbf{0}; \qquad t_0 \leq \sigma \leq t, \tag{12–15}$$

where

$$\boldsymbol{\epsilon}(t_1 | t) = \hat{\boldsymbol{x}}(t_1 | t) - \boldsymbol{x}(t)$$

$$\begin{aligned} \boldsymbol{\Psi}_{xz}(t_1 - \sigma) &= \mathrm{E}\{\boldsymbol{x}(t_1)\boldsymbol{z}^T(\sigma)\} \\ \boldsymbol{\Psi}_z(\tau - \sigma) &= \mathrm{E}\{\boldsymbol{z}(\tau)\boldsymbol{z}^T(\sigma)\}. \end{aligned} \tag{12–16}$$

*Proof:* Rather than prove the theorem by means of the calculus of variations arguments used in Chapter 11, we shall call upon the orthogonal-projection theorem for optimal estimators.

Let $X$ denote the space generated by the random vectors $\{\boldsymbol{x}(t_1)\}$. The subspace $U \subseteq X$ is generated from the set of observables $\{\boldsymbol{z}(t)\}$ by elements of the type

$$\boldsymbol{u}(t_1) = \int_{t_0}^{t} \mathbf{B}(t_1, \tau)\boldsymbol{z}(\tau)\, d\tau, \tag{12–17}$$

where $\mathbf{B}^{[m \times p]}(t_1, \tau)$ is continuously differentiable in both arguments.

The orthogonal-projection Theorem 3.3 can be called upon to show that the minimum of the norm

$$N = \|\boldsymbol{x} - \boldsymbol{u}\|; \qquad \boldsymbol{x} \in X,\ \boldsymbol{u} \in U \tag{12–18}$$

must be the projection of $\boldsymbol{x}$ on $U$. Denote this projection by $\hat{\boldsymbol{x}} = \mathrm{P}\circ\boldsymbol{x} \in U$. It then follows, by the definition of a projection and the decomposition theorem, that the inner product

$$\mathrm{E}\{[\hat{\boldsymbol{x}}(t_1 | t) - \boldsymbol{x}(t_1)]\boldsymbol{u}^T(t_1)\} = \mathbf{0} \tag{12–19}$$

or

$$
\begin{aligned}
\mathrm{E}\{\boldsymbol{\epsilon}(t_1 \mid t)\boldsymbol{u}^T(t_1)\} &= \mathrm{E}\left\{\int_{t_0}^{t} \boldsymbol{\epsilon}(t_1 \mid t)\boldsymbol{z}^T(\tau)\mathbf{B}^T(t_1, \tau)\, d\tau\right\} \\
&= \int_{t_0}^{t} \boldsymbol{\Psi}_{\epsilon z}(t_1 - \tau \mid t)\mathbf{B}^T(t_1, \tau)\, d\tau = \mathbf{0}.
\end{aligned} \tag{12–20}
$$

Assuming that the interchange of expectation and integration is a valid operation, then $\boldsymbol{\Psi}_{\epsilon z} = \mathbf{0}$ establishes the sufficiency of the theorem, because $\mathbf{B}$ was an arbitrary matrix selected subject only to differentiability conditions.

The necessity of the Wiener-Hopf equation must next be established to conclude the proof of the theorem.

Let $\mathbf{B}(t_1, \tau) = \boldsymbol{\Psi}_{\epsilon z}(t_1 - \tau \mid t)$, then $\mathbf{BB}^T$ is certainly positive semidefinite. The continuity of the integrand in (12–20) leads to the conclusion that $\mathbf{BB}^T$ and hence also $\mathbf{B}(t_1, \tau)$ must vanish identically for all $t_0 \leq \tau < t$. Therefore, the necessity of (12–15) is verified.

### 12.1.2 *CANONICAL FORM OF THE OPTIMAL FILTER*

A canonical form for the optimal filter can be formulated as a differential equation derived from the Wiener-Hopf equation. Let $t_1 = t$ in (12–14), and differentiate both sides with respect to $t$. Interchanging the order of operations of differentiation and expectation, we find the derivative of the left-hand side is

$$
\begin{aligned}
\frac{\partial}{\partial t}\boldsymbol{\Psi}_{xz}(t - \sigma) &= \frac{\partial}{\partial t}\mathrm{E}\{[\boldsymbol{x}(t) - \mathrm{E}\{\boldsymbol{x}(t)\}][\boldsymbol{z}(\sigma) - \mathrm{E}\{\boldsymbol{z}(\sigma)\}]^T\} \\
&= \mathrm{E}\left\{\frac{\partial \boldsymbol{x}(t)}{\partial t}\boldsymbol{z}^T(\sigma)\right\} - \mathrm{E}\left\{\frac{\partial \boldsymbol{x}(t)}{\partial t}\right\}\mathrm{E}\{\boldsymbol{z}^T(\sigma)\} \\
&= \mathrm{E}\{\mathbf{F}(t)\boldsymbol{x}(t)\boldsymbol{z}^T(\sigma) + \mathbf{G}(t)\boldsymbol{u}(t)\boldsymbol{z}^T(\sigma)\} \\
&\quad - \mathrm{E}\{\mathbf{F}(t)\boldsymbol{x}(t) + \mathbf{G}(t)\boldsymbol{u}(t)\}\,\mathrm{E}\{\boldsymbol{z}^T(\sigma)\} \\
&= \mathbf{F}(t)\boldsymbol{\Psi}_{xz}(t - \sigma) + \mathbf{G}(t)\boldsymbol{\Psi}_{uz}(t - \sigma).
\end{aligned} \tag{12–21}
$$

By assumption, $\boldsymbol{u}(t)$ is independent of $\boldsymbol{v}(\sigma)$ and $\boldsymbol{x}(\sigma)$ when $\sigma < t$, hence $\boldsymbol{\Psi}_{uz}(t - \sigma) = \mathbf{0}$. After interchanging the order of differentiation and expectation, the derivative of the right-hand side of (12–14) is expressible as

(12–22)

$$
\frac{\partial}{\partial t}\int_{t_0}^{t}\mathbf{A}(t, \tau)\boldsymbol{\Psi}_z(\tau - \sigma)\, d\tau = \int_{t_0}^{t}\frac{\partial \mathbf{A}(t, \tau)}{\partial t}\boldsymbol{\Psi}_z(\tau - \sigma)\, d\tau + \mathbf{A}(t, t)\boldsymbol{\Psi}_z(t - \sigma).
$$

An alternative form of (12–22) is also useful. This is

$$
\begin{aligned}
&\frac{\partial}{\partial t}\int_{t_0}^{t}\mathbf{A}(t, \tau)\boldsymbol{\Psi}_z(\tau - \sigma)\, d\tau \\
&\qquad = \frac{\partial}{\partial t}\int_{t_0}^{t}\mathbf{A}(t, \tau)\,\mathrm{E}\{[\boldsymbol{z}(\tau) - \bar{\boldsymbol{z}}][\boldsymbol{z}(\sigma) - \bar{\boldsymbol{z}}]^T\}\, d\tau
\end{aligned}
$$

$$(12\text{–}22\text{a}) \quad = \frac{\partial}{\partial t}\int_{t_0}^{t} \mathbf{A}(t, \tau)\, \mathrm{E}\{[\boldsymbol{y}(\tau) - \bar{\boldsymbol{y}} + \boldsymbol{v}(\tau)][\boldsymbol{y}(\sigma) - \bar{\boldsymbol{y}} + \boldsymbol{v}(\sigma)]^T\}\, d\tau$$

$$= \frac{\partial}{\partial t}\int_{t_0}^{t} \mathbf{A}(t, \tau)\boldsymbol{\Psi}_y(\tau - \sigma)\, d\tau + \frac{\partial}{\partial t}\mathbf{A}(t, \sigma)\mathbf{R}(\sigma)$$

$$= \int_{t_0}^{t} \frac{\partial \mathbf{A}(t, \tau)}{\partial t}\boldsymbol{\Psi}_y(\tau - \sigma)\, d\tau + \mathbf{A}(t, t)\boldsymbol{\Psi}_y(t - \sigma) + \frac{\partial \mathbf{A}(t, \sigma)}{\partial t}\mathbf{R}(\sigma).$$

Using (12–8), the statement following (12–21), and (12–14), the last term in (12–22) can be written as

$$(12\text{–}23) \quad \begin{aligned} \boldsymbol{\Psi}_y(t - \sigma) &= \mathrm{E}\{\boldsymbol{y}(t)\boldsymbol{y}^T(\sigma)\} \\ &= \mathrm{E}\{[\mathbf{H}(t)\boldsymbol{x}(t) + \boldsymbol{v}(t)][\boldsymbol{z}(\sigma) - \boldsymbol{v}(\sigma)]^T\} \\ &= \mathbf{H}(t)\boldsymbol{\Psi}_{xz}(t - \sigma) \\ &= \mathbf{H}(t)\int_{t_0}^{t} \mathbf{A}(t, \tau)\boldsymbol{\Psi}_z(\tau - \sigma)\, d\tau. \end{aligned}$$

Combine (12–14), (12–21), (12–22), (12–22a), and (12–23) to obtain the condition

$$(12\text{–}24) \quad \int_{t_0}^{t}\left[\mathbf{F}(t)\mathbf{A}(t, \tau) - \frac{\partial \mathbf{A}(t, \tau)}{\partial t} - \mathbf{A}(t, t)\mathbf{H}(t)\mathbf{A}(t, \tau)\right]\boldsymbol{\Psi}_z(\tau - \sigma)\, d\tau = 0, \quad t_0 \le \sigma < t.$$

Equation (12–24) will be satisfied if the *optimal* matrix operator $\mathbf{A}$ is a solution of the differential equation

$$(12\text{–}25) \quad \mathbf{F}(t)\mathbf{A}(t, \tau) - \frac{\partial \mathbf{A}(t, \tau)}{\partial t} - \mathbf{A}(t, t)\mathbf{H}(t)\mathbf{A}(t, \tau) = 0; \qquad t_0 \le \tau \le t.$$

Kalman and Bucy showed that not only is (12–25) a sufficient condition for $\mathbf{A}$ to be optimal, but, if $\mathbf{R}(\tau)$ is positive definite in the interval $t_0 \le \tau \le t$, then (12–25) is also a necessary condition.

The differential equation for the optimal filter is generated by differentiating (12–11) with respect to $t$ and combining the result with (12–25). Thus,

$$(12\text{–}26) \quad \begin{aligned} \frac{d\hat{\boldsymbol{x}}(t\,|\,t)}{dt} &= \int_{t_0}^{t} \frac{\partial \mathbf{A}(t, \tau)}{\partial t}\boldsymbol{z}(\tau)\, d\tau + \mathbf{A}(t, t)\boldsymbol{z}(t) \\ &= \int_{t_0}^{t} [\mathbf{F}(t)\mathbf{A}(t, \tau) - \mathbf{A}(t, t)\mathbf{H}(t)\mathbf{A}(t, \tau)]\boldsymbol{z}(\tau)\, d\tau + \mathbf{A}(t, t)\boldsymbol{z}(t), \end{aligned}$$

or

$$(12\text{–}27) \quad \begin{aligned} \frac{d\hat{\boldsymbol{x}}(t\,|\,t)}{dt} &= \mathbf{F}(t)\hat{\boldsymbol{x}}(t\,|\,t) + \mathbf{K}(t)[\boldsymbol{z}(t) - \mathbf{H}(t)\hat{\boldsymbol{x}}(t\,|\,t)]; \\ \mathbf{K}(t) &\overset{d}{=} \mathbf{A}(t, t). \end{aligned}$$

The estimate error is defined as

$$(12\text{–}28) \quad \begin{aligned} \text{Error} &= \text{estimated value} - \text{true value} \\ \boldsymbol{\epsilon}(t\,|\,t) &= \hat{\boldsymbol{x}}(t\,|\,t) - \boldsymbol{x}(t). \end{aligned}$$

A differential equation for the error can readily be obtained by differentiating (12–28) with respect to $t$ and then inserting (12–1) and (12–27). These operations lead to

$$\begin{aligned}\frac{d\boldsymbol{\epsilon}(t|t)}{dt} &= \frac{d\hat{\boldsymbol{x}}(t|t)}{dt} - \frac{d\boldsymbol{x}(t)}{dt} \\ &= \mathbf{F}(t)\hat{\boldsymbol{x}}(t|t) + \mathbf{K}(t)[\boldsymbol{z}(t) - \mathbf{H}(t)\hat{\boldsymbol{x}}(t|t)] \\ &\quad -\mathbf{F}(t)\boldsymbol{x}(t) - \mathbf{G}(t)\boldsymbol{u}(t),\end{aligned} \tag{12–29}$$

or

$$\frac{d\boldsymbol{\epsilon}(t|t)}{dt} = [\mathbf{F}(t) - \mathbf{K}(t)\mathbf{H}(t)]\boldsymbol{\epsilon}(t|t) - \mathbf{G}(t)\boldsymbol{u}(t) + \mathbf{K}(t)\boldsymbol{v}(t). \tag{12–30}$$

The next step is to exhibit an explicit form of the optimal weighting matrix $\mathbf{K}(t) = \mathbf{A}(t, t)$. Equation (12–14) will be modified for this purpose. Make the following transformations:

$$\begin{aligned}\boldsymbol{\Psi}_{xz}(t-\sigma) &= \mathrm{E}\{\boldsymbol{x}(t)\boldsymbol{z}^T(\sigma)\} \\ &= \mathrm{E}\{\boldsymbol{x}(t)[\boldsymbol{y}^T(\sigma) + \boldsymbol{v}^T(\sigma)]\} \\ &= \mathrm{E}\{\boldsymbol{x}(t)\boldsymbol{y}^T(\sigma)\} = \boldsymbol{\Psi}_{xy}(t-\sigma);\end{aligned} \tag{12–31}$$

and

$$\begin{aligned}\boldsymbol{\Psi}_z(\tau-\sigma) &= \mathrm{E}\{\boldsymbol{z}(\tau)\boldsymbol{z}^T(\sigma)\} \\ &= \mathrm{E}\{[\boldsymbol{y}(\tau) + \boldsymbol{v}(\tau)][\boldsymbol{y}(\sigma) + \boldsymbol{v}(\sigma)]^T\} \\ &= \boldsymbol{\Psi}_y(\tau-\sigma) + \boldsymbol{\Psi}_v(\tau-\sigma) = \boldsymbol{\Psi}_y(\tau-\sigma) + \mathbf{R}(\tau)\,\delta(\tau-\sigma).\end{aligned} \tag{12–32}$$

Hence,

$$\begin{aligned}\boldsymbol{\Psi}_{xz}(t-\sigma) &= \int_{t_0}^{t} \mathbf{A}(t,\tau)\boldsymbol{\Psi}_z(\tau-\sigma)\,d\tau; \qquad t_0 < \sigma < t \\ \boldsymbol{\Psi}_{xy}(t-\sigma) &= \int_{t_0}^{t} \mathbf{A}(t,\tau)\boldsymbol{\Psi}_y(\tau-\sigma)\,d\tau + \mathbf{A}(t,\sigma)\mathbf{R}(\sigma).\end{aligned} \tag{12–33}$$

Since (12–33) is continuous in $\sigma$, let $\sigma = t$. Then the resulting equality implies that

$$\begin{aligned}\mathbf{A}(t,t)\mathbf{R}(t) &= -\mathrm{E}\{[\hat{\boldsymbol{x}}(t|t) - \boldsymbol{x}(t)]\boldsymbol{y}^T(t)\} \\ \mathbf{K}(t)\mathbf{R}(t) &= -\mathrm{E}\{\boldsymbol{\epsilon}(t|t)\boldsymbol{x}^T(t)\mathbf{H}^T(t)\} \\ &\overset{d}{=} -\boldsymbol{\Psi}_{\epsilon x}(0|t)\mathbf{H}^T(t).\end{aligned} \tag{12–34}$$

Define

$$\mathbf{P}(t) = -\boldsymbol{\Psi}_{\epsilon x}(0|t). \tag{12–35}$$

Because $\mathbf{R}^{-1}$ exists (assumed positive definite), (12–34) can be solved for the weighting matrix

$$\mathbf{K}(t) = \mathbf{P}(t)\mathbf{H}^T(t)\mathbf{R}^{-1}(t). \tag{12–36}$$

$\mathbf{P}(t)$ is also the covariance matrix of the estimate error $\boldsymbol{\epsilon}(t|t)$. This observation follows from the definitions of terms. Thus

$$\begin{aligned}
\boldsymbol{\Psi}_{\epsilon}(0|t) &= \mathrm{E}\{\boldsymbol{\epsilon}(t|t)\boldsymbol{\epsilon}^T(t|t)\} \\
&= \mathrm{E}\{[\hat{\boldsymbol{x}}(t|t) - \boldsymbol{x}(t)][\hat{\boldsymbol{x}}(t|t) - \boldsymbol{x}(t)]^T\} \\
&= -\,\mathrm{E}\{[\hat{\boldsymbol{x}}(t|t) - \boldsymbol{x}(t)]\boldsymbol{x}^T(t)\} \\
&\quad + \mathrm{E}\{[\hat{\boldsymbol{x}}(t|t) - \boldsymbol{x}(t)]\hat{\boldsymbol{x}}(t|t)\} \\
&= \mathbf{P}(t) + \mathrm{E}\{[\hat{\boldsymbol{x}}(t|t) - \boldsymbol{x}(t)]\hat{\boldsymbol{x}}(t|t)\}.
\end{aligned} \tag{12–37}$$

The last term in (12–37) can be evaluated by combining (12–11) and (12–15). We find that

$$\mathrm{E}\left\{[\hat{\boldsymbol{x}}(t|t) - \boldsymbol{x}(t)]\int_{t_0}^{t} \boldsymbol{z}^T(\tau)\mathbf{A}^T(t,\tau)\,d\tau\right\} = \mathbf{0},$$

or

$$\mathbf{P}(t) = \boldsymbol{\Psi}_{\epsilon}(0|t) = -\boldsymbol{\Psi}_{\epsilon x}(0|t). \tag{12–38}$$

### 12.1.3 *VARIANCE RELATIONS*

The general solutions of the differential equations (12–27) and (12–30) will have the same transition, or fundamental, matrix $\mathbf{\Lambda}(t, \tau)$. Using previous definitions, corresponding to (12–1) and (12–3) write the solution to (12–30) in the form:

$$\boldsymbol{\epsilon}(t|t) = \mathbf{\Lambda}(t, t_0)\boldsymbol{\epsilon}(t|t_0) + \int_{t_0}^{t} \mathbf{\Lambda}(t - \tau)[\mathbf{K}(\tau)\boldsymbol{v}(\tau) - \mathbf{G}(\tau)\boldsymbol{u}(\tau)]d\tau.$$

Multiply this expression by its transpose and take the expected value of the result. This operation yields:

(12–39)

$$\begin{aligned}
&\mathbf{P}(t) - \mathbf{\Lambda}(t, t_0)\mathbf{P}(t_0)\mathbf{\Lambda}^T(t, t_0) \\
&= \mathrm{E}\left\{\int_{t_0}^{t} \mathbf{\Lambda}(t, \tau)[\mathbf{K}(\tau)\boldsymbol{v}(\tau) - \mathbf{G}(\tau)\boldsymbol{u}(\tau)]\,d\tau \right. \\
&\qquad\left. \times \int_{t_0}^{t} [\boldsymbol{V}^T(\sigma)\mathbf{K}^T(\sigma) - \boldsymbol{u}^T(\sigma)\mathbf{G}^T(\sigma)]\,\mathbf{\Lambda}^T(t, \sigma)d\sigma\right\} \\
&= \int_{t_0}^{t} \mathbf{\Lambda}(t, \tau)[\mathbf{G}(\tau)\mathbf{Q}(\tau)\mathbf{G}^T(\tau) + \mathbf{K}(\tau)\mathbf{R}(\tau)\mathbf{K}^T(\tau)]\mathbf{\Lambda}^T(t, \tau)\,d\tau.
\end{aligned}$$

Differentiate (12–39) with respect to $t$. Using (12–4) and (12–36), we find that

$$\begin{aligned}
&\frac{d\mathbf{P}(t)}{dt} - \frac{d\mathbf{\Lambda}(t, t_0)}{dt}\mathbf{P}(t_0)\mathbf{\Lambda}^T(t, t_0) - \mathbf{\Lambda}(t, t_0)\mathbf{P}(t_0)\frac{d\mathbf{\Lambda}^T(t, t_0)}{dt} \\
&= \mathbf{\Lambda}(t, t)[\mathbf{G}(t)\mathbf{Q}(t)\mathbf{G}^T(t) + \mathbf{K}(t)\mathbf{R}(t)\mathbf{K}^T(t)]\mathbf{\Lambda}^T(t, t) \\
&\quad + \int_{t_0}^{t} \frac{d\mathbf{\Lambda}(t, \tau)}{dt}[\mathbf{G}(\tau)\mathbf{Q}(\tau)\mathbf{G}^T(\tau) + \mathbf{K}(\tau)\mathbf{R}(\tau)\mathbf{K}^T(\tau)]\mathbf{\Lambda}^T(t, \tau)\,d\tau \\
&\quad + \int_{t_0}^{t} \mathbf{\Lambda}(t, \tau)[\mathbf{G}(\tau)\mathbf{Q}(\tau)\mathbf{G}^T(\tau) + \mathbf{K}(\tau)\mathbf{R}(\tau)\mathbf{K}^T(\tau)]\frac{d\mathbf{\Lambda}^T(t, \tau)}{dt}\,d\tau,
\end{aligned} \tag{12–40}$$

$$\frac{d\mathbf{P}(t)}{dt} - \mathbf{F}(t)\mathbf{\Lambda}(t, t_0)\mathbf{P}(t_0)\mathbf{\Lambda}^T(t, t_0) - \mathbf{\Lambda}(t, t_0)\mathbf{P}(t_0)\mathbf{\Lambda}^T(t, t_0)\mathbf{F}^T(t_0)$$
$$= \mathbf{G}(t)\mathbf{Q}(t)\mathbf{G}^T(t) + \mathbf{K}(t)\mathbf{R}(t)\mathbf{K}^T(t)$$
$$+ \mathbf{F}(t)[\mathbf{P}(t) - \mathbf{\Lambda}(t, t_0)\mathbf{P}(t_0)\mathbf{\Lambda}^T(t, t_0)]$$
$$+ [\mathbf{P}(t) - \mathbf{\Lambda}(t, t_0)\mathbf{P}(t_0)\mathbf{\Lambda}^T(t, t_0)]\mathbf{F}^T(t).$$

Therefore, the desired differential equation for the variance of the error $\boldsymbol{\epsilon}(t)$ is

(12–41)
$$\frac{d\mathbf{P}(t)}{dt} = \mathbf{G}(t)\mathbf{Q}(t)\mathbf{G}^T(t) + \mathbf{F}(t)\mathbf{P}(t) + \mathbf{P}(t)\mathbf{F}^T(t) - \mathbf{P}(t)\mathbf{H}^T(t)\mathbf{R}^{-1}(t)\mathbf{H}(t)\mathbf{P}(t).$$

Equation (12–41) is the variance differential equation. It is a system of $n(n + 1)/2^4$ nonlinear differential equations of the first order and is of the type known as the *Riccati equation*. The initial condition for the variance equation is obtained from the observation that (12–11) implies

(12–42)
$$\hat{\boldsymbol{x}}(t_0 \,|\, t_0) = 0.$$

Therefore, (12–38) yields the initial condition

(12–43)
$$\mathbf{P}(0) \stackrel{d}{=} \mathbf{P}(t_0) = \mathrm{E}\{\boldsymbol{x}(t_0)\boldsymbol{x}^T(t_0)\}.$$

If we relax the generality of the Kalman and Bucy development, which did not require the asymptotic stability of (12–10), and now require (12–10), then (12–43) can be evaluated explicitly as

(12–44)
$$\mathbf{P}(t_0) = \mathrm{E}\left\{\int_{-\infty}^{t}\int_{-\infty}^{t} \mathbf{\Phi}(t_0, \tau)\mathbf{G}(\tau)\boldsymbol{u}(\tau)\boldsymbol{u}^T(\sigma)\mathbf{G}^T(\sigma)\mathbf{\Phi}^T(t_0, \sigma)\, d\tau\, d\sigma\right\}$$
$$= \int_{-\infty}^{t} \mathbf{\Phi}(t_0, \tau)\mathbf{G}(\tau)\mathbf{Q}(\tau)\mathbf{G}^T(\tau)\mathbf{\Phi}^T(t_0, \tau)\, d\tau.$$

#### 12.1.4 *TRANSITION RELATION*

If $t_1 > t$, then (12–3) becomes

(12–45)
$$\boldsymbol{x}(t_1) = \mathbf{\Phi}(t_1, t)\boldsymbol{x}(t) + \int_{t}^{t_1} \mathbf{\Phi}(t_1, \tau)\mathbf{G}(\tau)\boldsymbol{u}(\tau)\, d\tau.$$

Since in the interval $t < \tau \leq t_1$, $\boldsymbol{u}(\tau)$ is independent of $\boldsymbol{x}(\tau)$ in the interval $t_0 \leq \tau \leq t$, Equation (12–14) can be used to show that the optimal estimator for the right-hand side of (12–45) is $\mathbf{0}$. Thus, we conclude that

(12–46)
$$\hat{\boldsymbol{x}}(t_1 \,|\, t) = \mathbf{\Phi}(t_1, t)\hat{\boldsymbol{x}}(t \,|\, t), \qquad t_1 \geq t.$$

It should be remarked that the same conclusion cannot be drawn for the interpolation case in which $t_1 < t$ because, in this case, one does not know if $\boldsymbol{x}(\tau)$ and $\boldsymbol{u}(\tau)$ would be independent in the required interval. Equation (12–46) is important in the applications of the theory because it shows that, under the stated hypothesis, the optimal estimator can be extrapolated by means of the transition matrix.

The optimal filter is diagrammed in Figure 12–2.

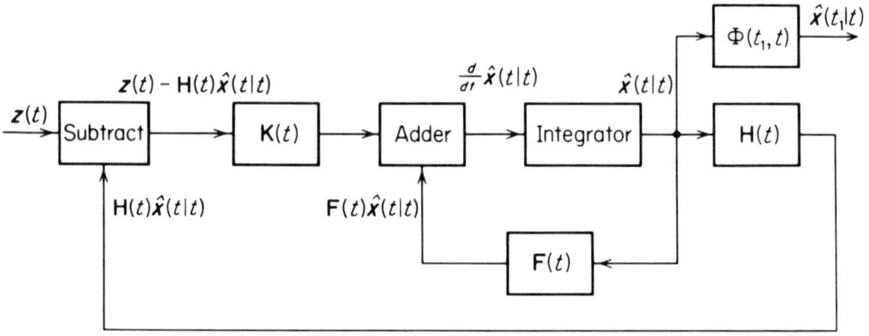


**Fig. 12-2** Optimum continuous linear filter.

### 12.1.5 *CORRELATED NOISE*

The preceding derivation of the Kalman-Bucy theory, as contained in their original paper [81], for the optimal filter for a continuous time-varying dynamic system was limited to the situation in which all measurements were perturbed by white noise. This hypothesis runs into trouble when dealing with physical systems for which the assumption of white noise cannot be justified. Moreover, the original theory requires modification for the ideal situation of noise-free measurements. In the noise-free case, the matrix $\mathbf{R}^{-1}$ does not exist.

Bryson and Johansen extended the Kalman-Bucy theory to include cases of correlated-noise and noise-free measurements [19]. Their extension is based upon the concept that the correlated noise can, with sufficient accuracy, often be simulated by an auxiliary conceptual linear dynamic system having white noise as an input signal. In this approach, the correlated noise vector becomes a part of an augmented state variable vector, and the measurements then contain only linear combinations of the augmented state variables. The details of the theory closely parallel the preceding sections.

## 12.2 *DISCRETE TIME DIFFERENCE EQUATIONS*

The formulas for the discrete time optimal-filter solution can be written by analogy with those already derived for the continuous time situation. Equations followed by the letter $D$ will denote the discrete analog to the continuous formulations which are summarized from the preceding section.

(a) System model

(12–47) $\dfrac{d\boldsymbol{x}(t)}{dt} = \mathbf{F}(t)\boldsymbol{x}(t) + \mathbf{G}(t)\boldsymbol{u}(t),$ (12–1).

(12–48) $\boldsymbol{z}(t) = \mathbf{H}(t)\boldsymbol{x}(t) + \boldsymbol{v}(t),$ (12–8).

(12–47$D$) $\boldsymbol{x}_{k+1} = \mathbf{A}\boldsymbol{x}_k + \mathbf{G}_k\boldsymbol{u}_k.$

(12–48$D$) $\boldsymbol{z}_k = \mathbf{M}_k\boldsymbol{x}_k + \boldsymbol{v}_k.$

(b) Statistics

(12–49)
$$\begin{aligned}
&\mathrm{E}\{\boldsymbol{u}(t)\} = \mathrm{E}\{\boldsymbol{v}(t)\} = \boldsymbol{0}.\\
&\boldsymbol{\Psi}_u(\tau) = \mathbf{Q}(t)\,\delta(t-\tau) = \mathrm{E}\{\boldsymbol{u}(t)\boldsymbol{u}^T(t-\tau)\}, \qquad (12\text{–}9).\\
&\boldsymbol{\Psi}_v(\tau) = \mathbf{R}(t)\,\delta(t-\tau) = \mathrm{E}\{\boldsymbol{v}(t)\boldsymbol{v}^T(t-\tau)\}.\\
&\boldsymbol{\Psi}_{uv}(\tau) = \mathrm{E}\{\boldsymbol{u}(t)\boldsymbol{v}^T(t-\tau)\} = \mathbf{0}.
\end{aligned}$$

(12–49$D$)
$$\begin{aligned}
&\mathrm{E}\{\boldsymbol{u}_k\} = \mathrm{E}\{\boldsymbol{v}_k\} = \boldsymbol{0}.\\
&\boldsymbol{\Psi}_u(k) = \mathbf{Q}_k\,\delta_{kj} = \mathrm{E}\{\boldsymbol{u}_k\boldsymbol{u}_j^T\}.\\
&\boldsymbol{\Psi}_v(k) = \mathbf{R}_k\,\delta_{kj} = \mathrm{E}\{\boldsymbol{v}_k\boldsymbol{v}_j^T\}.\\
&\boldsymbol{\Psi}_{uv}(j-k) = \mathrm{E}\{\boldsymbol{u}_j\boldsymbol{v}_k^T\} = \mathbf{0}.
\end{aligned}$$

(c) Optimal filter

(12–50) $\dfrac{d\hat{\boldsymbol{x}}(t)}{dt} = \mathbf{F}(t)\hat{\boldsymbol{x}}(t\,|\,t) + \mathbf{K}(t)\,[\boldsymbol{z}(t) - \mathbf{H}(t)\hat{\boldsymbol{x}}(t\,|\,t)],$ (12–27).

(12–50$D$) $\hat{\boldsymbol{x}}_{k+1} = \mathbf{A}\hat{\boldsymbol{x}}_k + \mathbf{C}_k\,[\boldsymbol{z}_k - \mathbf{M}_k\hat{\boldsymbol{x}}_k].$

(d) Error of the optimal estimate

(12–51) $\boldsymbol{\epsilon}(t\,|\,t) = \hat{\boldsymbol{x}}(t\,|\,t) - \boldsymbol{x}(t),$ (12–28).

(12–52) $\dfrac{d\boldsymbol{\epsilon}(t\,|\,t)}{dt} = [\mathbf{F}(t) - \mathbf{K}(t)\mathbf{H}(t)]\,\boldsymbol{\epsilon}(t\,|\,t) - \mathbf{G}(t)\boldsymbol{u}(t) + \mathbf{K}(t)\boldsymbol{v}(t),$ (12–30).

(12–51$D$) $\boldsymbol{\epsilon}_k = \hat{\boldsymbol{x}}_k - \boldsymbol{x}_k.$

(12–52$D$) $\boldsymbol{\epsilon}_{k+1} = [\mathbf{A} - \mathbf{C}_k\mathbf{M}_k]\boldsymbol{\epsilon}_k - \mathbf{G}_k\boldsymbol{u}_k + \mathbf{C}_k\boldsymbol{v}_k.$

(e) Weighting matrix

(12–53) $\mathbf{P}(t) = \mathrm{E}\{\boldsymbol{\epsilon}(t\,|\,t)\boldsymbol{\epsilon}^T(t\,|\,t)\},$ (12–38).

(12–54) $\mathbf{K}(t) = \mathbf{P}(t)\mathbf{H}^T(t)\mathbf{R}^{-1}(t),$ (12–36).

(12–53$D$) $\mathbf{P}_k = \mathrm{E}\{\boldsymbol{\epsilon}_k\boldsymbol{\epsilon}_k^T\}.$

(12–54$D$) $\mathbf{C}_k = \mathbf{P}_k\mathbf{M}_k^T\mathbf{R}_k^{-1}.$

(f) Variance relation

(12–55)
$$\begin{aligned}
\frac{d\mathbf{P}(t)}{dt} = {}&\mathbf{F}(t)\mathbf{P}(t) + \mathbf{P}(t)\mathbf{F}^T(t) + \mathbf{G}(t)\mathbf{Q}(t)\mathbf{G}^T(t)\\
&-\mathbf{P}(t)\mathbf{H}^T(t)\mathbf{R}^{-1}(t)\mathbf{H}(t)\mathbf{P}(t), \qquad (12\text{–}41).
\end{aligned}$$

(12–55*D*) $$\mathbf{P}_{k+1} = \mathbf{A}\mathbf{P}_k + \mathbf{P}_k\mathbf{A}^T + \mathbf{G}_k\mathbf{Q}_k\mathbf{G}_k^T - \mathbf{P}_k\mathbf{M}_k^T\mathbf{R}_k^{-1}\mathbf{M}_k\mathbf{P}_k.$$

(g) Transition relation

(12–56) $$\hat{\mathbf{x}}(t_1 \mid t) = \mathbf{\Phi}(t_1, t)\hat{\mathbf{x}}(t \mid t), \qquad t_1 \geq t.$$

(12–56*D*) $$\hat{\mathbf{x}}_{k+j} = \mathbf{\Phi}(k + j, k + 1)\hat{\mathbf{x}}_{k+1}, \qquad j \geq 1.$$

We can now demonstrate that the discrete form of the optimal filter is exactly analogous to the sequential estimator generated in Section 8.3. Equation (12–50*D*) is identical with the linear sequential estimator (8–74) if the following quantities are set equal.

| (12–50*D*) | (8–74) |
|---|---|
| $\hat{\mathbf{x}}_{k+1}$ | $\hat{\boldsymbol{b}}_{k+1}$ |
| $\mathbf{A}$ | $\mathbf{I}$ |
| $\mathbf{C}_k$ | $\mathcal{M}_{k+1}$ |
| $\mathbf{z}_k$ | $\boldsymbol{W}_{k+1} - \boldsymbol{B}_{k+1}$ |
| $\mathbf{M}_k$ | $\mathbf{T}_k$ |
| $\mathbf{P}_k$ | $\mathbf{Q}_{k+1}$ |

The use of the identity matrix in (8–74) reflects the fact that this relation was obtained for fixed system parameters and not for state variables, which in (12–50*D*) are permitted to vary as a function of the estimation step.

It is a relatively simple exercise to verify the equivalence between all the relations of the discrete optimal filter with those of the sequential linear estimator. The equivalence is not unexpected. Although each set of relations was developed using a different theoretical approach, the results are the same because they represent the unique linear optimal estimator for the same mean-squared risk function.

The similarity between some of the results of Kalman and Bucy and the prior results of sequential estimators, should not be construed as any criticism of their work. Their development is much more rigorous and general than the few introductory aspects which have been exhibited in this chapter.

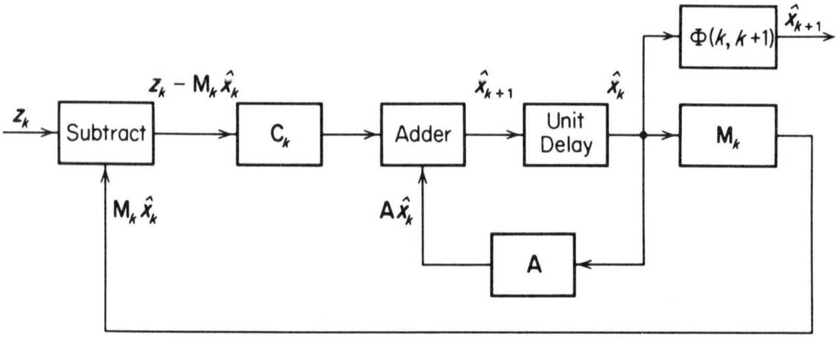


**Fig. 12-3** Optimum discrete linear filter.

One misses the point if he allows the similarity of some of Kalman and Bucy's formulations with previous results to obscure the fact that they have generated a new and powerful technique for both estimation and control problems. New results in these areas have already been discovered, and more important developments should be forthcoming. For our purposes, Kalman and Bucy's method primarily serves as a medium to gain further insight into some of the frequently obscured depths of estimation theory and to provide a good illustration of the universality of the theoretical concepts discussed in Chapters 2 and 3.

The discrete form of the optimal filter is diagrammed in Figure 12–3.

## 12.3
## *OPTIMAL NONSTATIONARY ESTIMATION*

A fundamental aspect of linear filtering theory, in the form considered in this chapter, is that a linear system can be described by state-transition equations. The prediction of the future behavior of a system requires the knowledge of the components of the state-transition matrix. However, suppose that these components are not known. This being true, one can use the present knowledge of the system state to provide a continuously updated optimal estimate of the transition matrix in an adaptive configuration.

Mayne has exhibited the versatility of sequential linear estimators in treating problems that closely represent the incomplete knowledge of the real world [99]. Consider a linear system

$$\frac{d\boldsymbol{x}(t)}{dt} = \mathbf{F}\boldsymbol{x}(t) + \boldsymbol{v}(t) \tag{12–57}$$

for which $\boldsymbol{x}(t)$ can be measured without error and $\mathbf{F}$ is a constant matrix with unknown elements. It is impossible to solve the problem of finding an unknown $\mathbf{F}$ unless we are willing to assume *some* estimate $\hat{\mathbf{F}}$ of the system matrix. The error in this estimate will be

$$\begin{aligned} \text{Error} &= \text{estimated value} - \text{true value} \\ \boldsymbol{\phi}(t) &= \hat{\mathbf{F}}(t) - \mathbf{F}. \end{aligned} \tag{12–58}$$

Moreover, to correlate $\mathbf{F}$ with the system state $\boldsymbol{x}$, we impose the condition that

$$\hat{\mathbf{F}}(t) = \mathrm{E}\{\mathbf{F} \mid \boldsymbol{x}(\tau), \tau \leq t\}. \tag{12–59}$$

We shall show that (12–57), (12–58), and (12–59), coupled with the assumption that $\mathbf{F}$ is a constant matrix, yield an effective system model equivalent to that described in Section 12.2. Once the equivalence has been demonstrated, the problem of determining $\mathbf{F}$ from error-free measurements of the state variables will be solved by simply identifying symbols in the equations summarized in Section 12.2. Write (12–57) in the form

$$\boldsymbol{z}^{[n\times 1]}(t) = \frac{d\boldsymbol{x}(t)}{dt} = \mathbf{H}^{[n\times n^2]}(t)\boldsymbol{f}^{[n^2\times 1]}(t) + \boldsymbol{v}^{[n\times 1]}(t), \tag{12–60}$$

where the equivalent input constraint, or *control matrix*, is chosen as

$$\mathbf{H}^{[n\times n^2]}(t) = \begin{bmatrix} \boldsymbol{x}^{T[1\times n]}(t) & & 0 \\ & \boldsymbol{x}^{T[1\times n]}(t) & \\ 0 & & \boldsymbol{x}^{T[1\times n]}(t) \end{bmatrix}. \tag{12–61}$$

$\mathbf{H}$ has $n(r-1)$ zeros in the $r$th row followed by $\boldsymbol{x}^T$ and $n(n-r)$ zeros.

$\boldsymbol{f}(t)$ consists of the $n$ rows of $\mathbf{F}$ arranged vertically,

$$\mathbf{F}^{[n\times n]}(t) = \begin{bmatrix} f_{11}(t) & f_{12}(t) & \cdots & f_{1n}(t) \\ f_{21}(t) & f_{22}(t) & \cdots & f_{2n}(t) \\ \cdots & \cdots & \cdots & \cdots \\ f_{n1}(t) & f_{n2}(t) & \cdots & f_{nn}(t) \end{bmatrix}$$

$$\boldsymbol{f}^{[n^2\times 1]}(t) = \begin{bmatrix} \boldsymbol{f}_1(t) \\ \boldsymbol{f}_2(t) \\ \cdots \\ \boldsymbol{f}_n(t) \end{bmatrix} \tag{12–62}$$

$$\boldsymbol{f}_j^T(t) = [f_{j1}(t) \quad f_{j2}(t) \quad \cdots \quad f_{jn}(t)].$$

Since $\mathbf{F}$ is constant,

$$\frac{d\boldsymbol{f}(t)}{dt} = \boldsymbol{0}. \tag{12–63}$$

The desired equivalence can now be formulated. In Section 12.2 make the replacements

| Section 12.2 | Becomes |
|---|---|
| $\boldsymbol{x}(t)$ | $\boldsymbol{f}$ |
| $\mathbf{F}(t)$ | $\mathbf{0}$ |
| $\mathbf{G}(t)$ | $\mathbf{0}$ |
| $\boldsymbol{\Psi}_u$ | $\mathbf{0}$ |
| $\boldsymbol{\Psi}_v$ | $\mathbf{0}$ |
| $\mathbf{P}(t)$ | $\mathbf{P}_f(t)$ |

where

$$\begin{aligned} \boldsymbol{\epsilon}_f(t) &= \hat{\boldsymbol{f}}(t) - \boldsymbol{f}(t) \\ \hat{\boldsymbol{f}}(t) &= \mathrm{E}\{\boldsymbol{f}(t)\,|\,\boldsymbol{z}(\tau), \tau < t\} \\ \mathbf{P}_f(t) &= \mathrm{E}\{[\hat{\boldsymbol{f}}(\sigma) - \boldsymbol{f}(\sigma)][\hat{\boldsymbol{f}}(\sigma - t) - \boldsymbol{f}(\sigma - t)]^T\}. \end{aligned} \tag{12–64}$$

The fundamental concept, of course, is to revamp the formulation so that the elements of the unknown constant matrix $\mathbf{F}$ appear in the form of state variables.

The final point to consider is whether or not the variance equation for this problem actually converges to some equilibrium value. This point is discussed in Section 12.5. We shall see that if $\mathbf{\Psi}_u = \mathbf{0}$, the equilibrium value is zero. Thus, as time proceeds, we are assured that a more accurate estimate is obtained for the coefficients of the system function matrix $\mathbf{F}$.

Mayne also showed how the preceding scheme can be extended to the situation in which the elements of $\mathbf{F}$ are random variables. Represent the auxiliary vector $\boldsymbol{f}$, defined in (12–62), in the form

$$\boldsymbol{f}(t) = \boldsymbol{f}'(t) + \boldsymbol{f}''(t), \tag{12–65}$$

where $\boldsymbol{f}'(t)$ denotes a constant, but unknown, component of $\boldsymbol{f}$ and the random second component $\boldsymbol{f}''$ satisfies the differential equation

$$\frac{d\boldsymbol{f}''(t)}{dt} = \mathbf{M}^{[n^2\times n^2]}\boldsymbol{f}''^{[n^2\times 1]}(t) + \boldsymbol{\mu}^{[n^2\times 1]}(t). \tag{12–66}$$

The vector $\boldsymbol{\mu}(t)$ symbolizes a noise process having zero mean value and covariance matrix,

$$\mathbf{\Psi}_\mu^{[n^2\times n^2]}(\tau) = \mathrm{E}\{\boldsymbol{\mu}(t)\boldsymbol{\mu}^T(t-\tau)\} = \mathbf{N}(t)\,\delta(t-\tau). \tag{12–67}$$

A system model can be written in the canonical form

$$\begin{bmatrix} \dfrac{d}{dt}\boldsymbol{f}'(t) \\ \dfrac{d}{dt}\boldsymbol{f}''(t) \end{bmatrix} = \begin{bmatrix} \mathbf{0} & \mathbf{0} \\ \mathbf{0} & \mathbf{M} \end{bmatrix} \begin{bmatrix} \boldsymbol{f}'(t) \\ \boldsymbol{f}''(t) \end{bmatrix} + \begin{bmatrix} \boldsymbol{0} \\ \boldsymbol{\mu} \end{bmatrix} \tag{12–68}$$

or, by identification of terms,

$$\frac{d}{dt}\mathscr{F}(t) = \mathscr{G}\mathscr{F}(t) + \mathscr{M}(t). \tag{12–69}$$

Furthermore, using the definition of (12–60) and (12–61),

$$\boldsymbol{z}(t) = [\mathbf{H}(t) \quad \mathbf{H}(t)] \begin{bmatrix} \boldsymbol{f}'(t) \\ \boldsymbol{f}''(t) \end{bmatrix} + \boldsymbol{v}(t). \tag{12–70}$$

Since (12–69) and (12–70) are in the canonical form of the linear estimation problem, the formulations of Section 12.2 can be used to obtain the optimal estimate $\hat{\mathscr{F}}(t)$.

## 12.4
## *BAYES' ESTIMATION FORMULATION*

A third method of deriving the equations for a sequential estimator, is based upon an application of Bayes' theorem [30, 31, 70, 141]. Although we shall obtain no substantially new results other than were obtained by means of the two previous techniques, the Bayes' estimation method does present an opportunity to provide still further insight into the theory of the optimal filter by looking at the problem from an alternative point of view. Cox [30] has ably demonstrated that the Bayes' procedure can be adapted to nonlinear systems if one does not insist upon *closed form* solutions, but is willing to work with numerical solution techniques.

For illustrative purposes, consider a discrete time linear-system model described by (12–47*D*) and (12–48*D*). Our task is to estimate the sequence of $k$ states $\{\boldsymbol{x}_1^{[n\times 1]}, \ldots, \boldsymbol{x}_k^{[n\times 1]}\}$ on the basis of the $k$ observations of the system output $\{\boldsymbol{z}_1^{[p\times 1]}, \ldots, \boldsymbol{z}_k^{[p\times 1]}\}$. The state $\boldsymbol{x}_j$ at any time $t_j$ is related to some arbitrarily selected initial state $\boldsymbol{x}_0$ by means of the transition relation (12–56*D*),

(12–71)
$$\begin{aligned}\boldsymbol{x}_j &= \boldsymbol{\Phi}(j, 0)\boldsymbol{x}_0\\ &\overset{d}{=} \boldsymbol{\Phi}_j\boldsymbol{x}_0.\end{aligned}$$

We can represent the entire sequence of observations as a single matrix equation in the following fashion:

(12–72)
$$\begin{bmatrix}\boldsymbol{z}_1\\ \boldsymbol{z}_2\\ \vdots\\ \boldsymbol{z}_k\end{bmatrix} = \begin{bmatrix}\mathbf{M}_1\boldsymbol{\Phi}_1 & \mathbf{0} & \cdots & \mathbf{0}\\ \mathbf{0} & \mathbf{M}_2\boldsymbol{\Phi}_2 & \mathbf{0} & \mathbf{0}\\ \cdots & \cdots & \cdots & \cdots\\ \mathbf{0} & \cdots & \mathbf{0} & \mathbf{M}_k\boldsymbol{\Phi}_k\end{bmatrix}\begin{bmatrix}\boldsymbol{x}_0\\ \boldsymbol{x}_0\\ \vdots\\ \boldsymbol{x}_0\end{bmatrix} + \begin{bmatrix}\boldsymbol{v}_1\\ \boldsymbol{v}_2\\ \vdots\\ \boldsymbol{v}_k\end{bmatrix}$$

or

(12–73)
$$\boldsymbol{Z}^{[pk\times 1]} = \mathbf{M}^{[pk\times kn]}\boldsymbol{\Phi}^{[kn\times kn]}\boldsymbol{x}_0^{[kn\times 1]} + \boldsymbol{V}^{[pk\times 1]}.$$

The covariance matrix of the initial state $\boldsymbol{x}_0$ is assumed to be known and is represented by

(12–74)
$$\begin{aligned}\mathbf{P}_0^{[n\times n]} &= \mathrm{E}\{\boldsymbol{x}_0\boldsymbol{x}_0^T\},\\ \mathrm{E}\{\boldsymbol{x}_0\} &= \boldsymbol{0}.\end{aligned}$$

The white noise $\boldsymbol{v}$ is postulated to be normal, with zero mean value and covariance

(12–75)
$$\boldsymbol{\Psi}_v(\tau) = \mathrm{E}\{\boldsymbol{v}\boldsymbol{v}^T\} = \mathbf{R}(t)\,\delta(t-\tau).$$

Therefore, the total noise vector $\boldsymbol{V}$ has the covariance

(12–76)
$$\boldsymbol{\Psi}_V(\tau) = \mathrm{E}\{\boldsymbol{V}(t)\boldsymbol{V}^T(t-\tau)\} = \mathbf{R}_V(t)\,\delta(t-\tau) = \begin{bmatrix}\mathbf{R}(t)\,\delta(t-\tau) & \cdots & \mathbf{0}\\ & \ddots & \\ \mathbf{0} & \cdots & \mathbf{R}(t)\,\delta(t-\tau)\end{bmatrix}.$$

Keeping in mind that, if the estimate of any state is available, the estimate of any other state can be found by applying the transition relation (12–56*D*), we shall first specifically indicate how $\hat{\boldsymbol{x}}_0$ can be found by means of the

Bayes' theorem. The theorem for our illustrative problem can be written in the form of the probability density functions:

$$f(\boldsymbol{x}_0 | \boldsymbol{Z}) = \frac{f(\boldsymbol{Z} | \boldsymbol{x}_0) f(\boldsymbol{x}_0)}{f(\boldsymbol{Z})}. \tag{12–77}$$

The desired estimate $\hat{\boldsymbol{x}}_0$ is the mean value of the random variable $(\boldsymbol{x}_0 | \boldsymbol{Z})$, Chapter 2. Because the system noise was assumed to be normal and white, it follows that the probability densities in (12–77) have the forms

(12–78)

$$\begin{aligned} f(\boldsymbol{Z} | \boldsymbol{x}_0) &= f(\boldsymbol{V}) = f(\boldsymbol{Z} - \mathbf{M\Phi}\boldsymbol{x}_0) \\ &= (2\pi)^{-pk/2} |\boldsymbol{\Psi}_V|^{-1/2} \exp\{-\tfrac{1}{2}(\boldsymbol{Z} - \mathbf{M\Phi}\boldsymbol{x}_0)^T \boldsymbol{\Psi}_V^{-1} (\boldsymbol{Z} - \mathbf{M\Phi}\boldsymbol{x}_0)\}, \end{aligned}$$

$$f(\boldsymbol{x}_0) = (2\pi)^{-n/2} |\mathbf{P}_0|^{-1/2} \exp\{-\tfrac{1}{2}\boldsymbol{x}_0^T \mathbf{P}_0^{-1} \boldsymbol{x}_0\}, \tag{12–79}$$

$$f(\boldsymbol{Z}) = (2\pi)^{-pk/2} |\mathbf{N}|^{-1/2} \exp\{-\tfrac{1}{2}\boldsymbol{Z}^T \mathbf{N}^{-1} \boldsymbol{Z}\}, \tag{12–80}$$

where, from (12–73), (12–74), and (12–76),

$$\mathbf{N} = \mathrm{E}\{\boldsymbol{Z}\boldsymbol{Z}^T\} = \mathbf{M\Phi P}_0 \mathbf{\Phi}^T \mathbf{M}^T + \boldsymbol{\Psi}_V. \tag{12–81}$$

Substitute (12–78), (12–79), and (12–80) into (12–77). The result can be written as

$$\begin{aligned} f(\boldsymbol{x}_0 | \boldsymbol{Z}) &= \frac{|\mathbf{N}|^{1/2}}{(2\pi)^{n/2} |\boldsymbol{\Psi}_V|^{1/2} |\mathbf{P}_0|^{1/2}} \\ &\quad \times \exp\{-\tfrac{1}{2}[\boldsymbol{x}_0 - \mathbf{\Lambda\Phi}^T \mathbf{M}^T \boldsymbol{\Psi}_V^{-1} \boldsymbol{Z}]^T \mathbf{\Lambda}^{-1} [\boldsymbol{x}_0 - \mathbf{\Lambda\Phi}^T \mathbf{M}^T \boldsymbol{\Psi}_V^{-1} \boldsymbol{Z}]\}, \end{aligned} \tag{12–82}$$

where

$$\mathbf{\Lambda} = (\mathbf{P}_0^{-1} + \mathbf{\Phi}^T \mathbf{M}^T \boldsymbol{\Psi}_V^{-1} \mathbf{M\Phi})^{-1}. \tag{12–83}$$

By inspection of the normal form of (12–82), we conclude that the mean value of the random variable $(\boldsymbol{x}_0 | \boldsymbol{Z})$ is

$$\hat{\boldsymbol{x}}_0 = \mathbf{\Lambda\Phi}^T \mathbf{M}^T \boldsymbol{\Psi}_V^{-1} \boldsymbol{Z}. \tag{12–84}$$

Moreover, the covariance matrix of the estimate error

$$\boldsymbol{\epsilon}_0 = \hat{\boldsymbol{x}}_0 - \boldsymbol{x}_0 \tag{12–85}$$

is simply $\mathbf{\Lambda}$.

If the estimate of a state $\boldsymbol{x}_k$ is required at any time $t_k \neq t_0$, then the transition relation is called upon to obtain

$$\begin{aligned} \hat{\boldsymbol{x}}_k &= \mathbf{\Phi}_k \hat{\boldsymbol{x}}_0 \\ &= \mathbf{\Phi}_k \mathbf{\Lambda\Phi}^T \mathbf{M}^T \boldsymbol{\Psi}_V^{-1} \boldsymbol{Z}. \end{aligned} \tag{12–86}$$

The corresponding covariance matrix for the estimate error $\boldsymbol{\epsilon}_k$ at time $t = t_k$ is

$$\begin{aligned} \mathbf{\Lambda}_k &= \mathrm{E}\{\boldsymbol{\epsilon}_k \boldsymbol{\epsilon}_k^T\} = \mathrm{E}\{(\boldsymbol{x}_k - \hat{\boldsymbol{x}}_k)(\boldsymbol{x}_k - \hat{\boldsymbol{x}}_k)^T\} \\ &= \mathbf{\Phi}_k \, \mathrm{E}\{(\boldsymbol{x}_0 - \hat{\boldsymbol{x}}_0)(\boldsymbol{x}_0 - \hat{\boldsymbol{x}}_0)^T\} \mathbf{\Phi}_k^T \\ &= \mathbf{\Phi}_k \mathbf{\Lambda\Phi}_k^T. \end{aligned} \tag{12–87}$$

Smith, Schmidt, and McGee [141] demonstrated that, if the individual observations $\mathbf{z}_j$ are statistically independent, then a sequential estimation procedure will reduce (12–86) and (12–87) to the formulations summarized in Section 12.2.

Write (12–86) in terms of the individual matrices, or component matrices, which constitute the total matrices. That is, express (12–86) as

$$\hat{\mathbf{x}}_k = \mathbf{\Phi}_k \cdot \left[\mathbf{P}_0^{-1} + \sum_{i=1}^{k} \mathbf{\Phi}_i^T \mathbf{M}_i^T \mathbf{R}_i^{-1} \mathbf{M}_i \mathbf{\Phi}_i\right]^{-1} \cdot \sum_{i=1}^{k} \mathbf{\Phi}_i^T \mathbf{M}_i^T \mathbf{R}_i^{-1} \mathbf{z}_i. \tag{12–88}$$

Because we are considering a sequential estimation process, $\hat{\mathbf{x}}_{k-1}$ is available and it is not necessary in this particular situation to refer each estimate back to some arbitrarily chosen reference state estimate $\hat{\mathbf{x}}_0$. Hence, for the preceding step, corresponding to (12–88), the estimate for $(k - 1)$ observations would have the same form with $k$ replaced by $(k - 1)$. The estimate $\hat{\mathbf{x}}_k$ based upon $(k - 1)$ preceding observations is expressible as a transition of the estimate $\hat{\mathbf{x}}_{k-1}$,

$$\begin{aligned} \hat{\mathbf{x}}_k &= \mathbf{\Phi}(k, k-1)\hat{\mathbf{x}}_{k-1} = \mathbf{\Phi}_k \mathbf{\Phi}_{k-1}^{-1} \hat{\mathbf{x}}_{k-1} \\ &= \mathbf{\Phi}_k \mathbf{\Phi}_{k-1}^{-1} \mathbf{\Phi}_{k-1} \cdot \left[\mathbf{P}_0^{-1} + \sum_{i=1}^{k-1} \mathbf{\Phi}_i^T \mathbf{M}_i^T \mathbf{R}_i^{-1} \mathbf{M}_i \mathbf{\Phi}_i\right]^{-1} \cdot \sum_{i=1}^{k-1} \mathbf{\Phi}_i^T \mathbf{M}_i^T \mathbf{R}_i^{-1} \mathbf{z}_i, \end{aligned} \tag{12–89}$$

or

$$\left(\mathbf{P}_0^{-1} + \sum_{i=1}^{k-1} \mathbf{\Phi}_i^T \mathbf{M}_i^T \mathbf{R}_i^{-1} \mathbf{M}_i \mathbf{\Phi}_i\right) \mathbf{\Phi}_k^{-1} \hat{\mathbf{x}}_k = \sum_{i=1}^{k-1} \mathbf{\Phi}_i^T \mathbf{M}_i^T \mathbf{R}_i^{-1} \mathbf{z}_i. \tag{12–90}$$

Write (12–88) in a form similar to (12–90) by subtracting indices, and subtract the two expressions to find that

$$\hat{\mathbf{x}}_k = \mathbf{\Phi}_k \mathbf{\Phi}_{k-1}^{-1} \hat{\mathbf{x}}_{k-1} + \mathbf{\Lambda}_k \mathbf{M}_k^T \mathbf{R}^{-1} \cdot (\mathbf{z}_k - \mathbf{M}_k \mathbf{\Phi}_k \mathbf{\Phi}_{k-1}^{-1} \hat{\mathbf{x}}_{k-1}). \tag{12–91}$$

Equation (12–91) is identical to (12–50*D*) if we make the equivalences:

| (12–50*D*) | (12–91) |
|---|---|
| $\hat{\mathbf{x}}_{k+1}$ | $\hat{\mathbf{x}}_k$ |
| $\hat{\mathbf{x}}_k$ | $\hat{\mathbf{x}}_{k-1}$ |
| $\mathbf{A}$ | $\mathbf{\Phi}_k \mathbf{\Phi}_{k-1} = \mathbf{\Phi}(k, k-1)$ |
| $\mathbf{C}_k$ | $\mathbf{\Lambda}_k \mathbf{M}_k^T \mathbf{R}^{-1}$ |
| $\mathbf{M}_k$ | $\mathbf{M}_k \mathbf{\Phi}(k, k-1)$ |

A similar set of arguments can be used to complete the demonstrations, which show that the Bayes' estimation procedure can be reduced to the form of all the relations previously developed for sequential estimators summarized in Section 12.2 [141].

## 12.5
## *STABILITY AND INITIAL CONDITIONS*

The sequential estimator as derived in Chapter 8 suffered from the fact that, in general, the initial estimate to start the process must be obtained from the solution of a minimal data set. The problems encountered in arbitrarily selecting initial estimates were discussed in Section 8.5. The same type of initializing problems must be faced with the versions of sequential estimators, whether continuous or discrete, which have been developed in this chapter.

Kalman has studied the initializing problems and the following theorems are due to him [79; 166, Chapter 11]. The fundamental problem is to demonstrate the necessary and sufficient conditions for stability in the sense that, for given restrictions on assumed initial values of the state vector and error covariance matrix, the state and error covariance matrices after a large number of steps are independent of the initial assumptions.

DEFINITION 12.1: A linear system of the canonical form

(12–92)
$$\frac{d\boldsymbol{x}(t)}{dt} = \mathbf{F}(t)\boldsymbol{x}(t) + \mathbf{G}(t)\boldsymbol{u}(t)$$
$$\boldsymbol{z}(t) = \mathbf{H}(t)\boldsymbol{\Phi}(t, T)\boldsymbol{x}(T) + \boldsymbol{v}(t)$$

is called *completely controllable* if, at any instant of time $t > 0$, the corresponding state vector $\boldsymbol{x}(t)$ can be transformed to the origin state $\boldsymbol{x}(0)$ by means of a suitable control function.

Kalman, Ho, and Narendra proved the following theorem on controllable systems.

THEOREM 12.1: A system of the canonical form (12–92) is completely controllable if and only if the matrix

(12–93)
$$W(t, T) = \int_t^T \boldsymbol{\Phi}(T, \tau)\mathbf{G}(\tau)\mathbf{Q}(\tau)\mathbf{G}^T(\tau)\boldsymbol{\Phi}^T(T, \tau)\, d\tau$$

is positive definite for some $T > t$.

For a constant system in which **F** and **G** are constants, Theorem 12.1 can be replaced by a simpler version:

THEOREM 12.2: For a constant linear system of the canonical form (12–92), a necessary and sufficient condition for complete controllability is

(12–94)
$$\text{rank}\,[\mathbf{G} \quad \mathbf{FG} \quad \cdots \quad \mathbf{F}^{n-1}\mathbf{G}] = n;$$

**G**, **FG**, . . . denote the columns of a matrix.

DEFINITION 12.2: The system

(12–95)
$$\frac{d\boldsymbol{x}(t)}{dt} = \mathbf{F}(t)\boldsymbol{x}(t) + \mathbf{G}(t)\boldsymbol{u}(t)$$
$$\boldsymbol{y}(t) = \mathbf{H}(t)\boldsymbol{x}(t)$$

is called *completely observable* if it is possible to determine the exact value of $\boldsymbol{x}(t_0)$, given the values of $\boldsymbol{y}(t)$ in a finite interval $(t_{-1}, t_0)$ preceding $t_0$.

Analogous to Theorem 12.1, Kalman proved the following:

THEOREM 12.3: A system of the canonical form (12–95) is completely observable if and only if the matrix

$$\mathbf{D}(t_0, T) = \int_{t_0}^{T} \mathbf{\Phi}^T(t, T)\mathbf{H}^T(t)\mathbf{R}^{-1}(t)\mathbf{H}(t)\mathbf{\Phi}(t, T)\,dt \tag{12–96}$$

is positive definite for some $T > t_0$.

THEOREM 12.4: For a constant system of the canonical form (12–95), a necessary and sufficient condition for complete observability is

$$\text{rank}\,[\mathbf{H}^T \quad \mathbf{F}^T\mathbf{H}^T \quad \cdots \quad (\mathbf{F}^T)^{n-1}\mathbf{H}^T] = n. \tag{12–97}$$

We can now state a version of Kalman's results which concerns the initial conditions.

THEOREM 12.5: If a constant system of the canonical form (12–95) is both uniformly completely observable and uniformly completely controllable, then

(i) The optimum filter is uniformly asymptotically stable;

(ii) Every solution $\mathbf{P}(t_j)$ of the variance equation (12–55) which results from initializing with a boundary condition $\mathbf{P}(t_0)$ as a symmetric nonnegative matrix tends uniformily to a unique positive definite matrix.

The property of *uniformity* always holds for constant systems [79].

An analogous set of definitions and theorems can be written for the case of sampled data, or discrete time systems. In fact, most continuous systems which are completely controllable in the absence of sampling remain completely controllable after sampling [80].

In view of these theorems, one can now explain why the limited form of the sequential estimator developed in Chapter 8 does not necessarily lead to stable solutions independent of arbitrary choices of the initial state and error covariance matrix. If the unknowns are fixed system parameters, then the state variables, in the terminology of this chapter, are not completely controllable. There is no general transition function which will transform the estimate at any stage back to some chosen origin.

Even when we have assured ourselves that the system we are considering is both completely observable and completely controllable, we are still faced with the problem of an initial estimate. The initial estimate could be obtained by the solution of a minimal data set or, equivalently, by numerically integrating (12–3) over some short interval of time. However, it can be argued readily that a good assumption is to choose $\hat{\mathbf{x}}(0) = \mathbf{0}$ and $\mathbf{P}(0)$ as a diagonal matrix whose elements are the best known guesses of the variances of each element of the state variable estimate $\hat{\mathbf{x}}(0)$. The choice of

$\hat{\boldsymbol{x}}(0) = \boldsymbol{0}$ follows from (12–42), and the arbitrariness of $\mathbf{P}(0)$ follows from Theorem 12.5. Choosing the elements as variance estimates usually helps speed the convergence of the estimation process, although such a choice is not mandatory.

## 12.6
## *INVERSION OF THE FUNDAMENTAL MATRIX*

The transition, or fundamental, matrix in discrete form (12–56*D*) can be factored into a product of two matrices by the following arguments:

(12–98)
$$\begin{aligned} \boldsymbol{x}(t_{k+1}) &= \boldsymbol{\Phi}(t_{k+1}, t_k)\,\boldsymbol{x}(t_k) \\ \boldsymbol{x}_k &= \boldsymbol{\Phi}(k, 0)\,\boldsymbol{x}_0 \overset{d}{=} \boldsymbol{\Phi}_k \boldsymbol{x}_0 \\ \boldsymbol{x}_{k+1} &= \boldsymbol{\Phi}(k+1, 0)\,\boldsymbol{x}_0 \overset{d}{=} \boldsymbol{\Phi}_{k+1} \boldsymbol{x}_0 \\ \boldsymbol{x}_{k+1} &= \boldsymbol{\Phi}_{k+1} \boldsymbol{\Phi}_k^{-1} \boldsymbol{x}_k. \end{aligned}$$

Frielander has derived a rather simple algorithm for inverting $\boldsymbol{\Phi}(t_k)$ that is applicable to an important class of systems in which there is an even number, $n$, of elements in the system state vector and the matrix $\mathbf{F}$ of the canonical system model (12–47) can be partitioned into four square submatrices, each of order $n/2$, such that the diagonal submatrices are equal to the null matrix and the off-diagonal submatrices are symmetrical [54]. The first condition is always satisfied in dynamical problems for which the state vector consists of a body's position and velocity components. If a given system does not immediately meet the second condition on the matrix $\mathbf{F}$, a transformation of variables can frequently correct the situation. In any event, the simplicity of the algorithm, when applicable, can avoid possible numerical problems of inverting the fundamental matrix.

From (12–5) and (12–6)

(12–99)
$$\begin{aligned} \boldsymbol{\Phi}(t_0, t)\boldsymbol{\Phi}(t, t_0) &= \boldsymbol{\Phi}(t_0, t_0) = \mathbf{I}, \qquad t > t_0 \\ \boldsymbol{\Phi}^{-1}(t, t_0)\boldsymbol{\Phi}(t, t_0) &= \mathbf{I}. \end{aligned}$$

Differentiate (12–99) with respect to $t$, and insert (12–4) to find

(12–100)
$$\frac{d}{dt}\boldsymbol{\Phi}^{-1}(t, t_0) = -\boldsymbol{\Phi}^{-1}(t, t_0)\,\mathbf{F}(t).$$

Using the hypothesis on $\mathbf{F}^{[n\times n]}$, (12–100) can be partitioned into the form

(12–101)
$$\begin{aligned} \frac{d}{dt}\begin{bmatrix} \mathbf{L}_1 & \mathbf{L}_2 \\ \mathbf{L}_3 & \mathbf{L}_4 \end{bmatrix} &= -\begin{bmatrix} \mathbf{L}_1 & \mathbf{L}_2 \\ \mathbf{L}_3 & \mathbf{L}_4 \end{bmatrix}\begin{bmatrix} \mathbf{0} & \mathbf{F}_2 \\ \mathbf{F}_3 & \mathbf{0} \end{bmatrix} \\ &= -\begin{bmatrix} \mathbf{L}_2\mathbf{F}_3 & \mathbf{L}_1\mathbf{F}_2 \\ \mathbf{L}_4\mathbf{F}_3 & \mathbf{L}_3\mathbf{F}_2 \end{bmatrix}, \end{aligned}$$

where each submatrix is of order $n/2$. Partition the fundamental matrix into four submatrices of order $n/2$,

$$\mathbf{\Phi}(t, t_0) = \begin{bmatrix} \mathbf{\Phi}_1 & \mathbf{\Phi}_2 \\ \mathbf{\Phi}_3 & \mathbf{\Phi}_4 \end{bmatrix}. \tag{12–102}$$

The transpose of (12–4) is also partitioned in an analogous fashion so that

$$\frac{d}{dt}\mathbf{\Phi}^T = \mathbf{\Phi}^T \mathbf{F}^T$$

$$\frac{d}{dt}\begin{bmatrix} \mathbf{\Phi}_1^T & \mathbf{\Phi}_3^T \\ \mathbf{\Phi}_2^T & \mathbf{\Phi}_4^T \end{bmatrix} = \begin{bmatrix} \mathbf{\Phi}_1^T & \mathbf{\Phi}_3^T \\ \mathbf{\Phi}_2^T & \mathbf{\Phi}_4^T \end{bmatrix}\begin{bmatrix} \mathbf{0} & \mathbf{F}_3 \\ \mathbf{F}_2 & \mathbf{0} \end{bmatrix} = \begin{bmatrix} \mathbf{\Phi}_3^T\mathbf{F}_2 & \mathbf{\Phi}_1^T\mathbf{F}_3 \\ \mathbf{\Phi}_4^T\mathbf{F}_2 & \mathbf{\Phi}_2^T\mathbf{F}_3 \end{bmatrix}. \tag{12–103}$$

We have used the condition that $\mathbf{F}_2$ and $\mathbf{F}_3$ are both symmetric matrices. Equations (12–101) and (12–103) will be equivalent if they have the same boundary conditions and if, equating the coefficients of $\mathbf{F}_2$ and $\mathbf{F}_3$,

$$\mathbf{L}_1 = \mathbf{\Phi}_4^T \qquad \mathbf{L}_2 = -\mathbf{\Phi}_2^T$$
$$\mathbf{L}_3 = -\mathbf{\Phi}_3^T \qquad \mathbf{L}_4 = \mathbf{\Phi}_1^T. \tag{12–104}$$

The boundary conditions are identical because the fundamental matrix has the property that $\mathbf{\Phi}^T(t_0, t_0) = \mathbf{I} = \mathbf{\Phi}^{-1}(t_0, t_0)$. Hence, the desired inverse relation is obtained from (12–101) and (12–104),

$$\mathbf{\Phi}^{-1} = \begin{bmatrix} \mathbf{\Phi}_4^T & -\mathbf{\Phi}_2^T \\ -\mathbf{\Phi}_3^T & \mathbf{\Phi}_1^T \end{bmatrix}. \tag{12–105}$$

## Problems

**12.1** Show that the following system is completely controllable:

$$\frac{d}{dt}\begin{bmatrix} x_1(t) \\ x_2(t) \end{bmatrix} = \begin{bmatrix} x_1(t) \\ x_2(t) \end{bmatrix} + \begin{bmatrix} u_1(t) \\ u_2(t) \end{bmatrix}$$
$$y(t) = x_1(t) + x_2(t).$$

**12.2** For the system in Problem 12.1, let

$$\mathrm{E}\left\{\begin{bmatrix} u_1 \\ u_2 \end{bmatrix}[u_1 \ u_2]\right\} = \mathbf{Q}\,\delta(t - \tau),$$

$$\boldsymbol{z} = \begin{bmatrix} x_1 \\ x_2 \end{bmatrix} + \begin{bmatrix} v_1 \\ v_2 \end{bmatrix},$$

$$\mathrm{E}\left\{\begin{bmatrix} v_1 \\ v_2 \end{bmatrix}[v_1 \ v_2]\right\} = \mathbf{R}\,\delta(t - \tau).$$

Write the differential equation for the optimal estimate and the equation for the error covariance matrix.

**12.3** Show whether or not the system defined in Problem 12.2 is completely controllable and completely observable.

**12.4** The differential estimation procedure can be applied to the problem of detecting a sinusoid signal in the presence of white noise. The system model is

$$\frac{dx_1}{dt} = -A_2(t) \sin (t - T)$$

$$\frac{dx_2}{dt} = A_1(t) \cos (t - T)$$

$$z(t) = A_1(t) \cos (t - T) + A_2(t) \sin (t - T) + v(t)$$

$$\mathrm{E}\{v(t)\, v(t - \tau)\} = R(\tau).$$

Verify if this system is completely observable and completely controllable. Find the optimal weighting, or filter, that will separate the signal from the noise.

**12.5** Show how (12–50), (12–50*D*), (12–55), and (12–55*D*) must be modified if in (12–9) we *do not* assume $\mathrm{E}\{\boldsymbol{u}(t)\boldsymbol{v}(t - \tau)\} = \mathbf{0}$.

**12.6** Demonstrate that all the relations for the linear sequential estimator in Section 8.3 are equivalent to the relations summarized in Section 12.2.

**12.7** Show that (12–87) can be used in a sequential fashion to lead to a form equivalent to (12–55*D*).

# Chapter 13

# DECISION THEORY

Throughout the preceding chapters, the estimation of system parameters, or system states, has been considered as an end in itself. This narrow point of view was convenient in developing an estimation theory, but it is really slightly inconsistent with the real world. That is, in almost all applications of estimation theory, one first estimates parameters, or states, and then makes some sort of decision based upon his *best* available estimates.

The input data, upon which our judgements are based, consist of a set of observations, or measurements, which yield values assumed by a set of random variables $\{\boldsymbol{x}\}$, whose probability distribution function $F_x(\boldsymbol{\xi}; \boldsymbol{\theta})$ may be known except for the specific values of the parameters $\boldsymbol{\theta}$. Estimation theory is concerned with methods for judiciously selecting values of $\hat{\boldsymbol{\theta}}$, which in certain specified senses are *close* to the true value of $\boldsymbol{\theta}$. On the other hand, decision theory is applied to select a course of action from a set of alternatives for which the degree of preference associated with each choice depends upon the distribution function $F_x(\boldsymbol{\xi}; \boldsymbol{\theta})$. Thus the observations provide information concerning the parameters in the distribution function; in turn, the distribution function provides guidance in the choice of a particular alternative in a given collection of choices, or a *best* decision. The decision problem is one of establishing a rule, which, based upon all the information contained in the observations, indicates which decision should be made.

Because a decision is influenced by the estimation of parameters in a distribution function, it will not surprise us to learn that decision theory can be formulated as a generalization of the loss and risk function formulation used in estimation theory. It is exactly this close, formal relation between decisions and estimations that justifies a discussion on decision theory. In fact, as we shall observe, estimation theory can be completely contained within the framework of decision theory.

## 13.1
## *DECISION FUNCTIONS*

The principle objective of decision theory is to formulate rules which can be applied to a sequence of observations to specify an *optimum* decision. As a mechanism for formulating decision rules, we shall expand our previous definition of a risk function. Let $x$ be a value representing an observation from a set $X$, and let $d = \delta(x)$ be an associated decision rule. The domain of $d$ is the set of possible decisions $D$. The conditional risk function introduced by Wald [150] is defined as

$$R(b, \delta) = \mathrm{E}_D\{l[b, \delta(x)] \mid X\}. \tag{13–1}$$

Thus the risk is now a function of the loss function $l$, which, in turn, depends upon both the parameter $b$ and the decision $\delta(x)$.

A frequently occurring difficulty encountered in attempting to minimize the risk function is that the minimizing decision function $\delta$ may, in turn, be dependent upon the unknown values of the parameters $b$. It can very well happen that a minimum value of the risk can be found for some $\delta$ and a given estimate $\hat{b}$ of $b$; however, it is frequently discovered that relatively small changes in $\hat{b}$ can correspond to large changes in the risk. If there does not exist a decision function which minimizes the risk for all $\hat{b}$, it is not at all self-evident as to just what is the *best* procedure in selecting a decision function.

If $R(b, \delta_1) < R(b, \delta_2)$ for all $b$, then it is almost intuitive that we say that $\delta_1$ is *better* than $\delta_2$. Unfortunately the inequality may not hold for *all* $b$ in many situations which we encounter. Therefore, it is necessary to introduce some method of ordering risk functions. It is exactly this ordering problem that exhibits a weakness in the theory of optimum decisions. That is, the theory of optimum decisions is dependent upon a selected scheme for ordering risk functions as well as upon knowledge of the loss function coupled with a priori knowledge of the distributions of the random variables. These dependency problems are serious points which must be scrutinized carefully when one applies decision theory to actual real-world situations.

Two methods are commonly used to optimize risk functions with respect to decisions depending upon an ordering of the risk functions.

(i) *Bayes' Solution:* Suppose that the probability density function $f(b)$ is known for the parameters $b$. The *average risk function* $r$ for a given loss function $l$ and decision $\delta$ is defined to be

$$\begin{aligned} r(f, \delta) &= \mathrm{E}_b\{R[b, \delta(x)]\} \\ &= \int R[b, \delta(x)] f(b)\, db. \end{aligned} \tag{13–2}$$

The optimization procedure is chosen as a process of selecting a decision $\delta$ that minimizes the average risk function $r(f, \delta)$. This procedure leads to what is known as the *Bayes' solution*, corresponding to a given probability density function $f(b)$. The minimum value of $r$ obtained in this manner is called the *Bayes' risk*, corresponding to the density function $f(b)$.

In order to apply the Bayes' solution, it is necessary to postulate that the parameter $b$ is a random variable and that one has a priori knowledge of the distribution, or density, function associated with $b$. Unfortunately, we frequently are faced with both theoretical and applied situations for which even the existence of $f(b)$ cannot be postulated; other situations are met in which, even when the existence of $f(b)$ can be assumed, its exact form is unknown and thus the Bayes' solution cannot be calculated explicitly.

(ii) *Minimax Solution:* Because of the practical problem of having to work occasionally without either explicit a priori knowledge of the distribution function of the parameters or perhaps an incomplete description of the distribution function, alternative solution techniques have been proposed to minimize the risk functions. One such alternative technique is to compute a *minimax solution*. That is, $\delta_0$ is called a minimax solution of the decision problem if the choice of this decision minimizes the maximum risk $R(b, \delta)$ with respect to $b$. In the form of an inequality, a minimax solution is one which satisfies

$$(13\text{–}3) \qquad \max_{b} \min_{\delta} R(b, \delta) \leq \max_{b} R(b, \delta).$$

Notice that (13–3) assures us that we have the worst average loss, or that a minimax solution represents the maximum protection against having large losses.

Wald [150] has shown that, under rather general assumptions,

$$(13\text{–}4) \qquad \max_{f} \min_{\delta} r(f, \delta) = \min_{\delta} \max_{f} r(f, \delta).$$

A great amount of interest has been focused upon minimax solutions of the decision problem because this approach appeals intuitively as a reasonable solution to the decision problem when the a priori distributions of the random variables are unknown. Wald demonstrated that the theory of minimax solutions plays a dominant role in the theory of important classes of decision functions. In particular, Wald showed that there is an intimate relation between Bayes' and minimax solutions. Under certain general conditions, it can be proved that a minimax solution is identical to the Bayes' solution for the same problem.

It should be pointed out that, while there are many investigators who believe in minimax solutions, there are also a number of people who have directed various adverse criticisms at the minimax approach. One critical argument is that the conservatism of a minimax solution reduces the usefulness of the result. On the other hand, it is admitted that in some situations there is no doubt that a minimax solution is an ideal device. An example in which a minimax solution is not an intuitively reasonable choice is shown in Figure 13–1. Most people would select the decision $\delta_2$ rather than $\delta_1$,

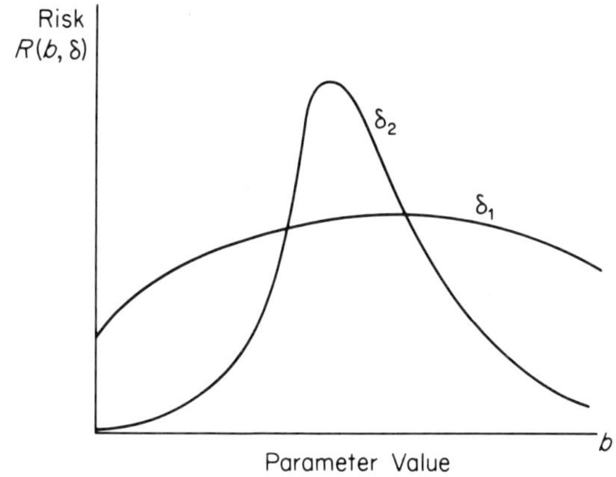


**Fig. 13-1** Risk functions.

although the risk function corresponding to $\delta_2$ has the larger magnitude for certain values of $b$.

(iii) *Properties of Decision Rules:* Because of the myriad of problems associated with attempts to find a unique solution to a decision process, investigations have been made of the extent to which a decision problem can be reduced without loss of relevant information. Let $\delta_1$ be a decision rule that is *better* than a rule $\delta_2$ in the sense of ordering risk functions:

$$
\begin{aligned}
&r(f, \delta_1) \leq r(f, \delta_2), \qquad \text{for all } f. \\
&r(f, \delta_1) < r(f, \delta_2), \qquad \text{for some } f.
\end{aligned}
\tag{13–5}
$$

If the inequalities (13–5) are satisfied, $\delta_2$ is called *inadmissible*. If no $\delta_1$ exists which satisfies the risk inequalities, $\delta_2$ is called an *admissible* decision function.

A *complete* class $\mathscr{D}$ of decision functions is one which, for any decision $\delta$ not in class $\mathscr{D}$, there exists a decision $\delta'$ in $\mathscr{D}$ such that $\delta'$ is *uniformly better* than $\delta$. That is, (13–5) is satisfied. Note that (13–5) implies that a decision function is admissible if no uniformly better one exists. An admissible decision function need not necessarily be uniformly better than any other decision function, because one could select decision rules which, as illustrated in Figure 13–1, could yield smaller risks at particular values, or ranges, of the parameters $b$. Furthermore, an admissible decision rule need not be minimax, because it is not at all unlikely that $\delta_1$ could yield a higher risk value than $\delta_2$ at some values of $b$ and yet still have a smaller maximum risk.

Further elaboration of properties of decision rules are contained in the books by Wald [150] and Middleton [100]. Wald has shown that the following statements hold for rather general conditions that are satisfied in most physical situations. These conditions are the usual ones regarding continuity and boundedness of domains.

a. The decision problem can be considered to be a strictly determined two-person, zero-sum game, in the game-theoretic sense, because

$$\max_f \min_\delta r(f, \delta) = \min_\delta \max_f r(f, \delta).$$

b. For any given a priori probability density function $f(b)$, there exists a Bayes' decision rule relative to $f(b)$.

c. There exists a least favorable a priori probability density function $f_0 = f(b)$ such that $\min_\delta r(f_0, \delta) = \max_f \min_\delta r(f, \delta)$.

d. Any minimax decision rule is a Bayes' rule relative to a least favorable a priori probability density function.

## 13.2
## *SIGNAL DETECTION*

One of the more important and widely used applications of decision theory is concerned with the detection of signals which are obscured by the unavoidable presence of noise. This particular application of the theory has received intense, widespread attention because of the dominant role it plays in the design and evaluation of radar and communication systems.

The signal detection problem is one of deciding whether or not a *desired* signal has really been received when it exists in a background environment of *undesired* signals, or noise. *Detection* can be defined as the act of discovering the existence, or presence, of an undefined object. Although this definition may be satisfactory for semantic purposes, it lacks the preciseness required for satisfactory mathematical models of detection processes which are encountered in communication systems.

Before an analytical model can be constructed for the concept of detecting an undefined object, it is first necessary to decide exactly what will constitute the detection process. A little reflection indicates that, for most *familiar* detection processes, the existence of a *detection threshold* is an integral member of the detection mechanism. As a simple example, recall that visual detection of an object is often described by stating that the light flux at the observer has exceeded some minimal acuity level. Furthermore, the most basic concept which must be incorporated into a mathematical model of detection is that of *penalty*. An observer can make two types of decision errors when attempting to detect an object, or signal in an environment of noise. Noise can be judged to be a signal in the absence of any signal, or the observer can fail to observe a signal when a signal is present. Because he can make two types of errors, the observer is in something of a quandary. If he is too sensitive in his responses, he may well report many signals when none is present or possibly when he is confused by noise. On the other hand, he may become very cautious and weigh his judgements so carefully that he fails to report a signal even when one is received.

The observer can resolve his quandary by playing a game. He assigns a *payoff** (reward) $a$ for making the first type of error of reporting a signal when only noise is present. Similarly, he assigns an amount $b$ as the payoff for making the second type of error of reporting no signal when there really is a signal present. We shall show that by judicious planning based upon the signal and noise statistics, the observer can maximize his rewards in the face of the two types of errors.

It is almost transparent that signal detection theory is being cast into the framework which is characteristic of hypothesis testing and decision theory. It is readily conceded that, in many respects, detection theory is formulated in this fashion for analytical convenience and possibly for mathematical elegance. However, there is more than elegance to motivate us, because practical experience and exhaustive laboratory experiments have amply demonstrated the logic and justification for formulating detection as a decision process.

A suitable, or acceptable, mathematical model for detection must encompass all the factors that are known to influence the physical detection processes encountered in the real world. Thus a *complete* theory must assign penalties to incorrect decisions and must include a measure for evaluating the performance of the detection process. Intuition also leads us to anticipate that a detection threshold concept will be encountered in the model.

## 13.3
## *NEYMAN-PEARSON DETECTION*

The theory of hypothesis testing during the last decades has been primarily advanced through the work of Fisher, Neyman and Pearson, and their schools. We shall briefly review the Neyman-Pearson test of a hypothesis against a single alternative [107, 108]. Their theory will be developed using the terminology of signal detection and then will be related to the generalistic

**Payoff* is used in the game-theoretic sense. That is, a penalty is assigned a negative payoff value, while a reward is assigned a positive payoff value.

formalism of decision, loss, and risk functions. This choice of development is specifically aimed at signal detection and is not completely framed in the statistical language of Neyman and Pearson. Middleton [100] has been very active in applying the formalism of hypothesis testing to signal detection and this section is largely motivated by his work.

The detection criterion which we shall use is motivated by the observation that the detection process is fundamentally postulated to be a problem in statistical hypothesis testing. In statistical terminology, the act of judging the presence or absence of a signal in a noise environment is equivalent to testing the hypothesis $H_0$ that noise alone is present against the alternative hypothesis $H_1$ that signal-plus-noise is present.

A detection decision based upon the finite amount of information which is available to the receiver is subject to two types of errors.

*Type* I: Decide that noise is a signal when only noise is present; probability of error is $\alpha$.

*Type* II: Decide that signal is noise when a signal is really present; probability of error is $\beta$.

The Neyman-Pearson Detector operates in the following manner. The probability $\alpha$ of a Type I error and the number of observations, $n$ (fixed integration, or observation, time in the terminology of detection theory), are kept constant at preassigned values. One then minimizes the probability $\beta$ corresponding to a Type II error. This procedure is the Neyman-Pearson test for the statistical hypothesis $H_0$ against $H_1$ for a fixed probability of Type I error, a test which has been demonstrated to be the best possible for a single alternative under these conditions.

Suppose that we have at our disposal $n$ observations $x_1, \ldots, x_n$ of a signal and the joint probability density function $f_n(x_1, \ldots, x_n; b)$ is known. $b$ is a parameter associated with the joint density function. In an observation-space region, known to contain a signal, $b = b_1$. In all other regions of this space $b = b_0 = 0$. For our illustrative purposes, $b_1$ will be the positive square root of the signal-to-noise power ratio, which plays a dominant role in communication theory.

The detection problem can now be stated explicitly. On the basis of the $n$ signal samples $x_1, \ldots, x_n$, we wish to test the hypothesis $H_0$ that $b_0 = 0$ against the alternate hypothesis $H_1$ that $b = b_1$. $H_0$ is called the *null hypothesis* because it is usually associated with the conditions that are known to occur most of the time and whose validity for the $n$ data elements in question is to be tested. Since there is but one alternative, clearly rejection of $H_0$ automatically implies acceptance of $H_1$, and conversely.

The test for accepting or rejecting $H_0$ requires that the observation space be divided into two regions. One region is associated with $H_0$ and the second region is associated with $H_1$. This division of the observation space is accomplished through the assignment of probabilities for the two types of errors.

(i) *Type-I error:* $H_0$ is rejected when it is in fact true. The probability of making this error is

$$\alpha = \int \cdots \int_{D_1} f_n(x_1, \ldots, x_n; b_0)\, dx_1 \ldots dx_n. \tag{13–6}$$

$D_1$ is the region of the $n$-dimensional observation space which is associated with the alternative hypothesis $H_1$. $D_1$ will be specified by the particular manner chosen to make the hypothesis test.

(ii) *Type-II error:* $H_0$ is accepted when $H_1$ is true. The probability of making this error is

$$\beta = \int \cdots \int_{D_0} f_n(x_1, \ldots, x_n; b_1)\, dx_1 \ldots dx_n. \tag{13–7}$$

$D = D_1 + D_0$ is the entire $n$-dimensional space for the signal samples $x_1, \ldots, x_n$. $D_0$ is called the *acceptance region.* $D_1$ is called the *critical region.* The *power of the test* is defined to be $1 - \beta$, and $\alpha$ is called the *significance level of the test.*

The detection decision is based upon the particular fashion selected for dividing the sample space $D$ into the regions $D_0$ and $D_1$. $H_0$ is accepted or rejected on the basis of whether or not the given sample point $\boldsymbol{x} = (x_1, \ldots, x_n)$ lies in $D_0$ or $D_1$. Although the division of the sample space $D$ is somewhat arbitrary, for various situations some divisions are better than others. It would be a reasonable investigation to determine the division of the sample space which leads to a *best* detection decision. Usually, for small probabilities of Type I errors, the probabilities of Type II errors are large, and conversely. For this reason, coupled with the fact that the statistical probability density function from which the probability $\alpha$ is calculated is not always known explicitly, Neyman and Pearson arbitrarily fixed $\alpha$ and then adjusted the critical region $D_1$ to minimize the probability $\beta$. This procedure is tantamount to making $D_1$ a most powerful region. An alternative course of action, which could be employed, is to fix $\beta$ and divide the regions to minimize $\alpha$. The alternative method would fix the probability of a Type II error and minimize the Type I error, or *false alarm.*

Equations (13–6) and (13–7) can be written in an abbreviated form by letting $Q$ denote the sample values $x_1, \ldots, x_n$:

$$\alpha = \int_{D_1} f_n(Q; b_0)\, dQ, \tag{13–8}$$

$$\beta = \int_{D_0} f_n(Q; b_1)\, dQ. \tag{13–9}$$

Let $p$ and $q$ respectively be the a priori probabilities of finding signal-plus-noise or finding noise alone in a given detection segment. These quantities are the probabilities that, out of a large number of trials, a fraction $p$ is known to contain signal-plus-noise and a fraction $q = 1 - p$ is known to contain only noise. Define the quantity $p\beta$ as the *total* Type II error and similarly define $q\alpha$ as the *total* Type I error. The Neyman-Pearson method is slightly modified at this point so that $p\beta$ will be minimized for a fixed value of $q\alpha$, [100]. The risk function for the detection problem is defined as

$$R = p\beta + \lambda q\alpha, \tag{13–10}$$

where $\lambda$ is an undetermined multiplier. The risk $R$ is to be minimized with respect to a decision rule $\delta$ for *terminal decisions*. Terminal decisions are those made at the termination of an experiment and, as such, are distinguished from decisions made during an experiment, which guide the course of action during the experiment.

Detection theory is categorized by having a finite number of discrete alternatives; consequently, the terminal decision rules can be represented as conditional probabilities. Given the sample set $Q = (x_1, \ldots, x_n)$, let $\delta(b_0 \mid Q)$ and $\delta(b_1 \mid Q)$ be the respective probabilities that $b_0$ and $b_1$ are selected. Because we have limited ourselves to a terminal decision, we must decide that either $b_0$ or $b_1$ exists. Hence,

$$\delta(b_0 \mid Q) + \delta(b_1 \mid Q) = 1. \tag{13–11}$$

Let $S = (s_1, \ldots, s_n)$ represent a signal sample in the absence of noise, and let $f_n(Q \mid S)$ be the conditional density function for $Q$, given $S$. With these definitions, (13–8) and (13–9) can be written as

$$\alpha = \int_D f_n(Q \mid 0)\,\delta(b_1 \mid Q)\,dQ, \tag{13–12}$$

$$\beta = \int_D \mathrm{E}_S\{f_n(Q \mid S)\}\,\delta(b_0 \mid Q)\,dQ. \tag{13–13}$$

Using these expressions in (13–10), the minimum value of the risk is

$$\begin{aligned} R_{\min} &= \min_{\delta}\left[p\int_D \mathrm{E}_S\{f_n(Q \mid S)\}\,\delta(b_0 \mid Q)\,dQ \right. \\ &\qquad \left. + \lambda q \int_D f_n(Q \mid 0)\,\delta(b_1 \mid Q)\,dQ\right] \\ &= \min_{\delta}\left[p\int_D \mathrm{E}_S\{f_n(Q \mid S)\}\,\delta(b_0 \mid Q)\,dQ \right. \\ &\qquad \left. + \lambda q \int_D f_n(Q \mid 0)\,[1 - \delta(b_0 \mid Q)]\,dQ\right] \\ &= \min_{\delta}\left[\int_D [p\mathrm{E}_S\{f_n(Q \mid S)\} - \lambda q f_n(Q \mid 0)]\,\delta(b_0 \mid Q)\,dQ\right] + \lambda q. \end{aligned} \tag{13–14}$$

It follows that $R$ will be a minimum if the decision rules are chosen in the following fashion:

(i) If $$pE_S\{f_n(Q \mid S)\} \geq \lambda q f_n(Q \mid 0),$$
let
$$\delta(b_1 \mid Q) = 1, \qquad \delta(b_0 \mid Q) = 0$$
and decide on the $H_1$ hypothesis that signal exists in the presence of noise.

(ii) If $$pE_S\{f_n(Q \mid S)\} < \lambda q f_n(Q \mid 0),$$
let
$$\delta(b_1 \mid Q) = 0, \qquad \delta(b_0 \mid Q) = 1$$
and decide on the $H_0$ hypothesis that only noise exists.

The decision rule also can be written as a single relation:

$$L = \frac{pE_S\{f_n(Q \mid S)\}}{q f_n(Q \mid 0)} = \lambda. \tag{13–15}$$

$L$ is called the *likelihood ratio*. The decision rule is: For a set of samples $Q$, the $H_1$ hypothesis is accepted if $L \geq \lambda$, and the $H_0$ hypothesis is accepted if $L < \lambda$.

Notice that $\lambda$ plays the role of a detection threshold, which by intuition we expected to find somewhere in the mathematical decision model. Moreover, $\lambda$ is not really arbitrary, but is determined by our restraint of a preassigned value of $\alpha$ (the probability of a Type I error) and the nature of the optimum decision rule.

A simple example will illustrate the application of the Neyman-Pearson detection criterion. Assume that observations are made on signals $s(t)$ in the presence of additive noise $n(t)$, the signal is constant but unknown, and the noise process is normally distributed and statistically independent between samples. This seemingly special situation is actually a representative model for many real detection problems. Successive samples of the signal-plus-noise $y(t) = s(t) + n(t)$ will be statistically independent; thus the joint probability density function of the samples $y_1, \ldots, y_N$ will be equal to the product of the individual density functions,

$$f_N(y_1, \ldots, y_N; b) = \prod_{i=1}^{N} f_1(y_i; b). \tag{13–16}$$

The normal density function for the noise alone, using the independence hypothesis and the definition of $b$ as the positive square root of the signal-to-noise ratio, is

$$\begin{aligned} f_N(n_1, \ldots, n_N; b = 0) &= (2\pi\sigma^2)^{-N/2} \prod_{i=1}^{N} \exp\left\{-\frac{1}{2\sigma^2}(y_i - s_i)^2\right\} \\ &= (2\pi\sigma^2)^{-N/2} \exp\left\{-\frac{1}{2\sigma^2}\sum_{i=1}^{N}(y_i - s_i)^2\right\}. \end{aligned} \tag{13–17}$$

Similarly the joint density function for the signal-plus-noise normal variates is,

(13–18) $$f_N(y_i, \ldots, y_n; b = b_1) = (2\pi\sigma^2)^{-N/2} \exp\left\{-\frac{1}{2\sigma^2}\sum_{i=1}^{N} y_i^2\right\}.$$

Insert (13–17) and (13–18) into (13–15) to calculate the likelihood ratio

(13–19) $$L = \frac{p \exp\left\{-\frac{1}{2\sigma^2}\sum_{i=1}^{N} y_i^2\right\}}{q \exp\left\{-\frac{1}{2\sigma^2}\sum_{i=1}^{N} (y_i - s_i)^2\right\}} = \frac{p}{q}\exp\left\{-\frac{1}{2\sigma^2}\sum_{i=1}^{N}(2y_i s_i - s_i^2)\right\}.$$

Instead of basing the detection criterion on $L$, we can just as well consider $\ln L$;

(13–20) $$\ln L = \ln\frac{p}{q} - \frac{1}{2\sigma^2}\sum_{i=1}^{N}(2y_i s_i - s_i^2).$$

The last term in the summation is simply the total signal-to-noise energy ratio corresponding to the $N$ samples. That is,

(13–21) $$b_1^2 = \frac{1}{2\sigma^2}\sum_{i=1}^{N} s_i^2.$$

For given values of $p$, $q$, $b_1$, and $\zeta$, the detection criterion can be reduced to

(13–22) $$\frac{1}{\sigma^2}\sum_{i=1}^{N} y_i s_i = \ln\frac{p}{q} - \ln L + b_1^2 \overset{d}{=} \zeta.$$

Thus, we accept the null hypothesis $H_0$ that no signal is present if the left side of (13–22) is less than $\zeta$ and accept the hypothesis $H_1$ that a signal is present if the left side is greater than $\zeta$. The left side is recognized as the discrete form of the correlation function of the signal-plus-noise $y_i$ with the signal $s_i$. Although this is a rather general result, it does not follow that the signal-detection criterion can always be reduced to the form of a covariance function. The example illustrates another general principle: The detection criterion is a function of the signal-to-noise ratio.

## 13.4
## *IDEAL DETECTOR*

The *Ideal Detector*, introduced by Siegert [38, 88, 100], represents one of the earliest formulations of signal detection as a problem in statistical hypothesis testing. Rather than present the original arguments, it is more expedient to treat the Ideal Detector as a modification of the Neyman-Pearson Detector.

The Ideal Detector can be modeled by means of the risk function

(13–23) $$R = q\alpha + p\beta.$$

The minimization differs from that in Section 13.3 where the risk was minimized with respect to $p\beta$ with $q\alpha$ kept fixed.

Insert (13–12) and (13–13) into (13–23), and the desired minimum risk has the form [The same as (13–14) with $\lambda = 1$]

$$R_{\min} = \min_{\delta} \left[ \int_D [p\mathrm{E}_S\{f_n(Q \mid S)\} - qf_n(Q \mid 0)]\delta(b_0 \mid Q)\, dQ \right] + q. \tag{13–24}$$

Hence, the risk will be a minimum for the Ideal Detector if the likelihood ratio is

$$L_I = \frac{p\mathrm{E}_S\{f_n(Q \mid S)\}}{qf_n(Q \mid 0)} = 1. \tag{13–25}$$

Therefore, the decision rule for the Ideal Detector is: For a set of samples $Q$, the $H_1$ hypothesis is accepted that signal-plus-noise is present if $L_I \geq 1$; the $H_0$ hypothesis is accepted that no signal is present if $L_I < 1$.

## 13.5
## *DETECTORS CHARACTERIZED BY LOSS FUNCTIONS*

Instead of individually discussing each of the signal-detection criterion that have been found to be either useful or interesting, it is perhaps proper at this point to exhibit a generalized theory. Pugachev [119] has shown that the general form of a loss function for signal detection should be

$$l(y, \hat{y}) = \begin{cases} 0; & y = 0,\ \hat{y} \leq c \quad \text{or} \quad y \neq 0,\ \hat{y} > c \\ 1; & y \neq 0,\ \hat{y} \leq c \\ \lambda; & y = 0,\ \hat{y} > c, \end{cases} \tag{13–26}$$

where $\lambda$ is an indefinite parameter which must be chosen to make the probability of a false alarm equal to a preassigned value. The probability of false alarm is the conditional probability of an erroneous decision on the presence of a signal, knowing that it is absent. As an illustrative example, we shall demonstrate (13–26) by showing that the Neyman-Pearson Detector is equivalent to minimizing the sum of two probabilities,

$$R' = \Pr(\hat{y} \leq c \mid y \neq 0) + \lambda' \Pr(\hat{y} > c \mid y = 0), \tag{13–27}$$

where $\lambda'$ is an indefinite multiplier. Multiply $R'$ by $p = \Pr(y \neq 0)$, the probability that a signal is present. The result is

$$\begin{aligned} pR' &= \Pr(y \neq 0) \Pr(\hat{y} \leq c \mid y \neq 0) + \lambda' \Pr(y \neq 0) \Pr(\hat{y} > c \mid y = 0) \\ &= \Pr(y \neq 0, \hat{y} \leq c) + \lambda' \frac{\Pr(y \neq 0)}{\Pr(y = 0)} \Pr(\hat{y} > c, y = 0) \\ &= \Pr(y \neq 0, \hat{y} \leq c) + \lambda \Pr(y = 0, \hat{y} > c), \end{aligned} \tag{13–28}$$

where the new arbitrary parameter is defined as

$$\lambda = \frac{\lambda' \Pr(y \neq 0)}{\Pr(y = 0)} = \frac{\lambda' p}{1 - p} = \frac{\lambda' p}{q}. \tag{13–29}$$

Equation (13–28) is nothing more than a restatement of the risk function (13–10), corresponding to the Neyman–Pearson Detector, or $R = pR'$. The important point is to observe that (13–28) is the result obtained by evaluating a risk function for a loss defined by (13–26). That is,

$$\begin{aligned} R &= \mathrm{E}\{l(y, \hat{y})\} \\ &= 0 \cdot \Pr\{y = 0, \hat{y} \leq c\} + 0 \cdot \Pr\{y \neq 0, \hat{y} > c\} \\ &\quad + 1 \cdot \Pr\{y \neq 0, \hat{y} \leq c\} + \lambda \cdot \Pr\{y = 0, \hat{y} > c\}. \end{aligned} \tag{13–30}$$

One might be tempted to introduce an even more general loss function than (13–26). In this vein, suppose we consider a general loss function defined as

$$l(y, \hat{y}) = \begin{cases} \alpha_1; & y = 0, \hat{y} \leq c \\ \beta_1; & y = 0, \hat{y} > c \\ \alpha_2; & y \neq 0, \hat{y} > c \\ \beta_2; & y \neq 0, \hat{y} \leq c, \end{cases} \tag{13–31}$$

where $\alpha_1, \alpha_2, \beta_1, \beta_2$, are weights associated with four possible decisions. The risk function associated with (13–31) is

(13–32)

$$\begin{aligned} R &= \mathrm{E}\{l(y, \hat{y})\} \\ &= \alpha_1 \Pr(y = 0, \hat{y} \leq c) + \beta_1 \Pr(y = 0, \hat{y} > c) \\ &\quad + \alpha_2 \Pr(y \neq 0, \hat{y} > c) + \beta_2 \Pr(y \neq 0, \hat{y} \leq c) \\ &= \alpha_1 \Pr(y = 0) \Pr(\hat{y} \leq c \mid y = 0) + \beta_1 \Pr(y = 0) \Pr(\hat{y} > c \mid y = 0) \\ &\quad + \alpha_2 \Pr(y \neq 0) \Pr(\hat{y} > c \mid y \neq 0) + \beta_2 \Pr(y \neq 0) \Pr(\hat{y} \leq c \mid y \neq 0) \\ &= \alpha_1 q \Pr(\hat{y} \leq c \mid y = 0) + \beta_1 q \Pr(\hat{y} > c \mid y = 0) \\ &\quad + \alpha_2 p \Pr(\hat{y} > c \mid y \neq 0) + \beta_2 p \Pr(\hat{y} \leq c \mid y \neq 0) \\ &= \alpha_1 q + \alpha_2 p + (\beta_2 - \alpha_2) p [\Pr(\hat{y} \leq c \mid y \neq 0) \\ &\quad + \frac{\beta_1 - \alpha_1}{\beta_2 - \alpha_2} \frac{q}{p} \Pr(\hat{y} > c \mid y = 0)], \end{aligned}$$

where

$$\begin{aligned} p &= \Pr(y \neq 0) \\ q &= \Pr(y = 0) \\ p &= 1 - q. \end{aligned} \tag{13–33}$$

Thus the result of minimizing (13–28) with

$$\lambda = \frac{\beta_1 - \alpha_1}{\beta_2 - \alpha_2} \tag{13–34}$$

is exactly equivalent to minimizing the risk in (13–32) with

$$\lambda' = \frac{q}{p}\frac{(\beta_1 - \alpha_1)}{(\beta_2 - \alpha_2)}. \tag{13–35}$$

The conclusion is that the loss function defined in (13–31) is no more general than the simpler loss function defined in (13–26). The loss function for the Ideal Detector is obtained from (13–26) by letting $\lambda = 1$. If $\lambda$ is to be specified by a given false alarm probability, (13–26) leads to the Neyman-Pearson Detector. If, in (13–34), $(\alpha_1, \alpha_2, \beta_1, \beta_2)$ are assigned values representing the weights for possible decisions, then (13–26) leads to a Neyman-Pearson Detector in which these decisions determine the false alarm threshold $\lambda$.

## 13.6
## *OPTIMUM DETECTION SYSTEM USING BAYES' CRITERIA*

After the preceding introduction to the theory of signal detection, it is almost natural to inquire if there exists an optimal detecting system in the sense of minimizing a risk function for a general class of loss functions, not necessarily limited to the class defined in (13–26). Pugachev [119, 120] has shown that such optimal detection systems do exist and can be formulated readily. Although signal detection theory is not intended to be a major topic, a simplified form of Pugachev's development serves as an excellent illustration of the strong connections between estimation theory, optimal systems, and decision theory. As a side issue, the formulation of the optimal detection system is in its own right an important contribution.

### 13.6.1 *SERIES REPRESENTATION OF A RANDOM PROCESS*

This section is intended to justify a series representation needed in our version of Pugachev's method.

Fourier series are an important analytical tool in conventional functional analysis and one can readily imagine that a similar type of series representation could be exceedingly useful when working with random processes. A series representation can be formulated for a complex (or real) wide sense stationary random process on a finite interval by means of a generalized Fourier-type expansion having independent coefficients. This series has been independently discovered by several investigators, but is now commonly known as the Karhunen-Loève expansion [75, 82, 83, 96].

Let $z(t)$ be a complex, wide-sense stationary stochastic process having the properties

$$\begin{aligned} &\mathrm{E}\{z(t)\} = 0 \\ &\mathrm{E}\{|z(t)|^2\} = \psi(0) \\ &\mathrm{E}\{z(t)z^*(t-\tau)\} = \psi(\tau), \end{aligned} \tag{13–36}$$

$$\lim_{|t-s|\to 0} \mathrm{E}\{|z(t) - z(s)|^2\} = 0, \qquad \text{continuity condition.} \tag{13–37}$$

A series representation will be formulated for $z(t)$ on the interval $0 \leq t \leq T$. For the defined process, it is known that [42]

(i) $\psi(\tau) = \psi^*(-\tau)$; covariance function is Hermitian symmetric;

(ii) $\psi(\tau)$ is positive semidefinite; i.e., for every $L^2$ function $g(t)$ on $(0, T)$,

$$\int_0^T \int_0^T g(s)g^*(t)\psi(s-t)\,ds\,dt \geq 0. \tag{13–38}$$

The series expansion of $z(t)$ will depend upon the eigenfunctions and eigenvalues of the following homogeneous integral equation with the Hermitian symmetric kernel $\psi(\tau)$:

$$\lambda^2 h(s) = \int_0^T \psi(s-t)h(t)\,dt. \tag{13–39}$$

The development requires the use of three properties, which are characteristic of homogeneous integral equations of the type (13–39). They are

(a) Eigenfunctions are mutually orthogonal and can be chosen to be orthonormal.

(b) Eigenvalues are all real.

(c) Mercer's theorem can be applied to express the positive semidefinite kernel, which is continuous on the space $(0, T) \times (0, T)$, as

$$\psi(s-t) = \sum_{j=1}^{\infty} \lambda_j^2 h_j^*(s) h_j(t), \tag{13–40}$$

where the series converges absolutely and uniformly on the space $(0, T) \times (0, T)$.

Introduce a set $\{G_n\}$ of orthogonal random variables such that

$$\begin{aligned} \mathrm{E}\{G_i\} &= 0 \\ \mathrm{E}\{G_i G_j^*\} &= \delta_{ij}. \end{aligned} \tag{13–41}$$

Now consider the series representation

$$z(t) \sim \lim_{N\to\infty} \sum_{j=1}^{N} \lambda_j G_j h_j(t). \tag{13–42}$$

It is a simple matter to exhibit that this representation yields the required covariance function. One simply computes

$$\text{(13–43)} \quad \begin{aligned} E\{z(t)z^*(s)\} &= E\left\{\sum_{i=1}^{\infty}\sum_{j=1}^{\infty} \lambda_i\lambda_j G_i G_j^* h_i(t) h_j^*(s)\right\} \\ &= \sum_{j=1}^{\infty} \lambda_j^2 h_j(t) h_j^*(s) \\ &= \psi(s-t). \end{aligned}$$

The Fourier coefficients of the series (13–42) are obtained in the usual way,

$$\text{(13–44)} \quad \begin{aligned} \int_0^T z(t) h_j^*(t)\,dt &= \int_0^T \sum_{i=1}^{\infty} \lambda_i G_i h_i(t) h_j^*(t)\,dt \\ &= \lambda_j G_j. \end{aligned}$$

$\lambda_j$ and $h_j$ are obtained from the solution of the integral equation (13–39), and therefore (13–44) is a condition on the auxiliary orthogonal random variables. A further condition on these variables results from the expected value

$$\text{(13–45)} \quad \begin{aligned} E\{z(t)G_j^*\} &= E\left\{\sum_{i=1}^{\infty} \lambda_i G_i h_i(t) G_j^*\right\} \\ &= \lambda_j h_j(t). \end{aligned}$$

The final point is to verify that the series representation converges in the mean to $z(t)$. This convergence follows since,

$$\text{(13–46)} \quad \lim_{N\to\infty} E\left\{\left|z(t) - \sum_{j=1}^{N} \lambda_j G_j h_j(t)\right|^2\right\} = \psi(0) - \lim_{N\to\infty} \sum_{j=1}^{N} \lambda_j^2 |h_j(t)|^2.$$

Mercer's theorem implies that the last limit converges absolutely and uniformly to $\psi(0)$, showing that the series does indeed represent $z(t)$ in the mean limit sense.

If $\{G_j\}$ were chosen as a set of independent normal variables, then (13–42) would be a series representation of a normal process.

### 13.6.2 *OPTIMAL DETECTOR*

Pugachev considered the following general model of a detection problem. The observables are of the form

$$\text{(13–47)} \quad Z(t) = \phi(\boldsymbol{U}, t) + x(t), \qquad s - T \leq t \leq s,$$

and the problem is to find a *best* estimate $\hat{W}(s)$ of a signal

$$\text{(13–48)} \quad W(s) = \theta(\boldsymbol{U}, y(s), s),$$

where $x(t)$ and $y(s)$ represent noise and $\boldsymbol{U}^{[p\times 1]}$ denotes unknown signal parameters. As we shall see, this model is sufficiently broad to include almost all special cases of signal detection and signal parameter estimations which previously have been almost always treated as discrete and individual problems.

The optimum detection and signal parameter estimation system can be formulated under the following assumptions:

(i) The probability density function $f(\boldsymbol{U})$ is known for the signal parameters.

(ii) $[x(t),\ y(s)]$ is a normal vector function which is statistically independent of the parameters $\boldsymbol{U}$. Assume that both $x(t)$ and $y(s)$ satisfy (11–36) and (11–37).

(iii) For each observation $z$ of $Z$, there exists a signal estimate $\hat{w}(s)$ such that a minimum of the risk function exists. That is,

$$R_{\min}(\hat{w}, z) = \mathrm{E}\{l(W, \hat{w})\,|\,z\} \leq \mathrm{E}\{l(W, w)\,|\,z\} = R(w, z), \tag{13–49}$$

where $w$ is any other estimate.

(iv) For all possible values $\boldsymbol{u}$ of $\boldsymbol{U}$, $\phi(\boldsymbol{u}, t)$ can be represented by a series of eigenfunctions generated by the covariance function of $x(t)$.

As a preliminary step, it is necessary to obtain several series representations. Applying the results of Section 13.6.1, write the two normal noise processes in the form

$$x(t) = \sum_{j=1}^{\infty} \lambda_j G_j h_j(t), \tag{13–50}$$

$$y(s) = \sum_{j=1}^{\infty} \lambda_j G_j g_j(s), \tag{13–51}$$

where $\{G_j\}$ is a set of orthonormal normal random variates and the functions $h_j(t)$ are generated from the covariance function of $x(t)$ by means of the integral equation

$$\begin{aligned} \lambda_j^2 h_j(s) &= \int_{s-T}^{s} \psi_x(s-t)\,h_j(t)\,dt, \\ \psi_x(s-t) &= \mathrm{E}\{x(s)x(t)\}. \end{aligned} \tag{13–52}$$

The functions $g_j(t)$ can be shown to be generated by $\mathrm{E}\{y(s)x(t)\} = \Psi_{yx}(s-t)$. From (13–51),

$$\mathrm{E}\left\{\sum_{j=1}^{\infty} \lambda_j G_i G_j g_j(s)\right\} = \lambda_i g_i(s) = \mathrm{E}\{y(s)G_i\}. \tag{13–53}$$

Analogous to (13–44), we now have

$$\lambda_i G_i = \int_{s-T}^{s} x(t)\,h_i(t)\,dt. \tag{13–54}$$

Substitute (13–54) into (13–53) to express the expansion eigenfunctions as

$$\begin{aligned} g_i(s) &= \frac{1}{\lambda_i^2}\int_{s-T}^{s} \mathrm{E}\{y(s)x(t)\}h_i(t)\,dt \\ &= \frac{1}{\lambda_i^2}\int_{s-T}^{s} \psi_{yx}(s-t)\,h_i(t)\,dt. \end{aligned} \tag{13–55}$$

Finally, assumption (iv) is symbolized as

$$\phi(\boldsymbol{u}, t) = \sum_{j=1}^{\infty} \lambda_j \alpha_j(\boldsymbol{u}) h_j(t). \tag{13–56}$$

Using the orthonormal property of the eigenfunctions,

$$\begin{aligned}\int_{s-T}^{s} \phi(\boldsymbol{u}, t) h_i(t)\, dt &= \sum_j \lambda_j \alpha_j(\boldsymbol{u}) \int_{s-T}^{s} h_j(t) h_i(t)\, dt \\ &= \lambda_i \alpha_i(\boldsymbol{u}).\end{aligned} \tag{13–57}$$

The observables $Z(t)$ can now be represented as

$$\begin{aligned}Z(t) &= \phi(\boldsymbol{U}, t) + x(t) \\ &= \sum_j \lambda_j [\alpha_j(\boldsymbol{u}) + G_j] h_j(t) \\ &= \sum_j F_j h_j(t);\end{aligned} \tag{13–58}$$

$$F_j \overset{d}{=} \lambda_j [\alpha_j(\boldsymbol{u}) + G_j]. \tag{13–59}$$

Notice that $F_j$ is a normally distributed random variable (because $\alpha_j$ is a constant and $G_j$ is normal) with mean value $\lambda_j \alpha_j(\boldsymbol{u})$ and variance $\lambda_j^2$. Define

$$\omega(\boldsymbol{u}, s) = \sum_j \lambda_j \alpha_j(\boldsymbol{u}) g_j(s), \tag{13–60}$$

which permits us to write (13–51) as

$$y(s) = \sum_j F_j g_j(s) - \omega(\boldsymbol{u}, s). \tag{13–61}$$

The important motivation for these series representations is that an equivalence has been established between the observables $Z$ and the set of random variables $\{F_j\}$. This equivalence will be used to compute the conditional expectation which appears in the definition of the risk function (13–49).

We start by considering only a finite set of $n$ random variables $F_j$. This is done by formally replacing the infinite limit in each of the appropriate series representations by $n$. Because the set $\{G_j\}$ is an independent set of normal variates, $\{F_j\}$ is also an independent set having the joint conditional probability density function,

$$f_n(F_1, \ldots, F_n \mid \boldsymbol{u}) = \prod_{j=1}^{n} (2\pi\lambda_j^2)^{-1/2} \exp\left\{-\tfrac{1}{2} \sum_{j=1}^{n} \frac{1}{\lambda_j^2} [F_j - \lambda_j \alpha_j(\boldsymbol{u})]^2\right\}. \tag{13–62}$$

The required conditional expectation is obtained from the relation

$$\begin{aligned}f_n(\boldsymbol{u} \mid F_1, \ldots, F_n) &= \frac{f(\boldsymbol{u}) f_n(F_1, \ldots, F_n \mid \boldsymbol{u})}{f_n(F_1, \ldots, F_n)} \\ &= \frac{f(\boldsymbol{u}) f_n(F_1, \ldots, F_n \mid \boldsymbol{u})}{\int_{-\infty}^{\infty} f(\boldsymbol{u}) f_n(F_1, \ldots, F_n \mid \boldsymbol{u})\, d\boldsymbol{u}}.\end{aligned} \tag{13–63}$$

Equation (13–63) is evaluated by using (13–62). The result can be written in the form

$$f_n(\boldsymbol{u}\,|\,F_1, \ldots, F_n) = \kappa_n(F_j) f(\boldsymbol{u}) \exp\left\{\sum_{j=1}^{n} \frac{1}{\lambda_j} \alpha_j(\boldsymbol{u}) F_j - \tfrac{1}{2}\beta_n(\boldsymbol{u})\right\}, \tag{13–64}$$

where

$$\begin{aligned} \beta_n(\boldsymbol{u}) &= \sum_{j=1}^{n} \alpha_j^2(\boldsymbol{u}) \\ \frac{1}{\kappa_n(F_j)} &= \int_{-\infty}^{\infty} f(\boldsymbol{u}) \exp\left\{\sum_{j=1}^{n} \frac{1}{\lambda_j} \alpha_j(\boldsymbol{u}) F_j - \tfrac{1}{2}\beta_n(\boldsymbol{u})\right\} d\boldsymbol{u}. \end{aligned} \tag{13–65}$$

The risk function, corresponding to $n$ observables, can now be evaluated. Hence, using the preceding results we find

$$\begin{aligned} R_n(\hat{W}, Z) &= \mathrm{E}\{l(W_n, \hat{W})\,|\,F_1, \ldots, F_n\} \\ &= \mathrm{E}\{l[\theta(s, \boldsymbol{u}, y(s)), \hat{W}]\,|\,F_1, \ldots, F_n\} \\ &= \mathrm{E}\left\{l\left[\theta\left(s, \boldsymbol{u}, \sum_{j=1}^{n} F_j g_j(s) - \omega_n(\boldsymbol{u}, s)\right), \hat{W}\right]\,\Big|\,F_1, \ldots, F_n\right\} \\ &= \kappa_n(F_j) \int_{-\infty}^{\infty} l\left\{\theta\left[s, \boldsymbol{u}, \sum_{j=1}^{n} F_j g_j(s) - \omega_n(\boldsymbol{u}, s)\right], \hat{W}\right\} \\ &\qquad \cdot f(\boldsymbol{u}) \exp\left\{\sum_{j=1}^{n} \frac{1}{\lambda_j} \alpha_j(\boldsymbol{u}) F_j - \tfrac{1}{2}\beta_n(\boldsymbol{u})\right\} d\boldsymbol{u}. \end{aligned} \tag{13–66}$$

The optimum signal estimate $\hat{W}$ is obtained by minimizing the integral in (13–66) for the case in which the observables are limited to be finite in number.

The corresponding risk function for the case in which $n \to \infty$ can be obtained formally from these same formulations. In the limit, for example, (13–64) becomes

$$f(\boldsymbol{u}\,|\,Z) = \kappa(Z) f(\boldsymbol{u}) \exp\{L(\boldsymbol{u}) \circ Z - \tfrac{1}{2}\beta(\boldsymbol{u})\} \tag{13–67}$$

where $L(\boldsymbol{u})$ is an operator such that

$$L(\boldsymbol{u}) \circ Z = \sum_{j=1}^{\infty} \frac{1}{\lambda_j} \alpha_j(\boldsymbol{u}) \int_{s-T}^{s} Z(t) h_j(t)\, dt, \tag{13–68}$$

and

$$\beta(\boldsymbol{u}) = \sum_{j=1}^{\infty} \alpha_j^2(\boldsymbol{u}). \tag{13–69}$$

In the limit, (13–66) assumes the form

$$\begin{aligned} R(\hat{W}, Z) = \kappa(Z) \int_{-\infty}^{\infty} & l\{\theta[s, \boldsymbol{u}, A^{(0)} \circ Z - \omega(\boldsymbol{u}, s)], \hat{W}\} \\ & \cdot f(\boldsymbol{u}) \exp\{L(\boldsymbol{u}) \circ Z - \tfrac{1}{2}\beta(\boldsymbol{u})\}\, d\boldsymbol{u}, \end{aligned} \tag{13–70}$$

where $A^{(0)}$ is the operator such that

$$A^{(0)} \circ Z = \sum_{j=1}^{\infty} g_j(s) \int_{s-T}^{s} Z(t) h_j(t)\, dt \tag{13–71}$$

and

$$\frac{1}{\kappa(Z)} = \int_{-\infty}^{\infty} f(\boldsymbol{u}) \exp\{L(\boldsymbol{u})\circ Z - \tfrac{1}{2}\beta(\boldsymbol{u})\}\, d\boldsymbol{u}. \tag{13–72}$$

We can quickly show that (13–70) reduces to a familiar form if the loss function is chosen as the difference squared function

$$l(W, \hat{W}) = (W - \hat{W})^2. \tag{13–73}$$

Substitute (13–73) into (13–70), and the mean-squared risk function is found to be

$$\begin{aligned} R(\hat{W}, Z) = \kappa(Z) \int_{-\infty}^{\infty} &(\theta[s, \boldsymbol{u}, A^{(0)}\circ Z - \omega(s, \boldsymbol{u})] - \hat{W})^2 \\ &\cdot f(\boldsymbol{u}) \exp\{L(\boldsymbol{u})\circ Z - \tfrac{1}{2}\beta(\boldsymbol{u})\}\, d\boldsymbol{u}. \end{aligned} \tag{13–74}$$

Differentiate (13–74) with respect to $\hat{W}$, equate the result to zero, and solve for the optimum signal estimate

$$\begin{aligned} \hat{W} = \kappa(Z) \int_{-\infty}^{\infty} &\theta[s, \boldsymbol{u}, \mathbf{A}^{(0)}\circ Z - \omega(s, \boldsymbol{u})] \\ &\cdot f(\boldsymbol{u}) \exp\{L(\boldsymbol{u})\circ Z - \tfrac{1}{2}\beta(\boldsymbol{u})\}\, d\boldsymbol{u}. \end{aligned} \tag{13–75}$$

The right side is recognized as the conditional expectation of the signal $W$ with respect to the observed function $Z$. This, of course, is exactly the condition for an optimal estimate which in Chapter 2 was derived in another context.

### 13.6.3 *SIGNAL DETECTION*

Equations (13–70) and (13–72) can be applied to determine the optimal signal detection system if the loss function (13–26) is used. In this case the signal $W$ is simply the vector $\boldsymbol{u}$, and its probability density function is

$$f(\boldsymbol{u}) = q\delta(\boldsymbol{u}) + pk(\boldsymbol{u}), \tag{13–76}$$

where $p = 1 - q$ is the probability that a signal exists in $Z$, $k(\boldsymbol{u})$ is the conditional probability density function of $\boldsymbol{u}$ when it is present in $Z$, and $\delta(\boldsymbol{u})$ is the Dirac-delta function. When (13–76) and (13–26) are substituted in (13–70) and (13–72), the risk function can be written as

$$R(Z, \hat{u}) = \begin{cases} \dfrac{pQ(Z)}{q + pQ(Z)}; & \hat{u} \leq c \\ \dfrac{q\lambda}{q + pQ(Z)}; & \hat{u} > c, \end{cases} \tag{13–77}$$

$$Q(Z) = \int_{-\infty}^{\infty} k(\boldsymbol{u}) \exp\{[L(\boldsymbol{u}) - L(\boldsymbol{O})]\circ Z - \tfrac{1}{2}[\beta(\boldsymbol{u}) - \beta(\boldsymbol{O})]\}\, d\boldsymbol{u}. \tag{13–78}$$

Equation (13–77) implies that the optimal signal estimate is of the form

$$\hat{u} = \zeta[Q(Z)], \tag{13–79}$$

where $\zeta$ is any increasing function of its argument, while the decision threshold is

$$c = \zeta\left(\frac{q\lambda}{p}\right). \tag{13–80}$$

For the Neyman-Pearson Detector, $c$ would be determined directly from a preassigned false alarm probability. It should be remarked that we are free to choose $\zeta(x) = \ln x$, which is the form of the optimal detector obtained by other methods for the case of normally distributed additive noise.

#### 13.6.4 *RELATION TO MAXIMUM LIKELIHOOD ESTIMATION*

By properly choosing the loss function, equations (13–70) and (13–72) will yield the maximum likelihood estimates for the signal parameters. Suppose $\boldsymbol{u}$ is the signal parameter vector which is to be estimated. Replace $W$ by $\boldsymbol{u}$ and choose the loss function

$$l(\boldsymbol{u}, \hat{\boldsymbol{u}}) = a - \delta(\hat{\boldsymbol{u}} - \boldsymbol{u}), \tag{13–81}$$

where $\delta(\cdot)$ is the Dirac-delta function. In this case, the risk function (13–70) is reduced to

$$R(\hat{\boldsymbol{u}}, Z) = a - \kappa(Z) f(\hat{\boldsymbol{u}}) \exp\{L(\hat{\boldsymbol{u}})\circ Z - \tfrac{1}{2}\beta(\hat{\boldsymbol{u}})\}. \tag{13–82}$$

Since (13–82) is now of the same form as (9–20), except for a constant $a$, it is apparent that minimizing (13–82) with respect to $\hat{\boldsymbol{u}}$ is exactly equivalent to finding the maximum likelihood estimator.

## Problems

**13.1** Let an observed signal have the form

$$y(t) = A \cos(\omega t + \theta) + N(t),$$

where $N(t)$ is white normal noise with zero mean value. Show that, for observations in the interval $-T \leq t \leq T$, the estimate for the signal amplitude is

$$\hat{A} = \frac{\int_{-T}^{T} y(t) \cos(\omega t + \theta)\, dt}{T + \dfrac{\sin 2\omega T \cos 2\theta}{2\omega}},$$

and the variance of the estimate is

$$\sigma_A^2 = N^2 \left[T + \frac{\sin 2\omega T \cos 2\theta}{2\omega}\right]^{-1}$$

$$N^2 = \mathrm{E}\{N^2(t)\}.$$

Find similar estimates for the signal parameters $\omega$ and $\theta$.

**13.2** Compute the detection criterion for the ideal observer for the example in Section 13.3. Instead of normally distributed signal samples, consider any other class of additive distributions and find the corresponding detection criterion.

**13.3** If the covariance function of a normal random process $z(t)$ has the form

$$\psi_z(\tau) = \mathrm{E}\{z(t)\, z(t - \tau)\} = Ae^{-\beta|\tau|},$$

obtain a series representation of $z(t)$.

**13.4** Modify the series representation given in Section 13.6 to remove the restriction that the random process be stationary.

**13.5** Fill in the details leading to Equations (13–64) and (13–66).

**13.6** Complete the steps leading from Equations (13–76) to (13–77).

**13.7** Suppose that the input signal to a receiver is known to be either $s_1(t)$ with probability $p_1$ or $s_2(t)$ with probability $p_2 = p_1 - 1$. If the signals occur in a background of additive normal noise, find the form of the Neyman-Pearson Detector for a preassigned false alarm probability.

**13.8** The radar range detector problem can be characterized by detecting a signal $s(t - \tau)$ in a background of additive normal noise. $s(t)$ is known, but $\tau$ is a random variable. If $\tau$ is uniformly distributed in the range $-T_1 \leq \tau \leq T_2$, what is the form of the Neyman-Pearson Detector? Hint: Consider a sequence of $k$ signals

$$s_j = s\left[t - \frac{j(T_2 - T_1)}{k}\right], \qquad j = 1, \ldots, i < k$$

$$s_k = s[t - (T_2 - T_1)].$$

Let each of these signals be equally probable with probability $1/k$. The limit as $k \to \infty$ will approximate the original signal [67, p. 237].

# REFERENCES


1. Aitken, A. C., "On least squares and linear combinations of observations," *Proc. Roy. Soc. Edinburgh, Sect. A*, **55** (1955), 42–48.
2. Anderson, T. W., "The integral of a symmetric unimodal function over a symmetric convex set and some probability inequalities," *Proc. Amer. Math. Soc.*, **6** (1955), 170–176.
3. Balakrishnan, A. V., "On a characterization of processes for which optimal mean-square systems are of a specified form," *IRE, Trans. PGIT*, **6** (Sept., 1960), 491–500.
4. Balakrishnan, A. V., "An operator theoretic formulation of a class of control problems and a steepest descent method of solution," *JSIAM Control, Ser. A*, **1** (1963), 109–127.
5. Balakrishnan, A. V., "Report on progress in information theory in the U.S.A., 1960–1963: Prediction and filtering," *IEEE Trans. PGIT*, **IT-9** (Oct., 1963), 237–239.
6. Bello, P., "Joint estimation of delay, Doppler, and Doppler rate," *IRE, Trans. PGIT*, **IT-6**, No. 3 (June, 1960), 330–341.
7. Bendat, J. S., "A general theory of linear prediction and filtering," *J. Soc. Indust. Appl. Math.*, **4** (Sept., 1956), 131–151.
8. Bendat, J. S., "Exact integral equation solutions and synthesis for a large class of optimum time variable linear filters," *IRE, Trans. PGIT*, **IT-3** (Mar., 1957), 71–80.
9. Benedict, T. R., and M. M. Sondhi, "On a property of Wiener filters," *Proc. IRE*, **45** (July, 1957), 1021–1022.
10. Berkson, J., "Estimation by least squares and by maximum likelihood," *Proceedings of the Third Berkeley Symposium on Mathematical Statistics and Probability*. Berkeley, Calif.: University of California Press, 1956, Vol. I, 1–11.
11. Bjerhammar, A., "Rectangular reciprocal matrices, with special reference to geodetic calculations," *Bull. Geod. Int.*, **52** (1951), 188–220.

**12.** Blackman, R. B., and J. W. Tukey, *The Measurement of Power Spectra from the Point of View of Communications Engineering.* New York: Dover Publications, Inc., 1959.

**12a.** Blackman, R. B., "Methods of orbit refinement," *Bell System Tech. J.*, **43** (May, 1964), 885–909.

**13.** Blum, M., "Best linear unbiased estimation by recursive methods," *J. Soc. Indust. Appl. Math.*, to be published 1965.

**14.** Bode, H. W., and C. E. Shannon, "A simplified derivation of linear least-squares smoothing and prediction theory," *Proc. IRE*, **38** (Apr., 1950), 417–425.

**15.** Bodewig, E., *Matrix Calculus.* New York: Interscience Publishers, Inc., 1959.

**16.** Booton, R. C., Jr., "An optimization theory for time-varying linear systems with nonstationary statistical inputs," *Proc. IRE*, **40** (Aug., 1952), 977–981.

**17.** Brouwer, D., "On the accumulation of errors in numerical integration," *Astronom. J.*, **46** (1937), 149–153.

**18.** Brown, J. L., Jr., "Asymmetric non-mean-square error criteria," *IRE, Trans. PGAC*, **AC-7** (Jan., 1962), 64–66.

**19.** Bryson, A. E., Jr., and D. E. Johansen, "Linear filtering for time-varying systems using measurements containing colored noise," *Research Rpt.* 385 (Jan., 1964), Applied Research Lab., Sylvania Electronic Systems, 40 Sylvan Rd., Waltham, Mass.

**20.** Bucy, R. S., "Optimum finite-time filters for a special nonstationary class of inputs," Johns Hopkins University/Applied Physics Lab. *Internal Memorandum*, BBD-600, 1959.

**21.** Cameron, J. M., "An algorithm for obtaining an orthogonal set of individual degrees of freedom for error," *J. Res. Nat. Bur. Std.*, **67B** (Jan.-Mar., 1961), 19–22.

**22.** Carlton, A. G., and J. W. Follin, Jr., "Recent developments in fixed and adaptive filtering," *Proc. of the Second AGARD Guided Missiles Seminar* (Guidance and Control), AGARDograph 21, (Sept., 1956).

**23.** Carrier, G. F., "Useful approximations in Wiener-Hopf problems," *J. Appl. Phys.*, **30** (Nov., 1959), 1769–1774.

**24.** Chauvenet, W., *A Manual of Spherical and Practical Astronomy: Vol. I, Spherical Astronomy; Vol. II, Theory and Use of Astronomical Instruments ———Method of Least Squares.* New York: Dover Publications, Inc., 1960 (reprint).

**25.** Chernoff, H., and L. E. Moses, *Elementary Decision Theory.* New York: John Wiley and Sons, Inc., 1959.

**26.** Claus, A. J., R. B. Blackman, E. G. Halline, and W. C. Ridgway, III, "Orbit determination and prediction, and computer programs," *Bell System Tech. J.*, **42** (July, 1963), 1357–1382.

**27.** Coddington, E. A., and N. Levinson, *Theory of Ordinary Differential Equations*. New York: McGraw-Hill Book Company, 1955.

**28.** Conte, S. D., "The computation of satellite orbit trajectories," *Advances in Computers*, Vol. 3. New York: Academic Press, Inc., 1962.

**29.** Courant, R., and D. Hilbert, *Methods of Mathematical Physics*. New York: Interscience Publishers, Inc., 1953.

**30.** Cox, H., "On the estimation of state variables and parameters for noise dynamic systems," IEEE, Trans. PGAC, **AC-9** (Jan., 1964), 5–12.

**31.** Cramér, H., *Mathematical Methods of Statistics*. Princeton, N. J.: Princeton University Press, 1946.

**32.** Curry, H. B., "The method of steepest descent for non-linear minimization problems," *Quart. Appl. Math.*, **2** (1944), 258–261.

**33.** Danby, J. M. A., "Integration of the equations of planetary motion in rectangular coordinates," *Astronom. J.*, **67** (June, 1962), 287–299.

**34.** Danby, J. M. A., "Matrix methods in the calculation and analysis of orbits," *J. AIAA*, **2** (Jan., 1964), 13–16.

**35.** Danby, J. M. A., "The matrizant of Keplerian motion," *J. AIAA*, **2** (Jan., 1964), 16–19.

**36.** Darlington, S., "Linear least-squares smoothing and prediction, with applications," *Bell System Tech. J.*, **37** (Sept., 1958), 1221–1293.

**37.** Darlington, S., "Nonstationary smoothing and prediction using network theory concepts," *IRE, Trans. PGIT*, **IT-5**, Special Supplement (May, 1959), 1–13.

**38.** Davenport, W. B., Jr., and W. L. Root, *An Introduction to the Theory of Random Signals and Noise*. New York: McGraw-Hill Book Company, 1956.

**39.** De Groot, M. H., and M. M. Rao, "Bayes estimation with convex loss," *Annals Math. Stat.*, **34** (Sept., 1963), 839–846.

**40.** Deutsch, R., *Nonlinear Transformations of Random Processes*. Englewood Cliffs, N. J.: Prentice-Hall, Inc., 1962.

**41.** Deutsch, R., *Orbital Dynamics of Space Vehicles*. Englewood Cliffs, N. J.: Prentice-Hall Inc., 1963.

**42.** Doob, J. L., *Stochastic Processes*. New York: John Wiley and Sons, Inc., 1950.

**43.** Dresher, M., *Games of Strategy: Theory and Applications*. Englewood Cliffs, N.J.: Prentice-Hall, Inc., 1961.

**44.** Dugué, D., "Application des proprietés de la limite au sens du calcul des probabilités à l'étude des diverses questions d'estimation," *École. Poly.*, **3**, No. 4 (1937), 305–372.

**45.** Edgeworth, F. Y., "On the probable error of frequency-constants," *Jour. Roy. Stat. Soc.*, **71** (1908), 381–397.

**46.** Fisher, R. A., "On an absolute criterion for fitting frequency curves," *Mess. of Math.*, **41** (1912), 155.

47. Fisher, R. A., "On the mathematical foundations of theoretical statistics," *Philos. Trans. Royal Soc. London*, **222** (1922), 309.

48. Fisher, R. A., "Theory of statistical estimation," *Proc. Cambridge Philos. Soc.*, **22** (1925), 700.

49. Foster, M., "An application of the Wiener-Kolmogorov smoothing theory to matrix inversion," *J. Soc. Indust. Appl. Math.*, **9**, No. 3 (Sept., 1961), 387–392.

50. Fox, A. H., *Fundamentals of Numerical Analysis*. New York: The Ronald Press Co., 1963.

51. Frame, J. S., "Part I—Matrix functions and applications," *IEEE Spectrum*, (Mar., 1964), 208–220.

52. Freund, R. J., R. W. Vail, and C. W. Clunies-Ross, "Residual analysis," *J. Amer. Statist. Assoc.*, **56** (1961), 98–104.

53. Friedland, B., "Least squares filtering and prediction of nonstationary sampled data," *Information and Control*, **1** (1958), 297–313.

54. Frielander, A. L., "Inversion property of the fundamental matrix in trajectory problems," *J. AIAA*, **1** (Apr., 1963), 971–973.

55. Gantmacher, F. R., *The Theory of Matrices*. New York: Chelsea Publishing Co., 1959.

56. Gauss, Karl F., *Theory of the Motion of the Heavenly Bodies Moving about the Sun in Conic Sections*. New York: Dover Publications, Inc., 1963 (reprint).

57. Goldberger, A. S., "Note on stepwise least squares," *J. Amer. Statist. Assoc.*, **56** (1961), 105–110.

58. Goldberger, A. S., "Stepwise least squares: residual analysis and specification error," *J. Amer. Statist. Assoc.*, **56** (1961), 998–1000.

59. Golub, G. H., "Comparison of the variance of minimum variance and weighted least squares regression coefficients," *Ann. Math. Statist.*, **34** (Sept., 1963), 984–991.

60. Graybill, F. A., and R. B. Deal, "Combining unbiased estimators," *Biometrics*, **15** (1959), 543–550.

61. Greene, A. H., and W. F. Jaros, Jr., "Comparison of error transfer matrices for circular orbits," *J. AIAA*, **1** (Nov., 1963), 2623–2625.

62. Grenander, U., and M. Rosenblatt, *Statistical Analysis of Stationary Time Series*. New York: John Wiley and Sons, Inc., 1957.

63. Gretz, R. W., "Error sensitivities in satellite ascent and orbital transfer," *J. Amer. Rocket Soc.*, **32** (Dec., 1962), 1860–1866.

64. Greville, T. N. E., "The pseudoinverse of a rectangular or singular matrix and its application to the solution of systems of linear equations," *SIAM Rev.*, **1** (1959), 38–43.

65. Greville, T. N. E., "Some applications of the pseudoinverse of a matrix," *SIAM Rev.*, **2** (1960), 15–22.

**66.** Hanson, J. E., "Some notes on the application of the calculus of variations to smoothing for finite time, etc.," JHU/APL *Internal Memorandum*, BBD-346, 1957.

**67.** Harman, W. W., *Principles of the Statistical Theory of Communication*. New York: McGraw-Hill Book Company, 1963.

**68.** Hartree, D. R., *Numerical Analysis*. Oxford: The Clarendon Press, 1958.

**69.** Ho, Y. C., "On the stochastic approximation method and optimal filtering theory," *J. Math. Anal. Appl.*, **6** (1962), 152–154.

**70.** Ho, Y. C., and R. C. K. Lee, "A Bayesian approach to problems in stochastic estimation and control," *IEEE, Trans. PGAC*, **AC-9** (Oct., 1964), 333–339.

**71.** Householder, A. S., *Principles of Numerical Analysis*. New York: McGraw-Hill Book Company, 1953.

**72.** Householder, A. S., "A survey of some closed methods for inverting matrices," *J. Soc. Indust. Appl. Math.*, **5**, No. 3 (Sept., 1957), 155–168.

**73.** Householder, A. S., "A class of methods for inverting matrices," *J. Soc. Indust. Appl. Math.*, **6**, No. 2 (June, 1958), 189–195.

**74.** Huzurbazar, V. S., "The likelihood equation, consistency and the maxima of the likelihood function," *Ann. Eugen., Lond.*, **14** (1948), 185–200.

**75.** Kac, M., and A. J. F. Siegert, "An explicit representation of a stationary Gaussian process," *Ann. Math. Statist.*, **18** (1947), 38.

**76.** Kale, B. K., "On the solution of the likelihood equation by iteration processes," *Biometrika*, **48** (1961), 452–456.

**77.** Kalman, R. E., "A new approach to linear filtering and prediction problems," *J. Basic Eng.*, Trans. ASME, **82 D** (1960), 33–45.

**78.** Kalman, R. E., and J. E. Bertram, "Control system analysis and design via the 'second method' of Lyapunov: I, Continuous-time systems; II, Discrete-time systems," *J. Basic Eng.*, Trans. ASME, **82 D** (1960), 371–393, 394–399.

**79.** Kalman, R. E., "New methods and results in linear prediction and filtering theory," *Tech. Rept.* 61–1, Research Institute for Advanced Studies, Baltimore, Md. (Nov. 1960).

**80.** Kalman, R. E., "On the general theory of control systems," *Proceedings of the First International Congress of the International Federation of Automatic Control. Moscow, 1960*. London: Butterworths, 1961.

**81.** Kalman, R. E., and R. S. Bucy, "New results in linear filtering and prediction theory," *J. Basic Eng.*, Trans. ASME, **83 D** (1961), 95–108.

**82.** Karhunen, K., "Über lineare methoden in der wahrscheinlichkeitsrechnung," *Ann. Acad. Sci. Fennicae Wer. A., I. Math. Phys.*, **37** (1947).

**83.** Kelly, E. J., I. S. Reed, and W. L. Root, "The detection of radar echoes in noise. I," *J. Soc. Indust. Appl. Math.*, **8** (June, 1960), 309–341.

**84.** Kiefer, J., and J. Wolfowitz, "Stochastic estimation of the maximum of a regression function," *Ann. Math. Statist.*, **23** (July, 1952), 462–466.

**85.** Kolmogorov, A. N., "Interpolation and extrapolation von stationären zufälligen folgen," *Bull. Acad. Sci. (USSR), Ser. Math.*, **5** (1941), 3–14.

**86.** Kolmogorov, A. N., "Interpolation and extrapolation of stationary random sequences," Trans. by W. Doyle and J. Selin, RM-3090-PR, 1962, The Rand Corp., Santa Monica, Calif.

**87.** Laning, J. H., and R. H. Battin, *Random Processes in Automatic Control.* New York: McGraw-Hill Book Company, 1956.

**88.** Lawson, J. L., and G. E. Uhlenbeck, *Threshold Signals.* New York: McGraw-Hill Book Company, 1950.

**89.** Leach, R., "Evaluating the quality of prediction for a position-predicting or tracking system," *J. Amer. Rocket Soc.*, **32** (Nov., 1962), 1697–1701.

**90.** LeCam, L., "On the asymptotic theory of estimation and testing hypotheses," *Proceedings of the Third Berkeley Symposium on Mathematical Statistics and Probability.* Berkeley and Los Angeles: University of California Press, 1956, 129–156.

**91.** Lee, Y. W., *Statistical Theory of Communication.* New York: John Wiley and Sons, Inc., 1960.

**92.** Legendre, A. M., *Nouvelles méthodes pour la détermination des orbites des comètes.* Paris: 1806.

**93.** Leitmann, G., ed., *Optimization Techniques with Applications to Aerospace Systems.* New York: Academic Press, Inc., 1962.

**94.** Levenberg, K., "A method for the solution of certain non-linear problems in least squares," *Quart. Appl. Math.*, **2** (1944), 164–168.

**95.** Levine, N., "A new technique for increasing the flexibility of recursive least squares data smoothing," *Bell System Tech. J.*, **40** (May, 1961), 821–840.

**96.** Lévy, P., *Processus Stochastiques et Mouvement Brownian.* Paris: Gauthier-Villars, 1948.

**97.** Magness, T. A., and J. B. McGuire, "Comparison of least squares and minimum variance estimates of regression parameters," *Ann. Math. Statist.*, **33** (1962), 462–470.

**98.** Marquardt, D. W., "An algorithm for least-squares estimation of nonlinear parameters," *J. Soc. Indust. Appl. Math.*, **11** (June, 1963), 431–441.

**99.** Mayne, D. Q., "Optimal non-stationary estimation of the parameters of a linear system with Gaussian inputs," *J. Electron. Control*, (Jan., 1963), 101–112.

**100.** Middleton, D., *An Introduction to Statistical Communication Theory.* New York: McGraw-Hill Book Company, 1960.

**101.** Miller, K. S., and L. A. Zadeh, "Solution of an integral equation occurring in the theories of prediction and detection," *IRE, Trans. PGIT*, **IT-2** (June, 1956), 72–75.

**102.** Monroe, A. J., *Digital Processes for Sampled Data Systems.* New York: John Wiley and Sons, Inc., 1962.

**103.** Mood, A. M., *Introduction to the Theory of Statistics*. New York: McGraw-Hill Book Company, 1950.

**104.** Morgenau, A., and G. M. Murphy, *The Mathematics of Physics and Chemistry*. New York: D. Van Nostrand Company, Inc., 1943.

**105.** Morrison, D., "A method for nonlinear minimization problems," *Internal Report* No. NN–140, 1959, Space Technology Labs., Redondo Beach, Calif.

**106.** Murphy, G. J., and K. Sahara, "A mean-weighted square-error criterion for optimum filtering of nonstationary random processes," *IRE, Trans. PGAC*, **AC-6** (May, 1961), 211–216.

**107.** Neyman, J., and E. S. Pearson, "The testing of statistical hypotheses in relation to probability a priori," *Proc. Cambridge Phil. Soc.*, **29** (1933).

**108.** Neyman, J., and E. S. Pearson, "Contributions to the theory of testing statistical hypotheses," *Stat. Res. Mem.*, Pts. I and II (1936, 1938).

**109.** Neyman, J., "Outline of a theory of statistical estimation based on the classical theory of probability," *Philos. Trans. Royal Soc. London, Ser. A.*, **236** (1937), 333–380.

**110.** Neyman, J., "Contributions to the theory of the $\chi^2$ test," *Proceedings of the Berkeley Symposium on Mathematical Statistics and Probability*. Berkeley and Los Angeles: University of California Press, 1949, 239–273.

**111.** O'Neill, E. L., "Spatial filtering in optics," *IRE, Trans. PGIT*, **IT-2** (June, 1956), 56–65.

**112.** Osborne, E. E., "On least squares solutions of linear equations," *J. Assoc. Comput. Mach.*, **8** (1961), 628–636.

**113.** Paley, R. E. A. C., and N. Wiener, "Fourier transforms in the complex domain," *American Math. Soc. Colloquium Publ.*, **19**, New York (1934).

**114.** Parzen, E., *Stochastic Processes*. San Francisco: Holden-Day, Inc., 1962.

**115.** Pearson, K., "Contributions to the mathematical theory of evolution," *Philos. Trans. Royal Soc. London*, **185** (1894), 71.

**116.** Pearson, K., "Contributions to the mathematical theory of evolution, IV: On the probable errors of frequency constants and on the influence of random selection on variation and correlation," *Philos. Trans. Royal Soc. London*, **191** (1898), 229.

**117.** Penrose, R. A., "A generalized inverse for matrices," *Proc. Cambridge Phil. Soc.*, **51** (1955), 406–413.

**118.** Pugachev, V. S., "General condition for the minimum mean square error in a dynamic system," *Avt. i Telemekh*, **17** (1956), 289–295; trans., 307–314.

**119.** Pugachev, V. S., "The method of determining optimum systems using general Bayes criteria," *IRE, Trans. PGCT*, **CT-7** (Dec., 1960), 491–505.

**120.** Pugachev, V.S., "Statistical theory of systems reducible to linear," *IRE Trans. PGCT*, **CT-7** (Dec., 1960), 506–513.

**121.** Rademacher, H. A., "On the accumulation of errors in processes of integration on high-speed calculating machines," *Proc. Symposium on Large Scale Digital Computing.* Cambridge, Mass.: Ann. Computing Lab. **16**, Harvard University, (1948), 176–186.

**122.** Rao, C. R., *Advanced Statistical Methods for Biometric Research.* New York: John Wiley and Sons, Inc., 1952.

**123.** Rao, C. R., "Analysis of dispersion for multiplying classified data with unequal numbers in cells," *Sankhyā*, **15** (1955), 253–280.

**124.** Rao, C. R., "A note on a generalized inverse of a matrix with applications to problems in mathematical statistics," *J. Roy. Statis. Soc., Ser. B*, **24** (1962), 152–158.

**125.** Richards, F. S. G., "A method of maximum-likelihood estimation," *J. Roy. Statist. Soc., Ser. B*, **23** (1961), 469–475.

**126.** Riesz, R., and B. Sz.-Nagy, *Functional Analysis.* New York: Frederick Unger Publishing Co., 1955.

**127.** Sakrison, D. J., "Iterative design of optimum filters for non-mean-square error performance criteria," *IEEE, Trans. PGIT*, **IT-9** (July, 1963), 161–167.

**128.** Sarhan, A. E., and B. G. Greenberg, eds., *Contributions to Order Statistics.* New York: John Wiley and Sons, Inc., 1962.

**129.** Scheffé, H., *The Analysis of Variance.* New York: John Wiley and Sons, Inc., 1959.

**130.** Schlegel, L. B., "Covariance matrix approximation," *J. AIAA*, **1** (Nov., 1963), 2672–2673.

**131.** Schlesinger, F., "On the errors in the sum of a number of tabular quantities," *Astronom. J.*, **30** (1917), 183–190.

**132.** Shenton, L. R., "Maximum likelihood and the efficiency of the method of moments," *Biometrika*, **37** (1950), 111–116.

**133.** Shenton, L. R., "Moment estimators and maximum likelihood," *Biometrika*, **45** (1958), 311–320.

**134.** Shenton, L. R., "The distribution of moment estimators," *Biometrika*, **46** (1959), 296–305.

**135.** Sherman, S., "A theorem on convex sets with applications," *Ann. Math. Statist.*, **26** (1955), 763–767.

**136.** Sherman, S., "Non-mean-square error criteria," *IRE, Trans. PGIT*, **IT-4** (Sept., 1958), 125–126.

**137.** Shinbrot, M., "A generalization of a method for the solution of the integral equation arising in optimization of time-varying linear systems with nonstationary inputs," *IRE, Trans. PGIT*, **IT-3** (Dec., 1957), 220–224.

**138.** Silvey, S. D., "A note on the maximum-likelihood in the case of dependent random variables," *J. Roy. Statist. Soc., Ser. B*, **23** (1961), 444–452.

**139.** Skolnik, M. I., *Introduction to Radar Systems.* New York: McGraw-Hill Book Company, 1962.

**140.** Slepian, D., "Estimation of signal parameters in the presence of noise," *IRE, Trans. PGIT*, **IT-3** (Mar., 1964), 68–89.

**141.** Smith, G. L., S. F. Schmidt, and L. A. McGee, "Application of statistical filter theory to the optimal estimation of position and velocity on board a circumlunar vehicle," *Tech. Rept.* R–135, Nov. 20, 1961, Ames Research Center, NASA, Moffett Field, Calif.

**142.** Sokolnikoff, I. S., and R. M. Redheffer, *Mathematics of Physics and Modern Engineering*. New York: McGraw-Hill Book Company, 1958.

**143.** Stumpers, F. L., "A bibliography of information theory communication——Cybernetics," *IRE, Trans. PGIT*, **IT-1** (Sept., 1955), 35–37.

**144.** Swerling, P., "A proposed stagewise differential correction procedure for satellite tracking and prediction," *Report* P-1292, Jan. 8, 1958, The Rand Corporation, Santa Monica, Calif.

**145.** Swerling, P., "First-order error propagation in a stagewise smoothing procedure for satellite observations," *J. Astronautical Sci.*, **6** (1959).

**146.** Swerling, P., "Parameter estimation accuracy formulas," *IEEE, Trans. PGIT*, **IT-10** (Oct., 1964), 302–314.

**147.** Tempelman, W. H., "Circular orbit partial derivatives," *J. AIAA*, **1** (May, 1963), 1187–1189.

**148.** Wainstein, L. A., and V. D. Zubakov, *Extraction of Signals from Noise*, trans. from the Russian by R. A. Silverman. Englewood Cliffs, N. J.: Prentice-Hall, Inc., 1962.

**149.** Wald, A., "Tests of statistical hypotheses concerning several parameters when the number of observations is large," *Trans. Amer. Math. Soc.*, **54** (1943), 426–482.

**150.** Wald, A., *Statistical Decision Functions*. New York: John Wiley and Sons, Inc., 1950.

**151.** Whittaker, E. T., *A Treatise on the Analytical Dynamics of Particles and Rigid Bodies*. New York: Dover Publications, Inc., 1944 (reprint).

**152.** Whittle, P., *Prediction and Regulation by Linear Least-Square Methods*. London: The English Universities Press, Ltd., 1963.

**153.** Wiener, N., *The Extrapolation, Interpolation and Smoothing of Stationary Time Series*. New York: John Wiley and Sons, Inc., 1949.

**154.** Wiener, N., *Nonlinear Problems in Random Theory*. New York: John Wiley and Sons, Inc., 1958.

**155.** Wilks, S. S., *Mathematical Statistics*. New York: John Wiley and Sons, Inc., 1962.

**156.** Wilson, E. B., "Probable inference, the law of succession, and statistical inference," *J. Amer. Statist. Assoc.*, **27** (1927), 209–212.

**157.** Wong, E., and J. B. Thomas," On the multidimensional prediction and filtering problem and the factorization of special matrices," *J. Franklin Inst.*, **272** (Aug., 1961), 87–99.

**158.** Woodward, P. M., *Probability and Information Theory with Applications to Radar*. New York: Pergamon Press, Inc., 1955.

**159.** Yaglom, A. M., *An Introduction to the Theory of Stationary Random Functions*. Englewood Cliffs, N.J.: Prentice-Hall, Inc., 1962.

**160.** Youla, D. C., "The use of the method of maximum likelihood in estimating continuous-modulated intelligence which has been corrupted by noise," *IRE, Trans. PGIT*, **IT-3** (Mar., 1954), 90–105.

**161.** Youla, D. C., "The solution of a homogeneous Wiener-Hopf integral equation occurring in the expansion of second-order stationary random functions," *IRE, Trans. PGIT*, **IT-3** (Sept., 1957), 187–193.

**162.** Zadeh, L. A., and J. R. Ragazzini, "An extension of Wiener's theory of prediction," *J. Appl. Phys.*, **21** (July, 1950), 645–655.

**163.** Zadeh, L. A., and J. R. Ragazzini, "Optimum filters for the detection of signals in noise," *Proc. IRE*, **40** (Oct., 1952), 1223–1231.

**164.** Zadeh, L. A., "What is optimal," *IRE, Trans. PGIT*, **4** (Mar., 1958), 2.

**165.** Zadeh, L. A., "Progress in information theory in the U.S.A., 1957–1960: Prediction and filtering," *IRE, Trans. PGIT*, **IT-7** (July, 1961), 139–144.

**166.** Zadeh, L. A., and C. A. Desoer, *Linear System Theory, The State Space Approach*. New York: McGraw-Hill Book Company, 1963.

**167.** Zakai, M., "On a property of Wiener filters," *IRE, Trans. PGIT*, **IT-5** (Mar., 1959), 15–17.

**168.** Zakai, M., "General error criteria," *IEEE, Trans. PGIT*, **IT-10** (Jan., 1964), 94–95.

# INDEX *



* Bracketed numbers refer to list of references.

## D



## E

## T



## U



## V



## W



## Y



## Z